The Butterflies of Hampshire

MATTHEW OATES, JOHN TAVERNER, DAVID GREEN *et al.*

Dedication
This book is dedicated to the memory of the New Forest,
and also to its future.

piscespublications

Published by Pisces Publications
in conjuction with the
Hampshire and Isle of Wight Branch
of Butterfly Conservation

**BUTTERFLY
CONSERVATION**

Sponsored by Hampshire County Council
and Heritage Lottery Fund
(Millennium Festival Awards for All)

First published 2000 by Pisces Publications in conjuction with the Hampshire and Isle of Wight Branch of Butterfly Conservation. Pisces Publications is the imprint of the **Nature**Bureau (formerly the Nature Conservation Bureau Limited).

British Library-in-Publication Data.
A catalogue record for this book is available from the British Library.

ISBN 1-874357-17-X

Designed and produced by the **Nature**Bureau, 36 Kingfisher Court, Hambridge Road, Newbury, Berkshire RG14 5SJ.

Printed by Information Press, Oxford

CONTENTS

FOREWORD

by Sir David Attenborough CH, FRS

This book describes the status of Hampshire butterflies in the closing years of the 20th century and looks back to those halcyon days when, for example, the Large Tortoiseshell, the High Brown Fritillary, the Black-veined White and the Wood White could be seen in profusion in Hampshire. Today those four butterflies are extinct in the county and two of them are extinct in Britain. Several other species (e.g. the Pearl-bordered Fritillary), formerly abundant in Hampshire, now hang on precariously on a very few sites. This sad falling-off is perhaps most spectacular and well-documented in the case of the New Forest, whose rides used to teem with butterflies to a degree difficult to imagine today.

On the credit side, the Speckled Wood and Comma have gained ground. But the general picture is overwhelmingly one of decline.

Butterfly Conservation exists to arrest this decline. It employs a team of professional entomologists but the majority of its vital recording work is carried out by dedicated and highly competent but unpaid Branch members. These are the kind of people who have always held an honourable place in the history of British nature conservation. And these are the people whom John Taverner has gathered round him to write this well-researched and readable book.

I commend the book to laymen and professional ecologists alike.

David Attenborough
President of Butterfly Conservation

THE TEAM

COORDINATOR AND EDITOR
John Taverner

LEAD AUTHOR AND NATURAL HISTORY ADVISOR
Matthew Oates

RESEARCH AND DISTRIBUTION MAPS
David Green

DATABASE
David Green, Alison Harper, Ken Bailey, Ian Small

TRANSECT COORDINATOR AND ADVISOR
Dr Andy Barker

WRITERS
Dr Andy Barker, Dr Susan Clarke, Sue Ellis, Brian Fletcher, Mike Gibbons, David Green, Adrian Hoskins,
Matthew Oates, John Taverner and Ken Willmott

PHOTOGRAPHERS
Dr Andy Barker, Pete Durnell, Brian Fletcher, Mike Gibbons, Barry Hilling, Tim Norriss, Matthew Oates,
Michael Skelton, John Taverner, Ashley Whitlock, Tim Wildridge and Ken Willmott

LINE DRAWINGS
Brian Fletcher, David Thelwell

COVER PAINTING
Rosemary Powell
White Admirals, Silver-washed Fritillary and Purple Emperor

EDITORIAL

This volume is essentially a team effort, regardless of whose names are on the cover, written by a group of people who have been co-authors of the annual Hampshire Butterfly Report for a number of years, each being responsible for a group of butterfly species. It began with Matthew Oates, who set out to write the book by himself. He was almost half way through a highly ambitious work but succumbed to the pressures that beset a family man in the 1990s with a time-consuming career. The Hampshire and Isle of Wight Branch of Butterfly Conservation took over the task and, as a retired person, I had time on my hands to organise *The Team* who used Matthew's original text as a base for much of the book. The resulting text was read by Matthew and The Team and modified as a result of their observations.

The names of this Team appear on an earlier page, whilst all those who have gathered field data appear in the *List of Observers* at the end of this volume. No book such as this is possible without a small army of field-workers who provide the basic data by spending countless hours monitoring butterfly populations and making a host of other observations. I consider all these helpers to be very much a part of The Team and I thank them all on behalf of The Branch.

Special mention must be made of David Green who has been in command of our database, aided by Alison Harper, Ken Bailey and Ian Small. David has spent countless hours processing data and producing all the species' distribution maps that appear in these pages, as well as helping to research historical records and performing valuable work preparing the Reference section.

Dr Andy Barker has also devoted much time to this book, organising Hampshire's enviable list of butterfly transects which are much used in the text to show the year to year fortunes of butterfly species, as well as offering much sound advice on the text. Such work is typical of the efforts made by volunteers to produce this volume and we count ourselves fortunate to have such expertise amongst our Branch members.

The text has been read by Barry Goater, whose name needs no introduction in the world of Lepidoptera, and we thank him for his observations. Barry's book on the moths of Hampshire and the Isle of Wight, written with Tim Norriss, will be published around the same time as this volume, which brings the written record of Hampshire's butterflies and moths conveniently up to date at the end of the Millennium.

The icing on the cake is the Foreword by Sir David Attenborough, the new President of Butterfly Conservation. It came as a final pleasure in my work as coordinator.

Originally, the book was intended to cover both Hampshire and the Isle of Wight, but Island lepidopterists have decided to produce their own butterfly book and so this volume is confined to Hampshire.

We acknowledge the generous help given by the British Geological Survey, Hampshire County Council and the Forestry Commission, who have provided indispensable custom-made maps for this book, and especially to Simon Rippon, Nicky Court and Berry Stone, respectively of those three establishments, who carried out the work on producing Figures 1 to 8. Hampshire County Council also made a generous contribution towards production costs; the cause of nature conservation in our county has been aided considerably by the policies of both our County Council and our local Councils. Heritage Lottery Fund (Millennium Festival Awards for All) also made a valuable contribution towards production costs. We also thank our publisher, Pisces Publications of Newbury, who has been of incalculable help with suggestions on layout, presentation and a host of other features that have added so much to this volume's final appearance, our thanks going especially to Peter Creed.

Producing this book has been a fascinating experience, but it has also been depressing. Throughout the text, one constant theme has been the decline or disappearance of so many of our butterfly species due to changes in their habitats brought about by our own activities. My hope is that the next volume of *Butterflies of Hampshire* will have a happier tale to tell.

John Taverner, Winchester, February 2000

PART ONE

INTRODUCTION

This is the first book to be devoted solely to a comprehensive account of Hampshire's butterfly fauna. It opens with a description of the geology and landscape, with particular attention paid to the New Forest, chalk downland, heaths and woodland other than those of the New Forest and to a few other habitats such as those on the coast. A brief resume of the weather experienced over the 1990s is then given, followed by a short account of past naturalists who have played an important part in the study and understanding of Hampshire's butterfly populations and another brief chapter that sets those populations in a national context. The bulk of the book is a Systematic List of species describing for each butterfly the present status, recent population trends, habitat and foodplants, flight periods, earliest and latest dates, conservation issues for a few of our key species, accounts of outstanding or interesting occurrences such as the Painted Lady invasion of 1996 and a historical review. The Systematic List concentrates mainly on the situation for each butterfly during the period 1990–1999, setting out the situation at the close of the 20th century, but attention is also given to the historical aspect of each species.

Since the end of World War II, there has been an impressive array of county natural history books with ornithology leading the way. This is much more than literature designed merely to interest those who go into the countryside in growing numbers to study or simply look at wildlife. These books are vital to conservation because they record in considerable detail the present status of species so that any future increases or decreases can be judged with some accuracy. All butterfly records sent to the Hampshire and Isle of Wight Branch of Butterfly Conservation are stored in our computerised database, but this is massive and public access is not readily available at the moment. This volume, together with the annual Butterfly Reports published by the Branch, can be looked upon as an index to that database so that researchers needing more detailed information will be able to see if it is available. As space in this volume is limited, readers may need to refer to our Annual Reports for more detail of some records, sets of such Reports being held by the Branch and bound copies of those Reports held by most of the major public libraries in Hampshire.

Those concerned with nature conservation in Hampshire would dearly love to have quantitative data from 1900 so that they can judge precisely how our birds, butterflies, dragonflies, flowers and other wildlife have fared over the century, but very few observers in those early days carried out census work. Incredibly, no data exists for butterfly numbers prior to the late 1970s. Our detailed records of today generally have to be compared with anecdotal accounts from the past and the researcher then has to assess the fate of species.

After World War II, there was a sudden and considerable increase in the study of natural history. Prior to that time, the study of wildlife had been mainly the preserve of a privileged few who had the time and facilities for such interests. In the world of ornithology, the numbers who took to the field almost amounted to a revolution as people had transport, leisure time and spare funds to purchase such items as binoculars. This revolution has spread to other fields and although many people collected butterflies before World War II, especially in Victorian times, the insects now have their own considerable following of those who go into the field to study, record or simply admire.

This book could not have seen the light of day were that not the case. It is the work of several hundred observers who have scoured Hampshire to map species and try to assess the size of populations and their trends from year to year. It *will* be of interest to those who have helped in that field-work and to those who visit Hampshire with butterflies in mind, but its main value will be in the future when lepidopterists will be able to look back and see how species have lost or gained ground and how Hampshire's habitats have changed. It joins recent books on Hampshire's birds and flora, and as a volume on Hampshire's moths is about to go to press, the county's wildlife is now well documented. For an overview of how Hampshire butterflies can be placed in a national context, we refer readers to Part Five of this volume and the forthcoming *Millennium Atlas of Butterflies* (Asher *et al.*, in press).

Maps – Distribution maps show the county boundary in the 1990s. However, administrative boundaries change, the main change in recent years being the transfer of the Bournemouth/Christchurch area and parts of the Avon valley to Dorset.

Branch activities deal with both moths and butterflies, and as moth recording follows the old Watsonian vice-county boundaries, our maps include records for the Bournemouth area and the lower Avon valley that are outside the modern county boundary so that moth and butterfly records cover the same area. To show the old county boundary would be misleading for present-day readers, but to omit records for the area removed to Dorset may mean that they are not recorded anywhere. Therefore we have an agreement with the Dorset Branch of Butterfly Conservation to gather data from the Bournemouth and Christchurch area. Distribution maps cover the period 1990–1999 inclusive and they are derived from the Branch database.

Transects – Much use is also made of transect data, the county being fortunate to have around 70 such transects in operation, coordinated and collated by Dr Andy Barker. Transects monitor butterfly populations at a particular site, showing the trend of population changes from year to year rather than attempting to measure the actual population size (Pollard, 1977). The data is gained by an observer walking a fixed route once a week in warm, sunny conditions from the beginning of April to the end of September, counting all butterflies seen within 5 m of the observer. The **Weekly Count** is the total number of any species seen in a specific week's walk. The **Annual Index** is the year's total of weekly counts for a given species.

Specific names – In the Systematic List, each butterfly is headed with its English and scientific names; in other parts of the text, only the English name is used. To save space in the text, only English names are used for flora and other forms of wildlife, scientific names being given in Appendix 1 at the end of the book. For all flora, both English and scientific names are those that appear in *The Flora of Hampshire* (Brewis, Bowman and Rose, 1996) to keep county literature consistent. This is the nomenclature developed by Stace (1991). For the same reason, both English and scientific names of birds are those used in *Birds of Hampshire* (Clark and Eyre, 1993).

PART TWO

LANDSCAPE AND GEOLOGY

The geology of Hampshire can be described simply as a central mass of chalk flanked by overlying Tertiary sands, gravels and clays to the north and south with a small area of older greensands and Gault Clay beneath the chalk in the east (see Figure 1). The younger Tertiary rocks in the north and south are mostly London Clay, Reading Beds, and the sand, gravel and clay complex of the Bagshot, Bracklesham, Barton and Hamstead Beds. The whole is overlain in places by even younger

Figure 1. The solid geology of Hampshire *Reproduced from Geological Map of the UK (1:625,000 scale) Solid by permission of the British Geological Survey. @NERC. All rights reserved. Map prepared by Simon Rippon.*

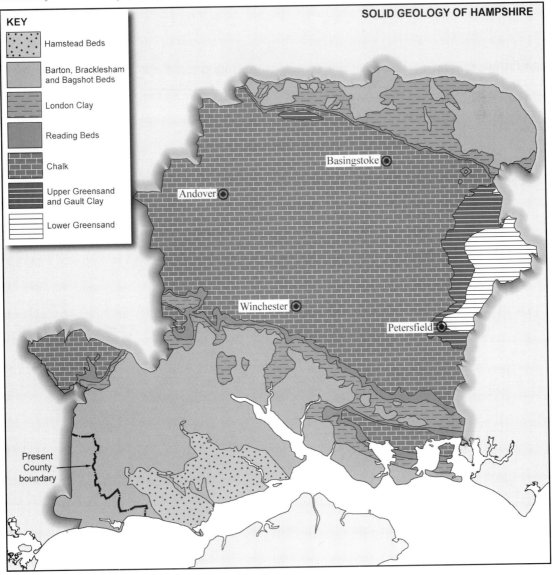

KEY

- Hamstead Beds
- Barton, Bracklesham and Bagshot Beds
- London Clay
- Reading Beds
- Chalk
- Upper Greensand and Gault Clay
- Lower Greensand

SOLID GEOLOGY OF HAMPSHIRE

Basingstoke ◉

Andover ◉

Winchester ◉

Petersfield ◉

Present County boundary

alluvial material in the river valleys, by Clay-with-flints that is mostly on the chalk, and by sands and gravels of uncertain origin along a wide coastal belt (see Figure 2).

Since chalk soils have pH values around neutral and the younger rocks produce soils that are mostly more acidic, the county flora is pleasantly diverse and as most butterflies have a small range of plants on which their larvae feed, this floral diversity gives rise to a healthy variety of butterfly species. This variety is aided by Hampshire's coastal and southerly position which allows species that occur in Britain towards the northern limit of their European range to survive, such as Adonis Blue and Glanville Fritillary. The result of the above is that Hampshire has a Butterfly List that compares well with most English counties. However, it is a list that is shrinking. Hampshire has lost species such as Black-veined White, Wood White and Large Tortoiseshell, and perhaps the High Brown Fritillary. Others such as the Marsh Fritillary are on the point of being lost unless successful conservation measures can prevent such a happening.

Figure 2. Superficial deposits in Hampshire *Reproduced from Quaternary Map of the UK (1:625,000 scale) by permission of the British Geological Survey. @NERC. All rights reserved. Map prepared by Simon Rippon.*

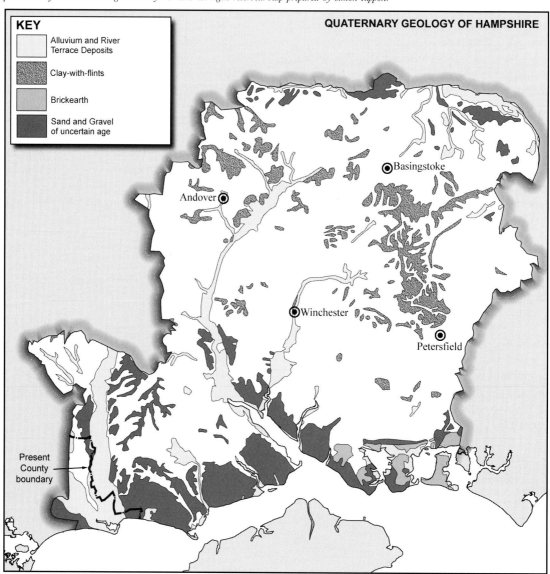

The central chalk is mainly the relatively soft Upper Chalk, a series of strata around 300 m in depth which forms rolling hill country. For the most part gradients are gentle because folding of the rock was not too severe and eroded scarp slopes are scarce, steep scarps being found mainly in the east near the West Sussex border where a small portion of Hampshire is included in the eroded Wealden anticline. Hampshire lacks the abundance of steep chalk slopes found in Dorset, Sussex and Wight. This is important because steep chalk slopes have mostly escaped the plough and remain as downland or wooded 'hangers', whereas most of Hampshire's gentle chalk slopes have become arable farmland. Consequently, in spite of the considerable area covered by chalk, there is a shortage of flower-rich downland and intensive arable farming dominates the landscape.

In places, the woodland cover has survived well on heavier soils where chalk is topped by Clay-with-flints. As chalk is so porous, there is a general shortage of surface water, rivers being confined to main streams such as the Avon, Itchen, Test and Meon which have cut through the chalk to the underlying water-table. Tributary chalk streams are small and often exist as winterbournes.

The main river valleys of central and southern Hampshire are wide and flat-floored. Over time, the rivers have meandered over the full width of these valleys, often in braided patterns where the channels constantly divide into smaller streams and then rejoin instead of flowing as one main river. This has resulted in river-borne material accumulating over a considerable area, giving rise to varied deposits which range from coarse gravels, in places such as the Avon valley above Ringwood, to peat in stretches such as the Test valley around Stockbridge.

In the past, parts of the valley floors were laid out as water-meadows with a series of small channels that inundated the areas to encourage the early growth of pasture, remains of the system still being evident in places such as the Itchen around Winchester. Today, weed is cut regularly from the main rivers to prevent flooding and so our modern streams are confined to clear-cut channels with surrounding valley floors given over to grassy fields or small woodland patches. Cuckooflower occurs frequently so that Orange Tips find the riverside meadows suitable habitat.

The younger rocks to the north and south of the central chalk have scarcely been folded by movements of the Earth's plates and being soft they have offered little resistance to erosion, presenting a rather flat landscape that is dissected by the valleys of streams that are now mostly very small. This flat horizon, with the surface cut by steep-sided valleys, is most noticeable in the northern New Forest, the valleys becoming less deep and wider to the south as land descends to The Solent because streams are close to sea-level and so cannot cut down below that mark.

From the butterfly point of view, all this has given rise to a wide variety of habitats, some of which are of particular importance, and the remainder of this opening chapter will concentrate on such areas. However, it will become obvious to the reader that all of Hampshire's butterfly habitats have been severely damaged by human development, causing most species to decline throughout the 20th century. Our destruction of habitat has unwittingly damaged butterfly populations far more than all the slaughter carried out by Victorian and Edwardian collectors.

The New Forest

The vegetation of the New Forest is due in part to its varied and predominantly acidic soils and in part to its history. It is an ancient royal hunting forest, only 40% of which is woodland, and is the largest area of semi-natural vegetation in lowland England. It is owned by the Crown and managed by the Forestry Commission. The Forest's boundary, or perambulation as it is known, encompasses some 37,907 ha of heath, grassland and woodland. The Forest includes 19,771 ha of unenclosed common land, the common rights of which are regulated by a statutory authority known as the Verderers of the New Forest, and holds the full complement of protection under UK and European wildlife and habitat legislation. It is of importance at European level for its lowland heath, notably for the valley bogs and for the ancient pasture woodlands which are noted for their epiphytic lichen and bryophyte floras, along with fungi and invertebrates associated with decaying wood. For a full and authoritative account of the New Forest's ecology, see Tubbs (1986).

The vegetation is *semi-natural* because much of the woodland was planted and the heath would soon revert to forest were it not for a programme of rotational burning and stock grazing which prevents trees from taking over. This burning is carried out in consultation with English Nature so that wildlife suffers minimum damage. Heathland is vital for the Commoners' grazing rights in the Forest, since it is this heathland that their stock of ponies, cattle and donkeys mostly graze.

Heathland is a specialist habitat for wildlife. Heathers play a dominant role in the vegetation, Bell Heather thriving in the drier parts, Cross-leaved Heath inhabiting the wetter areas, with Heather covering much of the land between the two, although the three do cross these boundaries and can occasionally be found together where a micro-habitat produces conditions suitable for all three. Gorse is widespread, thriving especially in places such as the old aerodromes at Beaulieu Heath, Stoney Cross and Holmsley where the soil has been recently disturbed, whilst Bracken is locally dominant and threatens to take over many sites. These New Forest heaths, together with the smaller area of heathland in the north and north-east of the county, account for around 40% of England's lowland heaths.

In the wetter 'bottoms', as the valleys are called, Bog-myrtle fills the air with its powerful scent, sphagnum mosses, Purple Moor-grass and Common Cottongrass abound and although the flora is not especially varied, it contains some rare and interesting species. The typical heathland butterflies are Silver-studded Blue, Small Copper, Gatekeeper and Grayling, the first-named also occurring along wet heath edges. Green Hairstreak colonies occur amongst Gorse stands and during the 18th and 19th centuries they were in some Inclosures.

Most of the woodland is in the form of fenced Inclosures that were created by various acts of Parliament. After their use as a hunting ground for the Normans and later royal houses, they consisted almost entirely of Pedunculate Oak for ship-building; for a time it was forbidden by law to plant other species. As wooden ships disappeared and a burgeoning population

Figure 3. Distribution of Inclosures and other woodland in the New Forest
Map created especially for this volume by the Forestry Commission. Map prepared by Berry Stone.

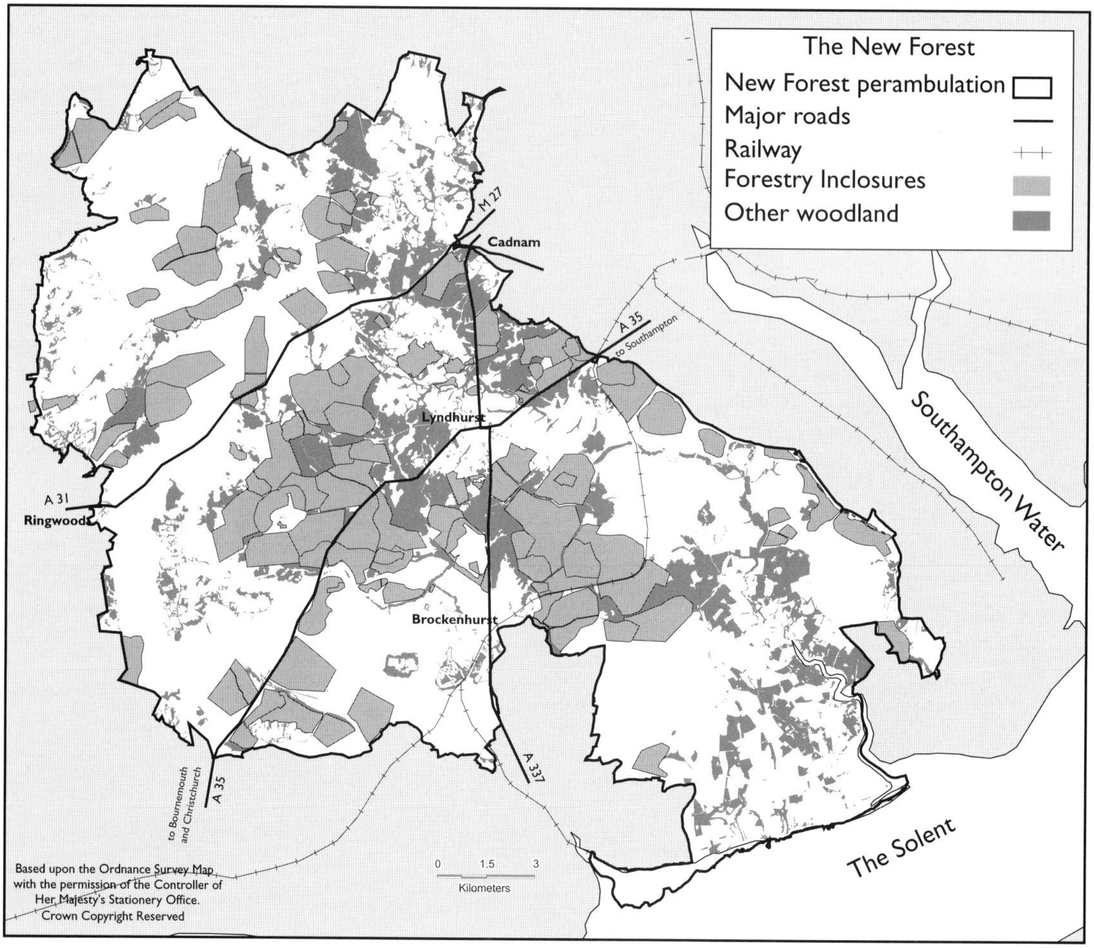

led to a growing demand for housing, fast-growing conifers began to appear and replace slow-growing hardwoods. Two world wars then brought about an accelerated programme of cutting with some areas even being used as a bombing range in World War II, incendiary bombs doing considerable damage. Further damage occurred between the two wars. The newly created Forestry Commission took control of timber production in 1924 with a policy of exploiting broad-leaved Inclosures and replanting with conifers. Woodland management practices which had been benign or beneficial towards butterflies were replaced by practices which were harmful, and at this point it must be made clear that the following criticism of forestry policy *is strictly in the past tense*, because in recent years this policy has been more sympathetic to wildlife conservation. Indeed, part of today's work by the Forestry Commission has such conservation in mind. Our Branch of Butterfly Conservation welcomes this trend in modern forestry where timber production and wildlife conservation are beginning to be seen as compatible ends.

The change in forestry policy in the early 20th century meant that modern Inclosures are very different from those of Victorian and Edwardian days. These Inclosures were the main butterfly areas. They were a mosaic of broad-leaved woodland of diverse age structure, heavily dissected by open rides which were lined with Bramble and shrubs, with frequent unplanted glades fringed with Bracken. The small number of forestry workers meant that this ride-side vegetation could be trimmed only at infrequent intervals and the luxurious growth formed ideal habitat for butterflies to obtain nectar. "At the cross-

Figure 4. Distribution of heathlands, valley mires and ponds in the New Forest
Map created especially for this volume by the Forestry Commission. Map prepared by Berry Stone.

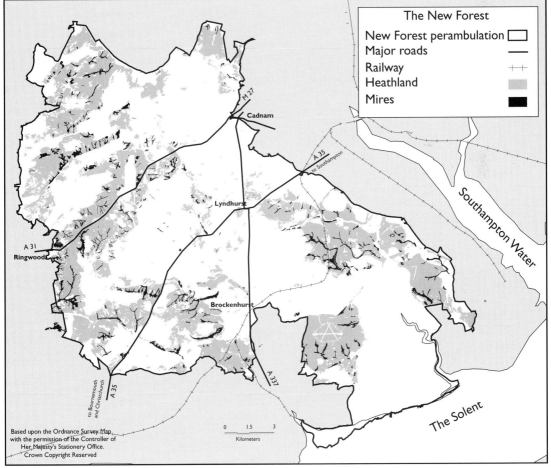

rides, where the sun shone from sunrise to sunset, the Bramble blossoms were crowded with insects of all kinds" (Castle Russell, 1952).

The New Forest was probably the finest area in Britain for woodland Lepidoptera. In the 19th century, collectors arrived in numbers during the summer for the High Brown Fritillaries, Silver-washed Fritillaries, White Admirals and others that swarmed in the Forest rides. The Crown lands of the New Forest, then administered by the Office of Woods, were open to visitors and the coming of railways made the area readily accessible to people journeying from places outside Hampshire. Butterfly collecting generated a valuable local industry, through board and lodging and transport, with some local people acting as guides or selling specimens to visiting collectors; sales of specimens and livestock took place at weekends.

In 'Hampshire Days', W.H. Hudson castigated Lyndhurst as being the place where "London vomits out its annual crowd of collectors, who fill its numerous and ever-increasing brand-new red-brick lodging houses, and who swarm through all the adjacent woods and heaths, men, women, and children (hateful little prigs!) with their vasculums, beer and treacle pots, green and blue butterfly nets, killing bottles, and all the detestable paraphernalia of what they would probably call 'Nature Study'".

Many Forest inns were virtually taken over in the season by dealers and collectors who were looking especially for atypical specimens such as Black Admirals and the *valezina* female form of the Silver-washed Fritillary. The history of butterflies in the New Forest has been documented by Oates (1996).

The wealth of the New Forest of old can be judged by three extracts from past lepidopterists. S.J. Castle Russell (1952), describing a visit to Ramnor Inclosure in 1892, wrote: "I entered by the gate leading from Holland wood into the ride in Ramnor Enclosure just as the sun became for a time obscured. As I walked slowly along, butterflies alarmed by my approach arose in immense numbers to take refuge in the trees above. They were so thick that I could hardly see ahead and indeed resembled a fall of brown leaves. As soon as the sun came out again they descended from the trees and resumed feeding on the bramble blossoms". The species involved were White Admiral, Silver-washed Fritillary, Dark Green Fritillary, High Brown Fritillary, Ringlet and Meadow Brown. Castle Russell then went on to investigate adjoining rides in Parkhill and Pignal, "and there I found the same abundance of butterflies".

J. Fowler, describing a visit to Roe Inclosure in the hot summer of 1893, wrote: "I followed the bed of one of the streams in search of water to drink, and was disappointed in not finding enough to quench my thirst, not a pool being left, but I was repaid by the sight I witnessed; the said bed of the stream for more than a mile was literally crowded with butterflies...", the bulk of which were High Brown Fritillary, Silver-washed Fritillary and White Admiral with numbers of Ringlet, Dark Green Fritillary and Small Pearl-bordered Fritillary.

F.W. Frohawk, the great lepidopterist and wildlife artist, described his first visit in 1888 in this way: "I shall never forget the impression it made upon my friend and self. Insects of various kinds literally swarmed. Butterflies were in profusion. *A. paphia* (Silver-washed Fritillary) were in hordes in every ride, the variety *valezina* was met with every few yards, as were *A. aglaia* (Dark Green Fritillary) and *A. adippe* (High Brown Fritillary). *L. camilla* (White Admiral) were sailing about everywhere. On a bank under a sallow in the sunshine a large female *A. iris* (Purple Emperor) sat with wings expanded, evidently washed out of the sallow by heavy rain. *N. polychloros* (Large Tortoiseshell) was of frequent occurrence" (quoted in Chatfield, 1987).

The outstanding summers of the golden era of butterfly collecting in the Forest were 1881, 1892, 1893, 1905, 1906, 1911 and 1917–19. The last two great butterfly years in the Inclosures were 1941 and 1942.

Since those halcyon days, several species have been lost from the Forest; the Black-veined White and Wood White are gone, the Brown Hairstreak and High Brown Fritillary are almost certainly extinct and the Duke of Burgundy may well have recently joined them. Furthermore, it is doubtful whether the Purple Emperor maintains a foothold and the two Pearl-bordered Fritillaries are reduced to remnant populations. A walker can go for hours in peak season and perhaps not see a single Silver-washed Fritillary or White Admiral, although a small number of Inclosures remain in relatively good condition for both, notably to the south and east of Lyndhurst. Indeed, lepidopterists living in the New Forest will travel outside of its boundary or to nearby private woods in search of these woodland species. As a butterfly habitat, the Forest Inclosures have been devastated and this demise is amongst the saddest aspects of the decline of British butterflies.

By the 1960s, populations of woodland species had collapsed. In sharp contrast to the three extracts given above from visitors in the 1880s are these reports from the 1950s and 1960s. One such visitor wrote: "Where insects once abounded we

Table I. Changes in the status of butterflies within the open forest and Crown Inclosures
Adapted from Oates (1996) and reproduced by courtesy of British Wildlife Publishing.

| | Pre-1900 | | 1901–1920 | | 1921–1940 | | 1941–1960 | | 1961–1980 | | 1990s | |
	OF	In	OF	In	OF	In	OF	In	OF	In	OF	In
Small Skipper	L	C	L	C	L	C	L	C	R	W	R	W
Essex Skipper	–	–	R	L	R	L	R	R	R	R	(E)	R
Silver-spotted Skipper	R	–	R	–	R	–	(E)	–	–	–	–	–
Large Skipper	C	C	C	C	C	C	C	C	W	C	W	W
Dingy Skipper	L	W	L	W	L	L	L	L	R	L	R	R
Grizzled Skipper	L	W	L	W	R	C	R	L	R	R	(E)	R
Wood White	–	E	–	E	–	E	–	E	–	E	–	E
Black-veined White	R	L	E	E	E	E	E	E	E	E	E	E
Brimstone	C	C	C	C	C	C	W	C	W	C	W	C
Large White	C	C	C	C	C	C	C	C	W	W	W	W
Small White	C	C	C	C	C	C	C	C	W	W	W	W
Green-veined White	W	C	W	C	W	C	L	L	L	L	R	R
Orange Tip	W	C	W	C	W	C	L	L	L	R	R	R
Green Hairstreak	C	L	C	L	C	L	W	L	W	L	W	R
Brown Hairstreak	L	L	L	R	L	R	R	(E)	(E)	E	E	E
Purple Hairstreak	C	C	C	C	C	C	C	W	C	W	C	W
White-letter Hairstreak	L	R	L	R	L	(E)	R	E	R	E	R	E
Small Copper	C	W	C	W	C	W	C	W	C	L	W	L
Silver-studded Blue	C	R	C	R	C	R	C	R	C	R	C	R
Brown Argus	W	V	W	V	R	V	R	V	V	V	V	V
Common Blue	C	W	C	L	C	L	W	L	L	L	L	R
Holly Blue	W	W	W	W	W	W	W	W	W	L	W	L
Duke of Burgundy	R	W	(E)	L	–	L	–	L	–	R	–	(E)
White Admiral	L	C	L	C	W	W	L	W	R	L	R	L
Purple Emperor	R	L	R	L	R	R	V	R	V	V	V	V
Red Admiral	W	W	W	W	W	W	W	W	W	R	W	R
Small Tortoiseshell	C	C	C	C	C	C	C	W	W	W	W	W
Large Tortoiseshell	W	W	L	L	R	R	R	R	E	E	E	E
Peacock	C	C	C	C	C	C	W	W	W	W	W	W
Comma	(E)	(E)	E	E	C	C	W	W	W	W	W	L
Small Pearl-bordered Fritillary	C	C	C	C	C	C	W	W	L	R	R	R
Pearl-bordered Fritillary	C	C	C	C	W	C	W	W	R	L	(E)	R
High Brown Fritillary	C	C	C	C	W	W	L	L	L	R	(E)	(E)
Dark Green Fritillary	W	W	W	W	L	R	L	R	R	R	R	R
Silver-washed Fritillary	W	C	W	C	W	C	L	W	L	L	R	L
Marsh Fritillary	–	–	R	–	R	–	(E)	–	E	–	E	–
Speckled Wood	W	C	W	C	W	C	W	C	L	W	L	W
Wall Brown	C	W	C	W	W	W	C	W	W	L	R	R
Grayling	C	W	C	W	C	W	C	L	W	L	W	L
Gatekeeper	C	C	C	C	C	C	C	C	C	W	C	W
Meadow Brown	C	C	C	C	C	C	C	C	C	W	W	W
Ringlet	L	C	L	C	L	C	R	C	(E)	L	(E)	L
Small Heath	C	W	C	W	C	W	C	W	W	L	L	R

OF = Open forest   **In** = Crown Inclosures
C = Common   W = Widespread   L = Local   R = Rare
(E) = Presumed extinct   E = Extinct   V = Vagrant   – = Absent

were shocked to see the forest razed to ground level" (Dyson, 1950). H.J. Turner (1951) reported that "Nearly every ride and Inclosure throughout the entire New Forest has received its quota of destruction in the form of cutting down of oaks, beeches, sallows and churning up of grassy rides into oceans of mud in winter and concrete hard surfaces in summer". C.M.R. Pitman (1963), in an article scathingly entitled *The New Forest That Was*, relates: "Vigorous clearing took place in the enclosures with such thoroughness that brambles were all but exterminated, honeysuckle burnt, all the undergrowth removed, and everything incinerated".

Table 1 shows the approximate status of butterflies in the Forest over the decades. Whereas, prior to 1900, some 19 species could be described as 'common' in the Inclosures, only one currently fits this category, although species such as Meadow Brown, Gatekeeper and Purple Hairstreak are locally common. In contrast, the status of butterflies in privately owned woodlands in and just outside the Forest boundary is much healthier, mainly on account of the presence of nectar sources and foodplants because grazing stock are absent.

How has this sad state of affairs come about? The golden era of butterfly abundance in the New Forest must have begun with the Deer Removal Act of 1851 which brought about the destruction of some 5,000–6,000 Fallow Deer so that only around 200 remained by 1900. This must have resulted in massive changes in the vegetation of the Inclosures. For example, Honeysuckle, which Fallow Deer favour, must have increased greatly. Optimum conditions for butterflies probably occurred during the 1890s, which were very much the golden years of collecting in the Forest. Removing padlocks from Inclosure gates to allow access for stock during the late 1960s and 1970s and the recovery of deer numbers then had a considerable adverse effect on ride-side vegetation.

Whereas the annihilation of deer undoubtedly benefited many butterflies, the switch from hardwoods to conifers was disastrous. Mature plantations of densely-packed, midnight-dark conifers provide poor butterfly habitat, because little light penetrates to the forest floor so that most ground flora disappears in such woodlands when they are past their early stages of growth. The accelerated cutting during two world wars incurred much adverse change by bringing about further losses of broad-leaved woodland and further planting of conifers. Then, in the 1950s and 1960s, the Forestry Commission planned to replace *all* the hardwoods with conifers, leaving a 'cosmetic fringe' of hardwood around the conifers to make the woods look more attractive from the outside. When this plan was leaked in 1970, the outcry was so great that the government stepped in and the scheme was abandoned (Tubbs, 1986). A Minister's Mandate was issued which curtailed the Forestry Commission's damaging activities.

Much of all this may have been unavoidable, but the wholesale and deliberate massacre of ride-side vegetation after World War II to make it easier for large machinery to move along the rides and have access to the timber was a final and devastating blow to the woodland species that could have been much better managed. This assault on ride-side vegetation started in the 1950s and by the 1960s a systematic policy of Bramble removal was in place (See Plates 42 and 43, p.33). Removal of nectar sources and larval foodplants is a more effective way of wiping out butterflies than all the slaughter carried out by Victorian collectors and those in charge of the New Forest at that time could scarcely have damaged butterflies more had they carried out a deliberate policy of extermination. Symes (1961) visited the renowned Islands Thorns Inclosure in the 1950s and found "all the ditches had been cleared and the brambles that used to overhang them ... had all been cut away and their roots smothered with an embankment of mud". Much depressed, Symes decided to return in a few years time to see if matters had improved. He did so in 1961 and found that the condition had worsened. He recorded just *one* Silver-washed Fritillary and *one* White Admiral.

Worse was to come, for in response to demands for more grazing land from the Commoners, resulting from the loss of grazing when the Forest boundary was gridded and fenced in the late 1960s, the Forestry Commission finally allowed stock into the Inclosures. Fences and gates were removed or allowed to fall into disrepair. This happened at a time when the Commoners' stock numbers were approaching an all time high, and deer numbers were also rising. As Tubbs (1986) writes: "Ponies, in particular, rapidly penetrated everywhere. The ecological effects have been dramatic". Within a few years, many Inclosures had become heavily grazed, their rides mostly devoid of flowers. Common woodland plants, such as Honeysuckle, Primroses and even thistles, disappeared from large areas of the Forest.

Today, efforts are being made to rectify ecological damage caused by 20th century forestry policies. However, in the New Forest the initial priorities lie in restoring heathland habitats, notably the mires which have been damaged by afforestation and attempted drainage, and in perpetuating pasture woodlands. For wildlife generally, the heathland and

▲ **Plate 1** (*Mike Gibbons*)

Hordle Cliffs in 1998 (Plate 1), where slumping material creates ideal habitat for Glanville Fritillaries. Currently, this is the only Hampshire site for the species which almost certainly arrived naturally from Isle of Wight colonies. A Glanville Fritillary (Plate 2) is shown perched on Thrift. Sexes are similar but the larger females are often a little darker than the males.

◀ **Plate 2** (*John Taverner*)

◀ **Plate 3** (*Pete Durnell*)

Sandy Point on the southern shore of Hayling Island in the mid-1990s, showing clumps of Bell Heather (Plate 3). The area is a Hampshire County Council Countryside Service site, home to Wall Brown (Plate 4) and Grayling (Plate 5), two butterflies that are distributed locally in Hampshire.

▼ **Plate 4** (*Barry Hilling*)

▼ **Plate 5** (*John Taverner*)

▲ **Plate 6** (*Ashley Whitlock*)

Pamber Forest, 1998, (Plate 6) is a Hampshire Wildlife Trust Reserve in the north of the county. Hampshire has an enviable amount of woodland containing deciduous areas that are managed for their wildlife. One species found in Pamber during the 1990s is the Purple Emperor (Plate 7), a spectacular insect that has suffered a serious decline in Hampshire since World War II.

◄ **Plate 7** (*Ashley Whitlock*)

Plate 8 *(Ken Willmott)*

The Hampshire and Isle of Wight Branch of Butterfly Conservation currently runs three Reserves, pictured here. Bentley Station Meadow, 1999 (Plate 8) is an area of ancient meadow that had become heavily overgrown with scrub, whilst Magdalen Hill Down, 1993 (Plate 9) and Yew Hill, 1999 (Plate 10) are two small areas of unimproved chalk downland that had also become overgrown. Scrub clearance and other conservation work by the Branch have returned the three to excellent butterfly habitats. Four species found on one or other of the three are pictured right; they are Brown Argus (Plate 11), Marbled White (Plate 12), Chalkhill Blue larvae with ants (Plate 13) and Orange Tip (Plate 14).

Plate 9 *(Andy Barker)*

Plate 10 *(John Taverner)*

▲ **Plate 11** *(John Taverner)*
▼ **Plate 13** *(Tim Norriss)*

▲ **Plate 12** *(John Taverner)*
▼ **Plate 14** *(Barry Hilling)*

▲ **Plate 15** (*John Taverner*)

◀ **Plate 16** (*Tim Wildridge*)

Noar Hill (Plate 15), 1998, is an area of chalk downland that has escaped the plough because chalk pits, dug in medieval times for a variety of uses, make the topography quite unsuitable for modern agriculture. Conservation by the Hampshire Wildlife Trust has created a rich wildlife habitat where the Duke of Burgundy (Plate 16) and Brown Hairstreak (Plate 17) maintain healthy populations.

◀ **Plate 17** (*Barry Hilling*)

▲ **Plate 18** *(John Taverner)*

Southern Water's Weeke Down reservoir (Plate 18), 1997, is especially set out by the company for wild flowers. No larger than a football pitch, it holds one of the largest Small Blue colonies in Hampshire. How the species arrived is something of a mystery since the reservoir is surrounded by Winchester's suburbs and unsympathetic cereal lands. Plate 19 shows a male Small Blue.

◄ **Plate 19** *(Tim Wildridge)*

Beacon Hill–Warnford, 1994
(Plate 20), an English Nature
NNR, is one of a few unimproved
chalk downland remnants around
the Meon valley. Together with
such sites as The Mountain and
Old Winchester Hill, it is vital
for species that require this
habitat. One scarce Hampshire
butterfly found at Beacon Hill is
the Silver-spotted Skipper (Plate
21), now showing signs of
recovery from a low ebb.

◀ **Plate 21** (*Barry Hilling*)

pasture woodlands are of far greater significance than the Inclosures. Furthermore, many of the Inclosures are probably too badly damaged to justify restoration, particularly those on the most acidic soils.

During the late 1990s, in response to pressure from nature conservationists and other bodies, the Forestry Commission began to exclude Commoners' stock from a number of Inclosures by erecting new fencing. Deer fencing was also erected around some of the richer broad-leaved Inclosures, notably in the eastern Forest. The latter initiative is largely that of John Gulliver, the local forest Keeper, who is a third generation entomologist; his father and grandfather acted as guides and collectors in bygone days and were also known to trade in livestock and specimens.

However, the Forestry Commission still wishes to replant former ancient woodland sites with conifers and remains loathe to open shaded rides in the Inclosures. Furthermore, the redevelopment of habitats for many woodland butterflies is hampered by the fact that the 1971 Minister's Mandate stipulates that the surviving areas of broad-leaved woodland are to be managed on a 200 year rotation and prohibits the felling of areas more than one acre or so in size. Whereas this stipulation assists the conservation of mature woodland flora and fauna, it cuts off the supply of fellings from broad-leaved woodland upon which so many woodland butterflies are dependent (Oates, 1996). The truth is that until management of the Inclosures ceases to be dictated by financial targets, takes account of wider objectives and addresses a number of practical problems, the chances of future generations of naturalists enjoying experiences remotely similar to those of Victorian lepidopterists will remain negligible. It is important to emphasise that the New Forest remains an area of outstanding potential for woodland butterflies, given the extent of unfragmented semi-natural habitat and the dynamic nature of woodland habitats and their associated butterfly faunas.

The new proposed National Park status of the New Forest, determined in the autumn of 1999, has cast the whole future of the Forest's butterfly population into the melting pot. Butterfly Conservation has started to develop an understanding with the Forestry Commission as to the importance of the Forest to Lepidoptera, but how will those in charge of a National Park weigh the needs of wildlife against the demands of tourism? As this book goes to press, the future of the Forest's butterflies hangs in the balance.

Chalk downland

In the days of Gilbert White, it was possible to ride on horseback from his Selborne home to Salisbury with much of the journey across sheepwalk and downland where Great Bustards still roamed. The 1729 map shows huge areas of downland, the largest of which stretched from just south of Andover to Broughton. There were also sizeable tracts to the east and north of Winchester, on the western South Downs and on the north Hampshire downs. Estimates suggest that 98% of Hampshire's downland has been lost during the last 150 years (Johnston, 1998).

The downland system declined during the late 18th century as corn began to be grown extensively, especially during the Napoleonic wars. As chalk country is so dry, it was not possible to grow cereals on a large scale until farming technique improved. Technology then produced powerful machines that could deep-plough and so conserve soil moisture, drought-resistant strains of cereals have been developed and the advent of artificial fertilisers improved the naturally low fertility of chalk soils. Such changes made arable farming possible on land which had been used mainly for sheep, the result being that cereals began to dominate Hampshire's chalklands, although the idyll of sheepwalk and weedy cereal fields persisted into the 20th century.

Once it became profitable to grow cereals on the productive chalk soil, the downland and sheepwalks rapidly began to vanish until only fragments remained. Then, as with the New Forest, two world wars brought about further inroads, massive patches of down being ploughed as submarine blockades made home food production a vital part of our survival. An example was the down around Cheesefoot Head, to the east of Winchester, which *was* proposed as a National Nature Reserve but was ploughed to form one of the county's bleakest cereal prairies.

The result is a pathetically small patchwork of down which has survived on old earthworks, on MoD land, in places such as Noar Hill where the man-made topography of old chalk-pits made it unsuitable for the plough, or on steep chalk scarps which, as the previous text has already explained, are scarce in Hampshire. This remnant was further damaged following myxomatosis in the early 1950s, when scrub developed over much grassland as Rabbit grazing decreased, whilst afforestation made further inroads into the remaining down.

Myxomatosis resulted in the vigorous growth of coarse grasses, notably Upright Brome and False Oat-grass, and a variety of bushes which developed over the short, broken turf that Rabbits maintained. Butterflies such as Silver-spotted Skipper, Adonis Blue, Silver-studded Blue and Grayling quickly declined, whereas the longer grass conditions favoured species such as Dark Green Fritillary, Duke of Burgundy and Marbled White. However, many downs where the turf had been heavily grazed and broken by Rabbits proved to be perfect seed beds for tree and shrub seedlings and developed quickly into dense scrub, to the detriment of even the coarse-grassland butterflies. Furthermore, with the decline of sheep grazing, many slopes became agriculturally redundant and were turned over to forestry. Beech and a range of conifers were planted, afforestation being particularly severe in the Hampshire sector of the South Downs. Figure 5 shows the distribution of chalk downland at the close of the 20th century.

Further agricultural intensification occurred, especially during the 1970s and early 1980s, as land values increased in response to profits made from cereals that were heavily subsidised by the Common Agricultural Policy. Conversion of downland to improved pasture also occurred widely; Beacon Hill, one of the richest butterfly downs in the Winchester area, was cleared of scrub in 1984 and partly reseeded and dressed with artificial fertiliser. The country's wildlife laws proved grossly inadequate in the face of this onslaught, even after the Wildlife and Countryside Act of 1981. Indeed, much of Hampshire's richest downland has survived because of Scheduled Ancient Monument designation.

Figure 5. Distribution of unimproved and semi-improved calcareous grassland in Hampshire
Map created and reproduced by permission of Hampshire County Council, our thanks going especially to Nicky Court.

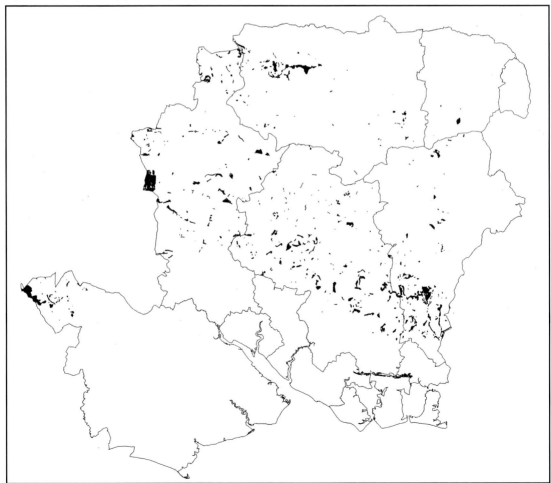

During the 1980s, many surviving areas of downland were taken over for Pheasant shoots, especially chalk combe systems. Fragments of old downland were ploughed for Pheasant feed crops, scrub or woodland was either planted or allowed to develop to provide cover for the birds, and stock grazing on these areas ceased altogether.

Rabbit populations recovered considerably since 1989 over much of Hampshire's downland so that numbers now approach or even exceed those of pre-myxomatosis days. Stockbridge Down, for instance, was infested with Rabbits, Philip Marshall (National Trust warden) counting over 600 on one evening in April 1998. This recovery in Rabbit numbers really came too late for Hampshire's specialist short-turf downland butterflies, which had long been restricted to a handful of nature reserves, and has had an adverse effect on butterflies which favour longer turf. Rabbit management has become the critical issue on important butterfly downs such as Old Winchester Hill and Stockbridge Down, but for many 'unmanaged' sites it is only Rabbit grazing that has saved the diversity of flowers and Lepidoptera.

There have been three ecological surveys of Hampshire's downland. In 1966, a survey by Blackwood and Tubbs identified some 2,115 ha, mainly in the form of downs less than 20 ha in size. This represented 2.18% of Hampshire's chalkland, although the figure should have been larger as the survey counted only sites larger than two hectares and so excluded numerous small fragments (Blackwood and Tubbs, 1970). During the early 1980s, Hampshire County Council conducted surveys which included 67 fragments under 2 ha in size and which identified some 2,053 ha of downland (Prescott, 1983). However, again many small fragments were missed. The County Council survey suggested that, in addition to loss to developing woodland through lack of grazing, chalk down was being destroyed at the rate of 1% (20 ha) per year. In response to the categorisation of chalk grassland as a priority habitat in the Biodiversity Action Plan for Hampshire, the most recent estimate by Hampshire County Council suggests that there are less than 2,800 ha of chalk downland left in the county, equating to about 5% of the UK resource (Johnston, 1998).

Today's downland remnant contains areas unusually rich in wildlife, although the long-term prosperity of their butterfly populations is threatened by isolation and by the hostile nature of the surrounding terrain; recolonisation will be difficult should local extinctions occur because several of the butterfly species involved are highly sedentary and therefore unlikely to move far to recolonise lost ground.

Few sizeable tracts of down are left and Hampshire is unfortunate in that the National Trust and the MoD hold very little of this land, although one of our two largest areas of downland is the Hampshire sector of the MoD (DERA) ranges at Porton Down. However, Hampshire *has* been fortunate in that the County Council has long had a policy of acquiring and managing chalk downland of high conservation value. Butser Hill NNR, the Farley Mount/Pitt Down complex and part of Martin Down NNR are owned by Hampshire County Council and these are amongst the largest and richest downs in the county. The Hampshire Wildlife Trust has also been active in managing important downland sites such as Noar Hill, which is a fine example of a chalk downland mosaic. The Trust also manages Old Burghclere lime quarry, whilst the Hampshire and Isle of Wight Branch of Butterfly Conservation manages important sites at Magdalen Hill Down and Yew Hill, both near Winchester. The reserve at Magdalen Hill Down includes a sizeable area of arable land which is being restored to downland (see p.35). Funding from Countryside Stewardship, the Environmentally Sensitive Area scheme, English Nature, Hampshire County Council, the National Lottery and various corporate and individual sponsors has helped considerably.

The dominant grasses of Hampshire's downland are Upright Brome, False Oat-grass, Red Fescue and Sheep's-fescue. Much of the county's downland therefore fits into the National Vegetation Classification categories CG2 (*Festuca ovina – Avenula pratensis* grassland) and CG3 (*Bromus erectus* grassland). Tor-grass, which is regarded as a troublesome coarse grass on many limestone areas in southern England, is very local in Hampshire.

The status of some flowers that are important butterfly foodplants on Hampshire downland is as follows: Horseshoe Vetch (locally frequent); Kidney Vetch (locally common); Common Bird's-foot-trefoil (common); Common Rock-rose (locally common) – (Brewis, Bowman and Rose, 1996).

Pressures on surviving downs are often immense, not least from recreational uses from a burgeoning population. Parts of Stockbridge Down, for example, are being cut to pieces by the hooves of riding-horses. At many sites a well-meaning public is insufficiently aware of the complexities of downland management that is essential for the perpetuation of chalk grassland communities so that conflict arises between conservationists on the one hand and recreational users on the other, both sides paradoxically wanting the same downland habitat.

Hampshire has been very much at the centre of pioneer work carried out on the management of downland for nature conservation during the late 20th century; the work of BUTT (1986), which pioneered research into the management requirements of downland butterflies, was centred on Hampshire. Indeed, considering the diversity of adverse factors, Hampshire's conservation movement has been largely successful to date in conserving the remnants of the county's downland.

Hampshire's remaining downland patches differ widely in their flora and therefore in their suitability for different butterfly species. The reasons for such differences are more complicated than simple factors such as aspect and soil properties, although these play a part in the local flora, and it is thought that the differing histories of management are largely responsible for floral differences in ways that are not fully understood. However, whatever the causes of local floral variations, downland remains one of our richest butterfly habitats.

Woodland outside the New Forest

Hampshire is one of most wooded counties in the UK, holding some 5% of the national resource of ancient semi-natural woodland. About 11% of Hampshire is covered in broad-leaved woodland, totalling some 42,000 ha (Johnston, 1998) – these figures include the New Forest. However, a large amount of woodland outside of the Forest has been lost as urban areas, agriculture, aggregate extraction and especially plantation forestry have expanded. Indeed, about half the county's

Figure 6. Distribution of broad-leaved woodland in Hampshire *Map created and reproduced by permission of Hampshire County Council, our thanks going especially to Nicky Court.*

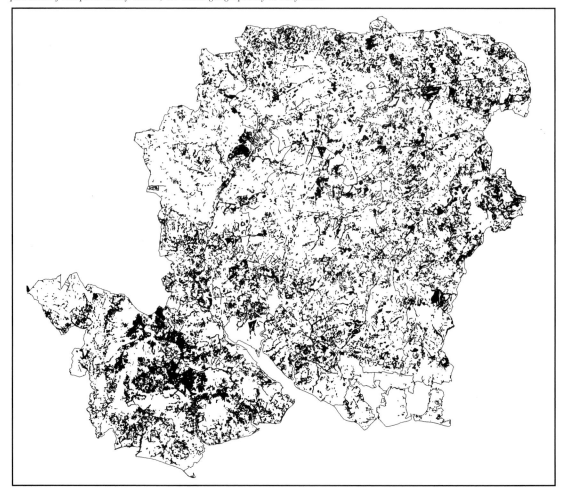

ancient woodland cover has been lost to these uses in the last 50 years. Plantations have done most damage to Hampshire's woodland butterfly fauna, replacing much of the Hazel-coppice woodland and oak timber woodland which were particularly rich habitats.

Away from the Forest, around 75% of Hampshire's ancient semi-natural woodland developed under the coppice management system (HCC, 1991). In 1895 there were in the region of 38,500 ha of worked Hazel-coppice in the county. In 1947, only 13,077 ha of Hazel-coppice existed, of which some 1,500 ha was in-cycle, but by 1981 over half had gone (Forestry Commission census figures). By the late 1970s, coppicing was only being practised on a few estates to the north and west of the New Forest, in the Kings Somborne area, to the south and north of Basingstoke and around Southwick.

Keeping a wood properly coppiced is expensive as it requires much manual labour. So, as Hazel became obsolete, owners allowed their woods to grow over because the cost of keeping them open had no financial return. However, flower seeds will remain dormant in the soil for many years and if an overgrown woodland is coppiced again, the flowers will come through in abundance in the next growing season and with them the insects that need such a habitat.

Since 1981, Hampshire County Council, supported by the Countryside Commission, has been running a scheme providing financial support for traditional coppice management in the county. This has helped the establishment of the Wessex Coppice Group, which helps with training in traditional skills and marketing of coppice products. In 1996, changes to the

Figure 7. Distribution of woodland (broad-leaved and coniferous) in Hampshire *Map created and reproduced by permission of Hampshire County Council, our thanks going especially to Nicky Court.*

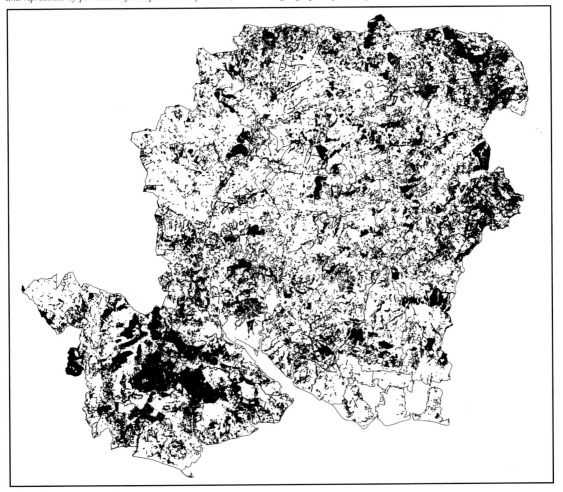

Forestry Commission's Woodland Grant Scheme further encouraged the reworking of coppice woodland. Currently, over 400 ha of Hazel-coppice are once again being worked over much of Hampshire. Sadly though, the associated butterflies, notably Pearl-bordered Fritillary and Duke of Burgundy, have only responded in mid-west Hampshire and there is much seemingly suitable but unoccupied habitat. Indeed, it is only in woods to the east of Stockbridge and to the north of Kings Somborne that these species still exist in coppiced woodland.

Hampshire County Council, some local authorities and the Hampshire Wildlife Trust have all been actively managing coppice woodland in the county for more than a decade. Crab Wood, close to Winchester, is an example of a wood that had become heavily overgrown so that butterfly populations declined. The Council foresters, led by Phil Allen, embarked on a programme of rotational coppicing, cutting areas year by year until the wood became a coppice patchwork of various ages with untouched woodland in between. It was remarkable to see how the scene changed after each cut. Within months, what had been dark, overgrown woodland became sunlit with a sea of colour on the flower-rich floor where butterflies found nectar and their larval foodplants.

Historically, the two main uses of oak timber were for ship-building and leather-tanning. Hampshire became a major centre for growing Pedunculate Oak and Beech timber for naval ships and during the Napoleonic wars, Hampshire produced enough oak to build 70 men-of-war. During the 19th century, leather-tanning became the more important industry and wood-ash was in great demand for the pottery industry. Oak was planted extensively in old Hazel-coppices during the late 18th and 19th centuries. For example, 65 ha of oak was planted in Alice Holt Forest, an old hunting forest, in 1814 alone (Colebourn, 1983). However, the price of oak collapsed in the late 19th century and much of the planted oak was used during the two world wars, only to be replaced with non-native conifers.

Coastal habitats

The entire coast of Hampshire is low-lying; cliffs line the coast west of Hurst spit, but rise to little more than 20 m, whilst small areas of cliff at Lepe, Brownwich and Hill Head seldom rise above 10 m. The highest cliffs are at Hengistbury Head where there is a trig point at 36 m. Two cliff areas are of special significance for butterflies. The first is at Hordle, which was formerly renowned for Small Blues and has been colonised recently by Glanville Fritillaries. The Small Blue died out from its headquarters around Becton Bunny following cliff stabilisation, but the Glanville Fritillary still remains at the close of the century. The second is at Southbourne Undercliff which is a sheltered, south-facing area that has been excellent for species such as Clouded Yellow and Small Copper.

Salt-marsh dominates the shore from Hurst spit to Lepe, along parts of the western side of Southampton Water and on considerable parts of Portsmouth, Langstone and Chichester Harbours. Whilst this is a rich habitat for much wildlife, no British butterfly utilises such habitat. However, behind the salt-marsh there are quite extensive areas of coastal grazing marshes, such as those along the Keyhaven/Pennington shore, at Park Shore, Needs Ore, Lepe and Farlington Marshes. These total some 750 ha (Johnson, 1998), attracting numbers of vagrant butterflies and large populations of grass-feeding species. The Wall Brown finds such areas to be excellent habitat; indeed, this species is now almost restricted to the coastal belt in Hampshire, having largely retreated from recently-used chalk downland sites, although in 1999 there is some evidence of a return to inland sites.

Some of these areas are nature reserves, but others are under considerable threat from development. In recent years, Dibden Bay and other parts on the western shore of Southampton Water have seen interesting developments with species such as Clouded Yellow and Brown Argus, but Dibden is threatened with a dock development and the remaining areas of shore along this stretch cannot be considered as safe from such ventures.

A few remaining areas of coastal heath occur at places such as Browndown and behind Hampshire's only sand dunes at Sinah Common and Hayling Island's Sandy Point. These coastal heaths and dunes form excellent butterfly habitat, notably for Grayling, Gatekeeper and Small Copper.

There are also patches of old and heavily compacted shingle that have become partly of wholly covered with vegetation, although their exposed nature limits their value to butterflies. Some such patches are of importance however; at Needs Ore Point, swathes of Sheep's Sorrel have developed on such habitat and support good numbers of Small Coppers, the adults taking nectar from a variety of flowers such as Smith's Pepperwort, Springbeauty, Sea Campion and Gorse.

The Hampshire coast has been much developed since 1945 and valuable habitat has been lost. Much of the remaining 'wild' coast is now nature reserve run by English Nature, the Hampshire Wildlife Trust and Hampshire County Council, which gives those areas considerable protection. Pressures remain however, and we cannot be complacent about their future.

Heathland outside the New Forest

The Tertiary rocks of northern Hampshire mirror those of the New Forest so their acidic soils are of limited agricultural use. As a consequence they have developed a heathland habitat not unlike that of the New Forest, although lacking the protection that history has given the latter, these northern heaths have been eroded by human development into a piecemeal distribution. Over 90% of this heathland has been lost over the last 200 years (Johnston, 1998), especially during recent decades. Losses have been due to urban development, forestry, roads and especially to natural succession of woodland due to the absence of grazing and increased water abstraction. Heathland survival has been best on land owned by the MoD in the Thames Basin and Western Weald, although grazing ceased on these heaths several decades ago and is only now being restored locally.

Figure 8. Distribution of heath, acid fenland and mire in Hampshire *Map created and reproduced by permission of Hampshire County Council, our thanks going especially to Nicky Court.*

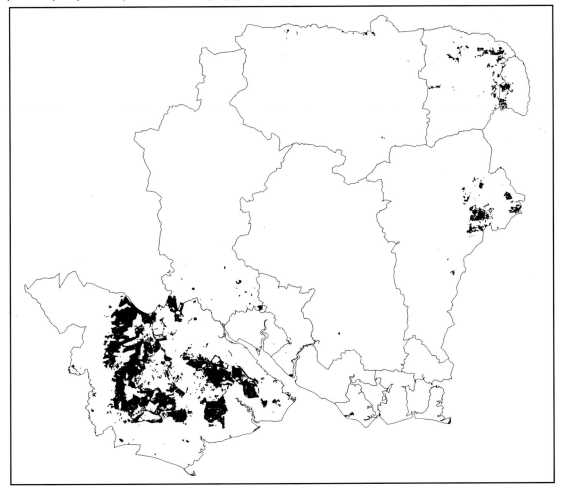

Heathland on similar geology bordering the New Forest in southern Hampshire and the adjoining parts of Dorset covered by this book have suffered similar losses; places such as Chandlers Ford, land on the outskirts of Southampton and considerable areas around the outskirts of Bournemouth have experienced heavy loss of such land to housing since the 1950s.

Outside of the New Forest, around 2,500 ha of undeveloped land with obvious heathland characteristics remain, the vast majority of which is, or could easily be, dry heath. Silver Birch, Scots Pine and oaks are invading much of this heath and it is ironic that the arboreal Purple Emperor is now established on many of the Western Weald heaths.

Another important issue, particularly in the conservation of wet heaths and mires, is the lowering of water-tables by ground water extraction and developing woodland. However, colonies of heathland butterflies, such as Grayling, Green Hairstreak and Silver-studded Blue, still occur on a number of these heaths, although recent trends have been towards a steady decline and these species are now absent from large areas of heath.

Conservation problems facing these heaths are immense, not least because the pastoral farming systems which created and maintained them have completely broken down. Conservation initiatives, initially led by Hampshire County Council's Heathland Project and now by the County Council's Hampshire Grazing Project, are reinstating the grazing which is essential for the restoration of neglected heathland. Hampshire County Council and the Hampshire Wildlife Trust manage a number of important relic heathland sites as nature reserves, such as Bartley Heath and Broxhead Common, whilst the National Trust has an important area of managed heath at Ludshott. However, management problems are manifold and are not helped by the unwillingness of many local people to accept fences and livestock which are necessary to perpetuate heathland. For example, in the early 1990s the National Trust was forced to abandon plans to fence and graze a neglected heathland SSSI at Conford when local people objected to fencing; colonies of Marsh and Small Pearl-bordered Fritillaries subsequently died out. This fencing issue is complicated by the fact that much of Hampshire's heathland is common land and there are legal issues in erecting fences on such land. Unless people accept the need for fencing and grazing animals, or a technological development obviates the need for conventional fencing, heathland and its associated wildlife will continue to decline.

Meadows

Away from the coast, Hampshire is an important county for unimproved meadows, holding some 3,000 ha out of a UK resource of no more than 15,000 ha (Johnston, 1998). These meadows occur on damp ground in river valleys and on soils which are either wet and acidic or on stiff clay. Even when they have escaped destruction by drainage or dressing with artificial fertilisers, they remain vulnerable to heavy grazing which is very damaging to butterfly populations. Recently, many unimproved pastures have either been too heavily grazed by horses, or neglected and consequently lost to woodland. Most notable in this latter category, from the butterfly conservation viewpoint, are the pastures around Fleet where abandonment of grazing brought about the apparent extinction of the Marsh Fritillary in what was its county stronghold. Bentley Station Meadow, a Butterfly Conservation reserve, is a rare example of an unimproved wood-edge meadow which is a valuable entomological habitat (see p.35). Richer meadows existed along the western edge of Alice Holt Forest until they were destroyed in the late 1970s. Given suitable grazing levels, unimproved meadows can support strong and varied butterfly populations for species such as Small Skipper, Small Copper, Common Blue, Marbled White and Meadow Brown.

There have also been losses of such habitat in the post-war years due to the development of housing, light industry and urban-edge shopping parks, especially in the Southampton/Portsmouth areas and in north east Hampshire. Construction of the M27 corridor led to further losses.

Other habitat types

Apart from the above, Hampshire has other habitats of importance. The weed-free cereal prairies of the chalk and the colourful fields of Rape, Flax and daffodils that have become such a feature of the landscape are of limited use to butterflies, although there are records of large gatherings of whites taking nectar on Rape. However, even in this intensively farmed land there are butterfly havens.

Plate 22 (*Ashley Whitlock*)

Plate 23 (*Ken Willmott*)

Martin Down, 1998, (Plate 22) and the Hampshire portion of Porton Down are the largest areas of unimproved chalk downland remaining in the county. Martin Down is run by The National Trust and parts are especially managed for scarce or disappearing species. It is the only remaining Hampshire site for Adonis Blue (Plate 23) and one of four remaining sites for Marsh Fritillary (Plate 24).

Plate 24 (*John Taverner*)

▲ **Plate 25** (*All photographs by Michael Skelton*)

▼ **Plate 26**   ▼ **Plate 27**   ▼ **Plate 28**

Plate 29 ▶

One of the most outstanding events of the 1990s in the butterfly world was the first successful over-wintering in Britain by Clouded Yellows, on the Southbourne Undercliffs (Plate 25) in 1998/99. Plates 26–29 record the main stages of this historic event. Ovum (Plate 26); 3rd instar larva (Plate 27); 5th instar larva (Plate 28); the first emerged adult (Plate 29).

▲ **Plate 30** *(John Taverner)*

Crab Wood, 1997 (Plate 30), on the outskirts of Winchester, is run by Hampshire County Council foresters whose belief is that commercial forestry and nature conservation are compatible aims. The wood is coppiced in rotation and rides are kept open so that Silver-washed Fritillaries (Plate 31) and White Admirals have larval foodplants for oviposition and nectar sources for adults.

◀ **Plate 31** *(John Taverner)*

◀ **Plate 32** *(John Taverner)*

**Stockbridge Down, 1998
(Plate 32) is a National Trust
area of chalk downland
where a variety of
conservation works have
created an excellent habitat
for species such as Dark
Green Fritillary (Plate 33).**

▼ **Plate 33** *(John Taverner)*

◀ **Plate 34** *(John Taverner)*

**The shore at English
Nature's Needs Ore Reserve,
1998 (Plate 34) is an old
coastal shingle formation,
parts of which have become
overgrown with Sheeps'
Sorrel, a foodplant for Small
Copper (Plate 35) larvae.**

▼ **Plate 35** *(John Taverner)*

Plate 36 (*Brian Fletcher*) ▶

Burghclere Lime-pits, 1994 (Plate 36) is a an area of old chalk diggings run by the Hampshire Wildlife Trust. The site is noted for Green Hairstreak (Plate 37).

▼ **Plate 37** (*Barry Hilling*)

Plate 38 (*Ashley Whitlock*) ▶

Ashford Hangers (Plate 38) is a wooded scarp where White-letter Hairstreaks (Plate 39) find the elms necessary for their larvae.

▼ **Plate 39** (*John Taverner*)

▲ **Plate 40** (*John Taverner*)

A New Forest heath, 1990 (Plate 40). Although the New Forest Inclosures have been devastated as a butterfly habitat, some heathland species still exist in considerable numbers. One heathland specialist is the Silver-studded Blue (Plate 41) and this species' map in the Millennium Atlas shows the New Forest as one of the main strongholds for this butterfly in Great Britain.

◄ **Plate 41** (*John Taverner*)

▲ **Plate 42** (*Matthew Oates*)

Pondhead Inclosure, 1995 (Plate 42) like the New Forest of old, with a broad ride through oak woodland, a zone of flower-rich grassland and a thick border of brambles and shrubs. **Perrywood, Hazeley Inclosure, 1995 (Plate 43)** shows what has gone wrong in the New Forest, with short, flowerless grassland grazed by ponies and deer, a complete absence of ride-side brambles and no understorey beneath the conifers.

◄ **Plate 43** (*Matthew Oates*)

▲ **Plate 44** (*Matthew Oates*)

▲ **Plate 45** (*Ken Willmott*)

▲ **Plate 46** (*Barry Hilling*)

▲ **Plate 47** (*Matthew Oates*)

Six species for which the New Forest was once noted. The High Brown Fritillary (Plate 44) has gone. The White Admiral (Plate 45), Pearl-bordered Fritillary (Plate 46) and Small Pearl-bordered Fritillary (Plate 47) remain in small numbers. The Large Tortoiseshell (Plate 48) is no longer found in England and the Purple Emperor (Plate 49) is now a vagrant in The Forest.

▼ **Plate 48** (*John Taverner*)

▼ **Plate 49** (*John Taverner*)

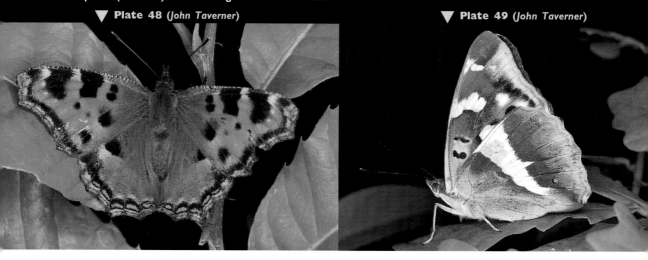

The **roadside and trackside hedgerows and verges** are much favoured by Green-veined Whites, whilst Gatekeepers, Orange Tips and the commoner skippers also occur in strength in such habitat. Garlic Mustard grows in abundance on many Hampshire verges and along rural footpaths, providing ideal habitat for Orange Tips. This habitat covers 13,000 ha along Hampshire's 10,000 km of roads (Johnston, 1998).

There are verges that harbour less common species, especially the wider verges. One such patch on Winchester's outskirts, carefully cut by the local Council to conserve a fine display of orchids, supports a colony of Small Blues. There are several places where roadside Wych Elms hold White-letter Hairstreaks, one or two trees being sufficient to support a colony. The sides of new by-passes, such as that at Alresford and the M3 at Winchester, are seeded with wild flowers and attract butterflies in spite of constant traffic and it is thought that Essex Skippers have extended their range by using such routes.

Hampshire has a considerable **urban and suburban area**, especially in the south. Towns may not seem ideal butterfly habitat, but they have gardens, parks and wasteland areas with many flowers that provide rich sources of nectar. *Buddleias* attract hordes of butterflies; allotments are often wonderful nurseries for Large and Small Whites; Ice Plants can be irresistible in autumn and a number of people especially lay out parts of their gardens to attract butterflies. Towns also have temperatures that are often one or two degrees above those of the surrounding countryside and this combination of nectar sources and slightly warmer temperatures means that our hibernating species are often attracted to urban areas as the season comes to an end, our buildings then providing winter quarters. Many of our early records come from towns. In the city of Southampton and its immediate surrounds, 35 butterfly species were recorded over the period 1990/96 (Barker and Budd, 1997), the local city Council being much concerned with nature conservation.

Butterfly Conservation reserves in Hampshire

In such limited space it is only possible to outline the main features of butterfly habitat in the county. Recent publications on Hampshire's wildlife have contained excellent chapters on such topics as the changes in habitat over time (Colin Tubbs writing in 'Birds of Hampshire' – Clark and Eyre, 1993) and the floral habitats of our area (Francis Rose writing in 'The Flora of Hampshire' – Brewis, Bowman and Rose, 1996). Hampshire has so many small pockets of valuable land, such as the tiny patch at Weeke Down reservoir, deliberately maintained by Southern Water as a flower-rich meadow and packed with Small Blues in the late 1990s, living in what was for them a living larder of Kidney Vetch. Let it suffice to close this section with a very brief reference to three rather special pieces of land, set aside especially for the benefit of butterflies.

The Hampshire and Isle of Wight Branch of Butterfly Conservation has three mainland reserves devoted mainly to butterflies, these being at Yew Hill, Magdalen Hill Down and Bentley Station Meadow (see Plates 8–10, p.14 and Figure 9, p.44). The first two are small areas of chalk down on the outskirts of Winchester; Bentley Station Meadow is unimproved meadow in the north east of the county.

Yew Hill was the first reserve to be created, opened on 9th May 1990. It consists of 2 ha of unimproved downland, where bushes had encroached to a certain extent, which Refuge Assurance generously granted to Butterfly Conservation on a 10-year, rent-free lease. Adjoining the reserve is a 2 ha covered reservoir where Southern Water have allowed a natural regeneration of downland flowers and grasses to take place. Around 30 butterfly species have occurred on the site, perhaps the most notable being the Duke of Burgundy whose larvae fed on the mass of Cowslips that are especially numerous on the reservoir area. Unfortunately, this species may have disappeared but there are hopes that it may recolonise the site.

Magdalen Hill Down was officially opened on 9th May 1992, set on a steep scarp slope of chalk on the northern side of the eroded Chilcomb anticline. It *was* 10 ha of ancient downland that had become much overgrown by scrub in the years following World War II, most of the scrub being cleared on acquisition. In 1996, the Hampshire and Isle of Wight Branch of Butterfly Conservation acquired a slightly larger neighbouring block of land which had been arable farmland because the slopes were much more gentle, owning part and leasing the remainder. Part of the money for this extension came from a National Lottery award that was matched with funds raised by the Branch. This extension is in the process of being converted to flower-rich calcareous grassland. Following initial preparation, it was sown in 1997 with wild flower and grass seed collected from local downs and was officially opened on 10th July 1999 by Sir David Attenborough. The area as a whole supports around 30 butterfly species.

Bentley Station Meadow was purchased in the summer of 1992 and consists of some 3.5 ha of ancient meadow that had become heavily overgrown with scrub. Much clearance work has created a varied habitat of open woodland, open meadow, grassland and an ensemble of tree species that includes Great Sallow, the food plant of Purple Emperor larvae. The reserve borders on Alice Holt Forest, which has a Purple Emperor population, and the meadow will no doubt benefit from this proximity to an important butterfly woodland. Like Yew Hill, some 30 butterfly species are likely to occur in a year.

A great deal of conservation work has been put into these areas, as is the case with other Hampshire reserves that are in the hands of English Nature, The Hampshire Wildlife Trust, The National Trust, local Councils and private owners. This has involved measures such as grazing with sheep and cattle, shrub clearance, Rabbit control and coppicing, much of the work carried out by volunteers from a number of organisations.

It is easy to become complacent about the future of our butterflies when all these reserves are considered together, but the future is far from secure. Population pressures will grow; government plans for new housing in Hampshire threaten 'green' areas, along with new out-of-town shopping centres; the mushrooming number of motorcars will lead to more roads; many developments in agricultural practice do not engender any great confidence for the future of wildlife, although organic farming and the withdrawal of land from production as *long-term* setaside have significant benefits for wildlife. Furthermore, central governments have not shown much understanding of nature conservation. Wildlife does not compete well with profit and the fight to conserve butterfly species has only just begun. On the other hand, Hampshire County Council and our smaller local authorities have shown an admirable attitude to nature conservation and we must hope that this enlightened approach not only continues in the future, but spreads to Westminster.

PART THREE

WEATHER
1990 to 1999

Weather has a profound influence on the fortunes of butterflies, so that population changes in the 1990s will be more meaningful if the weather for that period is known. The following section outlines the county's weather for the years 1990–1999.

1990 – Spring was very warm and sunny until the end of May when the weather deteriorated to a cool and dull June. Summer returned with a vengeance in mid-July and although the end of July and the whole of August were hot, there was sufficient rainfall to prevent severe drought problems.

1991 – Spring was cloudy but dry, with April and May dominated by a northerly airstream. May was the cloudiest since 1913, the driest since 1896, but one of the chilliest. However, emergence of spring species was good. June was the dullest since 1929 and often wet, whilst July started and finished well, with a poor middle section. August was excellent being warm, sunny and dry throughout and the remainder of the year was mild and mostly dry.

1992 – Late February and early March were sunny, but March then continued as a dry but dull month. Most of April was wetter and cooler than average, but then May produced settled and much warmer weather. In contrast with previous years, June was warm and sunny, but July's weather was very mixed with some dull, wet and thundery conditions. August was the wettest since 1956; September was dry but very cool; October was more like a normal November whilst November itself turned out to be mild but very wet. December was cold and rather wet.

1993 – Unrelieved rain and high winds made this the dullest January since 1975, but it was the fifth warmest of the century. Anticyclonic gloom made February the dullest since 1980, but spring broke on 11th March and the weather was mostly bright until early May. The rest of May and the first three weeks of June were a mixture of rain, sun and winds. A fortnight of fine weather followed, but the rest of July was damp and overcast. August was mostly hot and sunny; September was the wettest since 1976 and the first nine months of the year were the wettest since 1981. Autumn was also the coolest since 1952. After a very wet opening, October was rather dry and the year ended with December rainfall twice the average for that month.

1994 – Early January was very wet with snow on 6th/7th, but it became drier towards the end of the month. February was cold, with some bright days but snow fell on 14th/15th. Much of early March was overcast, but bright days did occur with the 21st and 26th being like the height of summer. April was a mixture of rain, overcast and a few warm and sunny days, whilst the first half of May was mostly warm and sunny. The weather was then rather poor until 11th June when summer burst and eventually developed into the hottest July on record with almost unbroken heat and sunshine. August continued in this vein. It was then generally mild for the remainder of the year, November being the mildest since records began in the 17th century.

1995 – January was one of the wettest since records began and although the 2nd and 4th February were like spring, a procession of depressions brought wet, windy but mild weather for most of that month. March was rather chilly but bright, with a few warm days and April was mostly dry with very variable temperatures. The first week of May was glorious, but the rest of the month was a mixture of sun, showers and overcast. June was overcast and cool until the 20th and from then, through July and August, the weather was *very* hot and sunny, apart from heavy rain on 23rd August. It was the hottest

August on record. September was the wettest for 20 years, almost making up for the summer drought; over 5 cm of rain fell on Southampton in one day. This was followed by the warmest October on record, but the weather then changed with the month and although November was unusually mild, torrential rain fell at times. December was gloomy, damp and cold.

1996 – January was even more miserable than December, and February was mostly cold with snow in the first week and on 19th/20th. Most of March was overcast and chilly with occasional days that threatened to be bright and this was followed by a mostly warm and sunny April. It was an appalling May for butterflies, one of the coldest since records began. June then flamed for nineteen days and the rest of the month was reasonable. Most of July, August and the first half of September were generally hot and sunny with the sun at times blazing from cloudless skies. The rest of September saw a good deal of overcast with almost continual rain on 30th. October was a mixture of sun and rain, although it was mild for much of the time, whilst early November had some fine days before the month became cold and wet. December was rather dry, ending with a bright, cold week.

1997 – January was the driest for 200 years, but rather cold; February was a month of mixed weather; March was mostly warm and sunny. April was splendid; few Aprils can have equalled this for butterflies. However, after a glorious 1st May, the month deteriorated and most of May and the last two weeks of June produced overcast, wet or showery weather, June being the wettest this century. July, August and September were then splendid, August especially being very hot and sunny. Temperatures for most of the remaining year were unusually mild, with isolated butterfly records up to the 31st December.

1998 – The first three months were amongst the warmest on record with the weather like a pleasant spring. Hibernators awoke early in January and these species were recorded at a number of sites to late March. April was rather wet and miserable but May was magnificent, warm and sunny days with temperatures well into the twenties being the norm until the last few days. June and July were wet, making the year poor for many species, but these were followed by a hot and sunny August. The rest of the year was not very suitable for butterflies and the season ended early.

1999 – From a butterfly viewpoint, 1999 was a mix of good and bad weather and overall it was one of the wettest years of the century. There was not much to encourage hibernators to awake until a fine but short-lived spell in mid-March, followed by mediocre weather in April. Both the beginning and end of May were briefly fine and sunny and then, after mixed weather in June, July was excellent. August had a few fine days between rain and overcast; September was very wet; October had two good but brief spells and the last two months produced only a handful of days when late butterflies were seen.

PART FOUR

A BRIEF HISTORY OF BUTTERFLY STUDY IN HAMPSHIRE

Shortly after the dawn of interest in British Lepidoptera, some 200 years ago, it became apparent that Hampshire was one of the best counties for butterflies in terms of both diversity and abundance of species. By the 1850s the New Forest had become the premier location for the pursuit of butterflies and moths in the country. Butterfly collectors also regularly visited a number of other sites in the county, particularly the woods and downs close to population centres. Indeed, localities such as St Catherine's Hill, Crab Wood, Pamber Forest and Portsdown Hill have been renowned butterfly sites since at least the mid-19th century. Conversely, many sites popular with butterfly enthusiasts today, such as Old Winchester Hill and Martin Down, were not frequented until well into the 20th century, not necessarily because of travelling constraints.

The early enthusiasts were essentially collectors, though many were also ardent breeders of Lepidoptera. Some were butterfly specialists, a few were moth purists, but the majority collected both and were therefore true lepidopterists. Many of them also collected birds' eggs. The majority of collectors were gentlemen from the upper and upper-middle classes, with the clerical, teaching, military and medical professions being particularly well represented. Between 1832 and 1890, six entomological journals dedicated to collecting were launched, though there were never more than three in publication at any one time. There are numerous references to collecting in Hampshire in these Victorian journals. In particular, there are many detailed descriptions of the abundance of butterflies and the pursuit of rarities in the New Forest. To the modern reader many of these accounts may seem fantastic, so great is the scale of abundance depicted.

Collectors were obsessed with variations (or aberrations): i.e. specimens which differed from the typical form, by having spots fused together, spots enlarged or distorted, white bands reduced or absent, and so on. Some variations are remarkably different from the type, such as the form *valezina* of the female Silver-washed Fritillary which in bygone days was regarded as a Hampshire speciality. Variations, or 'vars' and 'abs' as they were known, are strongly associated with large populations; where a species abounds, unusually marked specimens tend to occur, at least in some years. In the heyday of Lepidoptera collecting, during late Victorian and Edwardian times, butterflies occurred regularly in such profusion that interesting variations could be encountered with the frequency necessary to justify the effort and maintain enthusiasm. Nowadays, of course, there are relatively few situations wherein a species occurs in sufficient abundance to make the search for aberrations worthwhile. The extent to which the occurrence of variations has dwindled in Britain during the 20th century goes a long way towards explaining the demise of the popularity of butterfly collecting. In effect, not only were British butterflies considerably more abundant a hundred years ago, but they appeared in a far greater diversity of colour forms than they do now.

During the 1890s, at least three professional Lepidopterists were active in the New Forest – Tate and Jerrad of Lyndhurst and R.E. Salwey of Brockenhurst. They made their living from selling livestock (ova, larvae and pupae) and specimens to collectors, and by guiding collectors in the Forest. An unusual variation could fetch several guineas. In addition, many collectors built up and sold personal collections for relatively large sums of money. Thus, Salwey sold his collection at an auction in London in 1892 and F.W. Frohawk, a leading authority on butterflies and a regular visitor to Hampshire and the New Forest, sold his collection of 6,000 specimens for £1,000 in 1927, and purchased a sizeable house on the proceeds (Chatfield, 1987).

Several local accounts and lists were published in the Victorian entomological and natural history society journals. For example, a detailed account of the fauna of the Portsmouth district was published in *The Entomologist* (Pearce, 1890) and the Rev A.C. Harvey published a list of Hampshire Lepidoptera in the *Proceedings of the Hampshire Field Club* from 1887 to 1891. However, the first overview of Hampshire's butterfly fauna was written by H. Goss for the *Victoria County History for Hampshire and the Isle of Wight*, which was published in 1900. It is a fascinating and surprisingly confident account, which suggests that the overall status of Hampshire's butterflies was by then considered to be reasonably well understood.

There are, however, some curious omissions; for example, there is no reference to the occurrence of Silver-studded Blue on the chalk, although the butterfly was widespread on the Hampshire downs in those days.

In 1920, W.M. Fassnidge, the second master at King Edward VI School, Southampton, founded The Southampton and District Entomological Society. The Society staged regular meetings, mainly at University College, Southampton, and at Fassnidge's house in Tennyson Road. In 1924, with 31 members, it evolved into The Entomological Society of Hampshire and the Isle of Wight. This new society thrived and had amongst its membership some of the most knowledgeable and active entomologists in Britain, notably P.M. Bright, A.E. Burras, S.G. Castle Russell, B.M. Hobby, H.P. Jones and A.E. Stowell. The Society then developed into The Entomological Society of the South of England. In 1932, this new society had 134 members, many of whom were living in counties neighbouring Hampshire. At this point the Society started to lose its identity, particularly following the death or retirement from the region of some of its leading members. Then, in 1942, a tragic accident befell the Society's leading light when Fassnidge was seriously wounded in a 'friendly fire' incident at Imber Ranges on Salisbury Plain. He never recovered his health and died in 1949 at the age of 61.

On behalf of The Entomological Society of Hampshire and the Isle of Wight, Fassnidge published an annotated List of the Macro-Lepidoptera of Hampshire and the Isle of Wight, which was serialised in *The Entomologist's Record and Journal of Variation* between 1923–25. The list was the first attempt at coordinating Lepidoptera records in the two counties. It was updated in the *Transactions of the Entomological Society of the South of England* in 1930.

These early entomologists were men of considerable energy; S.G. Castle Russell (1866–1955), Hampshire's foremost butterfly collector, thought nothing of cycling from as far away as Woking to the New Forest for a day's collecting, returning at night! Their skills and knowledge were remarkably different to those of contemporary butterfly specialists, notably their ability to notice variations on the wing. Castle Russell, for example, could tell at 15 feet whether or not a male Orange Tip possessed the small black spot in the forewing orange splash.

However, the early entomologists' knowledge of the ecology and conservation of butterflies was essentially incipient, as is perhaps illustrated by the unrealistic nature of many of their releases of bred butterflies into the wild in order to establish new populations or boost existing ones (for a full account, see Oates and Warren, 1990). It was not until the early 1920s, in response to rapid habitat change precipitated by World War I, that the issue of the conservation of butterflies dawned. Fassnidge's society was amongst the first of the entomological bodies to react to the developing threat to British wildlife; in 1929 they issued a resolution condemning the Forestry Commission's treatment of the New Forest and calling for the Forest to be designated a Nature Reserve (see *Entomologist's Record*, Nov. 1929).

Although Hampshire's resident entomologists and regular visiting collectors were well-educated people and were often eminent society figures, they were not without their eccentricities. S.H. Kershaw (1958) writes of his friend Castle Russell: "Right and left conveyed little to him and he used them indiscriminately. Nor had he any idea of time ... In woods he often got lost: he had a total lack of a sense of direction ... In later years this habit of losing himself often caused anxiety to his friends ... The risk of an accident befalling him on these occasions was minimised to some extent by persuading him to carry a whistle; but of course he was never known to use it". Furthermore: "he did hate flies, particularly clegs (*Chrysops caecutiens*), and nearly blinded himself in the New Forest by painting a strong solution of nicotine on his forehead to keep them off; it was hot and the nicotine ran into his eyes". Incredibly for someone with such afflictions, Castle Russell was one of the country's pioneer electrical engineers!

Castle Russell spent much of his long life collecting in Hampshire, living at Ewshot, Aldershot, Andover, Fleet and Highcliffe, as well as London and Woking. His last years were spent at Cranleigh. Kershaw describes his collecting year: "CR devoted the earlier part of the season to the lesser fritillaries, later on the larger, and finally concentrating upon *coridon* (Chalkhill Blue), *aegon* (Silver-studded Blue) and *bellargus* (Adonis Blue) ... May and June were spent in Pamber, Chiddingfold and New Forests, July in Blean and New Forest and August and September divided between Royston, Folkestone, Salisbury Plain, Winchester, Eastbourne or Shoreham". Baron C.G. de Worms (1903–1979), himself one of Britain's most eminent 20th century lepidopterists and another regular visitor to Hampshire, rated "Sidney Castle Russell the most outstanding amongst the butterfly specialists of the older generation" (de Worms, 1973).

It must not be thought that the old collectors did not love butterflies. They loved them deeply, in their own way, calling them 'bugs' as a term of endearment. They would offer considerable help, especially to youngsters. Castle Russell periodically called in to Winchester College to encourage young collectors there. Many collectors were remarkably generous people. For example, R.W. Watson (1916–1982), one of the last great New Forest butterfly collectors, held open days every March for the viewing of his collection of immaculately set specimens, entertaining and encouraging all visitors with deep affection touched with a hint of eccentricity. A.W. Richards, a master at Farnborough Grammar School for many years after World War II, also encouraged many young naturalists, as well as making an intense study of the local butterfly fauna.

It is arguable that the famous 'long hot summer' of 1976 was the end of the era of butterfly collecting in Britain. Butterfly collecting has dwindled in popularity, due in the main to great changes in social values following World War II, coupled with the increasing concern over the loss of wildlife habitats, but collecting re-emerged during that remarkable summer to have one last halcyon day. During the mid-1970s, butterfly photography started to develop into a popular hobby amongst the growing number of conservation-minded naturalists. The recent success of Butterfly Conservation is partly based on the growth of butterfly photography as a hobby, along with the habit that many wildlife enthusiasts have of keeping 'lists' of species seen each year. Indeed, it is probable that butterfly collecting, in its broadest sense, is as popular now as in its heyday in the 1890s, only that it has become benign, with people collecting images and lists instead of specimens. The thrill of the chase is still present in the butterfly world.

In 1974, Barry Goater's book *The Butterflies and Moths of Hampshire and the Isle of Wight* was published by E.W. Classey, the specialist entomological publisher. The book largely consists of an annotated list of records for each species, with records being drawn from the entomological literature, data labels in a number of collections, and from the majority of lepidopterists active in the county at the time. It is not an ecological account. The butterfly texts list records for all species of note and present succinct summaries on the status of species regarded as being common or very widespread. What is incredible is that the Pearl-bordered Fritillary and Small Pearl-bordered Fritillary, two species now apparently threatened with extinction in the county, were so widespread in the late 1960s and early 1970s that they did not merit detailed record accounts. This example provides an indication of the rate of change in the status and distribution of many butterflies in the county in recent years. This work was followed in 1992 by a supplement, *The Butterflies and Moths of Hampshire and the Isle of Wight: additions and corrections*. This contains much additional information, including some transect data for selected species of butterflies. Barry Goater's work has helped greatly in the preparation of *The Butterflies of Hampshire*, especially by facilitating the necessary literature search.

The Hampshire and Isle of Wight Branch of Butterfly Conservation, formerly the British Butterfly Conservation Society, was formed late in 1981 by Matthew Oates. If its formation were more serendipitous than visionary, it is unquestionable that it was founded at the right time. The Branch grew steadily under the chairmanships of the late Pat Torrie, a retired hospital administrator, and the late Christopher Holt, a distinguished retired merchant banker who had grown up in the New Forest. In 1985 the Branch produced its first annual County Butterfly Report (which was the first such review ever produced in Britain). It prospered further under the leaderships of George Yorke, Alan Hold and Alan Green, gaining three important nature reserves and a membership of 700. This book is the product of the Branch's energy and dedication.

PART FIVE

HAMPSHIRE'S BUTTERFLY FAUNA – AN APPRAISAL AND A CHALLENGE

by Matthew Oates

A hundred years ago Hampshire was arguably the premier county for butterflies in Britain, being renowned for woodland, heathland and downland species. The county was nationally important for at least ten species: Silver-spotted Skipper, Silver-studded, Chalkhill and Adonis Blues, Duke of Burgundy, White Admiral, Purple Emperor, Pearl-bordered, High Brown and Silver-washed Fritillaries. This is clear from the entomological literature, of which that relating to Hampshire is unusually extensive.

Today, however, in terms of species-diversity, number of nationally important butterfly sites and county-holding of populations of national significance, Hampshire is not even one of the five most important counties for butterflies. It probably lies behind Devon, Dorset, Surrey, Sussex and Wiltshire. Also, it is arguable that Cumbria and the Isle of Wight are of more significance than Hampshire, despite supporting fewer species. Hampshire cannot boast a single species for which it holds larger populations or more colonies than any other county, the nearest to an exception being the Silver-studded Blue. This is not because other counties have become better for butterflies during the 20th century, for none has, but because conditions in Hampshire have deteriorated disproportionately, particularly of late.

Although during the 20th century only three species became extinct in Hampshire (Wood White, Large Tortoiseshell and High Brown Fritillary), most of the species for which the county was important have declined by orders of magnitude, notably the Fritillaries and downland Blues. Conversely, only three species underwent major expansions in Hampshire during the century (Essex Skipper, Comma and Speckled Wood), all of which increased strongly elsewhere. In addition, the Silver-spotted Skipper is now expanding in Hampshire, but only after having suffered a major contraction which took it to the brink of county extinction. It is the only nationally scarce species to have expanded in Hampshire during the second half of the 20th century. However, it is increasing elsewhere within its range.

Hampshire can still be considered a nationally important county for five of Britain's scarcer species (the heathland race of Silver-studded Blue, Duke of Burgundy, White Admiral, Purple Emperor and Silver-washed Fritillary). However, the county status of all of these is considerably reduced and at least two of them are in serious decline.

Four species can now be classified as being 'Endangered' within the county; i.e. they have declined drastically and are likely to become extinct in Hampshire if current factors adversely affecting their status are not rapidly countered. These are Brown Hairstreak and Pearl-bordered, Small Pearl-bordered and Marsh Fritillaries. In addition, four species can be classified as being 'Vulnerable'; i.e. they have declined greatly and could easily become 'Endangered' within the county. These are Small and Adonis Blues, Duke of Burgundy, Purple Emperor and away from the New Forest, Grayling. Silver-spotted Skipper seems to be in the process of removing itself from this list, hopefully permanently. These worrying trends are summarised in the following table, which involves one-third of the species which have been resident in Hampshire over the last 120 years.

Hampshire still boasts a number of rich sites which can be classed as nationally important butterfly sites, holding breeding populations of an exceptional range of species and constituting top national sites for one or more species. However, with the exception of the New Forest, which currently merits inclusion only as a heathland site, these are exclusively downland sites, *viz* Beacon Hill–Warnford NNR, Broughton Down, Martin Down NNR, Noar Hill, part of Porton Down and Old Winchester Hill NNR. A large number of Hampshire sites have been lost within the last 25 years. It is particularly disappointing that the county no longer supports any nationally important woodland butterfly sites, though the New Forest woodlands still have the potential to reach such standard. The latest top woodland butterfly site to lose this status is Alice Holt Forest, a Forestry Commission property which has recently lost six nationally scarce species.

Table 2. Hampshire's Extinct, Endangered, Vulnerable and Local/Declining Species

Recently Extinct	Endangered	Vulnerable	Local and Declining
High Brown Fritillary	Brown Hairstreak	Adonis Blue	Grizzled Skipper
Large Tortoiseshell	Marsh Fritillary	Duke of Burgundy	Silver-studded Blue *
	Pearl-bordered Fritillary	Purple Emperor	Silver-washed Fritillary
	Small Pearl-bordered Fritillary	Small Blue	Wall Brown
		Grayling *	
		Silver-spotted Skipper	

* = outside the New Forest

The truth is that changes in agriculture, silviculture and, more recently, urban development have been particularly severe in our county. Furthermore, many of these pressures are intensifying. Numerous fragments of actual or potentially viable butterfly habitat remain, but they are becoming islands within increasingly hostile landscapes and the management of many of them is either inadequate or economically unsustainable, or both. The main problem is that habitat connectivity, and the associated butterfly population structures, are being shattered in the county. All too often butterflies are now effectively restricted to occurring in isolated fragments in landscapes where beneficial pastoral processes have largely ceased and which are now dominated by urbanisation, roads, intensive agriculture, horse paddocks and commercial forestry.

The natural state is for butterflies to exist in clusters of colonies within intact landscapes, where a roughly equal number of local extinctions and colonisations can be expected to occur. In biological conservation, such clusters are termed *metapopulations* (see Marsh Fritillary account), the current belief being that for most species the conservation of isolated populations in fragmented landscapes is simply not sustainable. Whereas butterfly status and distribution, and population size at site level, have always been in a state of flux, the major difficulty in Hampshire today is that natural colonisation is being steadily reduced by the increasing fragmentation of habitats by man's activities. In effect, butterflies' powers of colonisation are not what they were, or need to be. This is not because butterflies are becoming physically weaker but because habitat patches are becoming smaller and further apart and because source populations are generally decreasing. Consequently, we should be more concerned about the paucity of new colonisations in the county than the accelerating rate of local extinctions.

On the credit side, Hampshire can boast of what is possibly the most effective county nature conservation structure in Britain, with a first rate County Wildlife Trust, a County Council with an unrivalled record in conservation, a strong English Nature presence founded on the solid base laid down by the late Colin Tubbs and, for Lepidoptera, a thriving branch of Butterfly Conservation. Others need to come properly on board, most notably the Forestry Commission which is the most significant landowning body for butterflies in central southern England after the National Trust (see analysis in Warren, 1993a).

The challenge is enormous, if the county is not to haemorrhage species but to restore habitat quality and connectivity and endeavour to win back its status as Britain's premier butterfly county. To do this we must seek to restructure the landscape, devise and introduce new cultural processes which actually benefit nature conservation and which address the widespread neglect of surviving habitat and, above all, convince a population which is becoming a hybrid between rural and urban extremes of the necessity for, and requirements of, nature conservation. The main components of the context in which the task will have to be conducted are the probability of population increase, plus the associated demands on the countryside, and climate change due to global warming. The last of these will certainly have a massive impact on butterflies. To achieve what needs to be done, we must have vision, immense practical ability, adequate resources and faith.

PART SIX

SYSTEMATIC BUTTERFLY LIST

Figure 9. Major butterfly sites in Hampshire

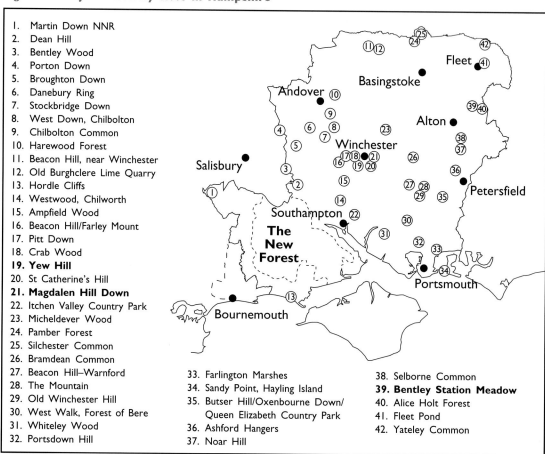

1. Martin Down NNR
2. Dean Hill
3. Bentley Wood
4. Porton Down
5. Broughton Down
6. Danebury Ring
7. Stockbridge Down
8. West Down, Chilbolton
9. Chilbolton Common
10. Harewood Forest
11. Beacon Hill, near Winchester
12. Old Burghclere Lime Quarry
13. Hordle Cliffs
14. Westwood, Chilworth
15. Ampfield Wood
16. Beacon Hill/Farley Mount
17. Pitt Down
18. Crab Wood
19. **Yew Hill**
20. St Catherine's Hill
21. **Magdalen Hill Down**
22. Itchen Valley Country Park
23. Micheldever Wood
24. Pamber Forest
25. Silchester Common
26. Bramdean Common
27. Beacon Hill–Warnford
28. The Mountain
29. Old Winchester Hill
30. West Walk, Forest of Bere
31. Whiteley Wood
32. Portsdown Hill

33. Farlington Marshes
34. Sandy Point, Hayling Island
35. Butser Hill/Oxenbourne Down/
    Queen Elizabeth Country Park
36. Ashford Hangers
37. Noar Hill

38. Selborne Common
39. **Bentley Station Meadow**
40. Alice Holt Forest
41. Fleet Pond
42. Yateley Common

COUNTS: In the Systematic List, specific counts are often given for species on particular days at various sites. These are not estimates of the total day's population for that site unless the text states that the entire site was covered. Counts are used because they give *some* indication of absolute numbers whereas transect figures represent an index to evaluate trends from year to year. Both types of count are useful, showing quite different aspects of a species' strength or weakness at a site. For example, at Stockbridge Down in 1996, the *Annual Index* for Chalkhill Blue was just 381 but between 0730 hrs and 0800 hrs on 5th August, at least 3,000 (mostly males) were seen in a clearing that was little larger than a football pitch. The Annual Index of 381, based on a fixed route through a small part of the site, gives no indication of such a population and although continued walking showed that the figure of 3,000 was just a proportion of the down's population on that date, it gives some idea of the size of the colony. Where counts are given, they are probably minima since care is taken not to overestimate.

In Transect tables (see example), the figures in bold print are our highest-ever Annual Index for that species. An asterisk (*) shows that an Index is not available for that year.

Example - Transect table

	1990	1991	1992	1993	1994	1995	1996	1997	1998	1999
Ashford Hangers	25	23	107	68	93	66	87	45	28	37
Botley Wood	*	*	*	*	*	116	322	248	199	43
Magdalen Hill Down	32	38	31	24	6	24	7	3	15	8
Noar Hill	37	47	122	67	71	120	64	44	41	31
Pamber Forest	96	31	97	126	241	304	308	174	106	100
Winnall Moors	122	30	38	34	45	46	82	86	53	45

Throughout the text, statements concerning habitat, foodplants and like subjects refer *only* to our experience in Hampshire. It may well be that the situation is different in other parts of a species' range.

Species' distribution maps. The distribution maps in each species' account are compiled from records collected during the period 1990 to 1999. Maps are plotted on a tetrad basis (2 x 2 kilometre squares). Each closed circle represents at least one record from a tetrad in the 1990s. Open circles that appear in some maps signify records of presumed vagrants or attempted introductions.

Figure 10. Observer coverage in the 1990s   **Example - Species distribution map**

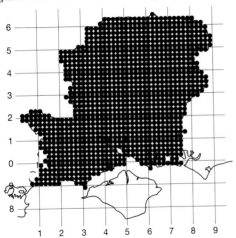
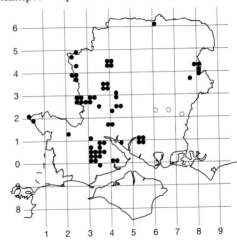

Small Skipper
Thymelicus sylvestris

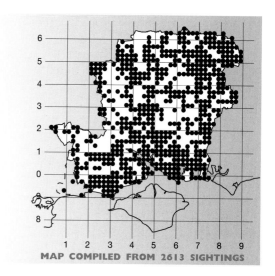

MAP COMPILED FROM 2613 SIGHTINGS

DISTRIBUTION 1990–1999 Apart from Hampshire's heathlands, where it is scarce, this small skipper is widely distributed across the whole of the county and is strongly associated with a single species of grass.

HABITAT AND FOODPLANTS Colonies are confined to ungrazed or lightly grazed tall swards where there is an abundance of nectar-rich flowers in high summer. It is equally at home on chalk grassland, dry coastal grassland or open woodland and can be common along roadside verges, country paths and on urban or industrial wasteland. Most Hampshire colonies are based on Yorkshire-fog, this being the grass most commonly chosen by ovipositing females. False Oat-grass and occasionally Creeping Soft-grass and Common Couch are also selected. Later on, these and other broad-leaved grasses, such as Creeping Bent, are foodplants used by the developing larvae.

MAJOR SITES For such a common and widespread species, the concept of major sites is misleading, but two localities are worthy of mention on account of the huge numbers that have been recorded there. They are Noar Hill and Pamber Forest and as chalk grassland and open forest they represent two of the main habitat types used by this species. The species and its favoured grass increased considerably at Pamber following heavy thinning work at the start of the decade; prior to that time, it was effectively restricted to two clearings.

POPULATION TREND AND SIZE, 1990–1999 *Trend* – In drought years, such as 1990, the species tends to do poorly, especially on chalk grassland sites as can be seen from the following transect figures. However, only 1998 proved to be a poor year for the county as a whole, although the table below also shows that particular sites have had years when their counts have been low whilst others were doing very well.

	1990	1991	1992	1993	1994	1995	1996	1997	1998	1999
Farlington Marshes	77	275	356	205	301	230	356	*	255	230
Hengistbury Head	132	83	198	112	257	123	71	88	99	193
Magdalen Hill Down	138	148	214	176	307	218	84	141	137	125
Martin Down (Kitts)	95	232	319	239	329	294	163	123	68	216
Noar Hill	234	671	985	648	1123	629	540	431	192	362
Pamber Forest	223	572	1607	1500	1754	1289	**2297**	935	544	274
Stockbridge Down	115	127	156	72	211	141	34	29	23	89
The Mountain	213	358	203	234	477	226	125	163	128	116
Yew Hill	34	117	94	90	162	135	190	70	148	107

Due to the similarity between Small and Essex Skippers, the above counts will include numbers of Essex Skippers, but they still give a guide to trends.

Size – It is by no means uncommon for observers to record over 100 at a site in a single visit. The current record was 576 in Pamber Forest on 23rd July 1994, a year in which a combination of a wet spring and a warm summer produced the tall grasses favoured by the species. The highest count in 1999 was 329 on 18th July from an area of Martin Down.

FLIGHT PERIOD The Small Skipper is on the wing for six to eight weeks at most sites. At 'early' sites in good summers, individuals can be seen in early June. Normally, emergence begins around Midsummer Day, numbers peaking in mid-July with few seen after mid-August. September specimens are rare. There is some evidence to suggest that the flight season in Hampshire now commences earlier than was the case during the 1970s and 1980s.

EARLIEST/LATEST DATES, 1990–1999 The earliest sighting was at Burghclere on 30th May 1996, our only record of a Small Skipper on the wing in May. The latest sighting was at Bishop's Waltham Moors on 19th September 1991.

OUTSTANDING OCCURRENCES This golden skipper is subject to some variation in colour. In 1979, the pale ab. *pallida* was seen at Noar Hill by Matthew Oates whilst he was searching for an as yet unnamed blue variety, first seen on 17th August 1978. This moderately fresh male had wings of a steely blue verging on buff, with sky blue body hairs. Either this individual, or another similar one, was photographed by Tony Croucher and three of these photographs were published in the *Entomologists' Gazette* (Huxley and Carter, 1981). On 3rd August 1981, another freshly emerged blue male, with both wings and body hairs the colour of a moderately fresh Chalkhill Blue, was seen by Matthew Oates and his wife. Ten days later, another with uniformly grey wings and light blue body hairs was seen at the site. The most recent sighting of the blue form was on 10th August 1991, also at Noar Hill, when Matthew Oates and Mike Gibbons were able to study an old, worn male from close quarters. As yet, this blue aberration has not been reported from any location other than Noar Hill.

HISTORICAL CHANGES The scant coverage afforded to this species in entomological literature suggests that it has always been one of the commonest butterflies in Hampshire. However, it must be one of the species to have suffered most from agricultural intensification during the 20th Century. It has undoubtedly become heavily reliant on road verges and other forms of 'wasteland'.

Essex Skipper
Thymelicus lineola

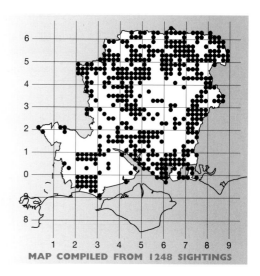

MAP COMPILED FROM 1248 SIGHTINGS

DISTRIBUTION 1990–1999 Many an Essex Skipper is reported as the very similar Small Skipper, and vice versa, especially as female Small Skippers often have dark brown antennae undersides. Because of such confusion, the map for this species is probably the most inaccurate of all the maps in this book. Careful field studies in the past ten years have greatly increased our knowledge of the abundance and distribution of the Essex Skipper to the point where it may now be concluded that the species is generally widespread but unevenly distributed throughout much of the county.

High numbers have been reported from the north-eastern grass heaths and around Fareham, Portsmouth, Southampton and Tidworth, whilst in the north-western corner of the county the species has been discovered in over half of the tetrads that cover five ten-kilometre squares. Until recently, it was virtually absent from the New Forest and parts of west Hampshire; this may have been due in part to less comprehensive observer coverage because very recent work in the New Forest has shown the species to be reasonably widespread. New colonies are reported every year, due either to continued extension of the species' range or to more diligent searching by observers.

HABITAT AND FOODPLANTS The preferred habitat is well-drained tall grassland, particularly early successional stage grassland. This can be in a variety of locations, such as on chalk or sandy soils, roadside cuttings and embankments or sea-walls. The last three of these environments make use of the species' apparently greater resistance to salt spray when compared with the Small Skipper.

The grasses favoured by the Essex Skipper in Hampshire have not been studied, though judging from aggregations of adults it would appear that Creeping Soft-grass, Cock's-foot, False Oat-grass, Common Couch, Timothy and perhaps Sea Couch are the most readily utilised species.

MAJOR SITES High numbers have been reported at Butter Wood, Greywell, Hayling Island (where about 70% of small golden skippers are Essex Skippers) and Wicor Meadows, but our knowledge of numbers is such that this should not be taken to be a list of Hampshire's main Essex Skipper sites.

POPULATION TREND AND SIZE, 1990–1999 Colonies of Small and Essex Skippers occur alongside one another and various ratios of the two have been reported at a number of sites. Small Skippers have usually been in the majority, but ratios of Small to Essex have ranged from 10:1 to 1:3, although since the two species do not have identical flight periods, such ratios must be interpreted with care. For instance, populations of Essex Skippers tend to increase spectacularly 2–4 years after colonisation, regularly outnumbering Small Skippers for a while before declining. The reasons for this are not known. The Basingstoke ring road, Fort Nelson on Portsdown Hill, Hayling Island and the seashore at Hook-with-Warsash are sites where Essex Skippers have outnumbered Small Skippers.

Present data do not allow us to make meaningful statements about population trend or size. Determined observers have counted more than 30 Essex Skippers at one site, but counts of over 100 are unusual. All that can be said is that the species has increased dramatically in Hampshire since the early 1980s, new colonies being discovered each year, and that constant monitoring will eventually give an idea of population sizes and trends.

FLIGHT PERIOD The species usually emerges two to three weeks after the Small Skipper, with the first being seen during the last week in June or the first week in July. Good numbers are on the wing in late July and during the first half of August, with the flight season ending in late August or early September. There is little correlation between the ends of the flight seasons of the Small and Essex Skippers.

EARLIEST/LATEST DATES, 1990–1999 The earliest sighting was at Castle Meadow, Portchester, on 15th June 1997. Our latest date was on 21st September 1996 near Aldershot, at Bourley Road.

OUTSTANDING OCCURRENCES After rain on 6th July 1992, 241 Essex Skippers and Small Skippers were observed taking water from a puddle along a track at Holly Bush Hill, Farnborough. Such occurrences are associated with more southerly climes and are distinctly rare in Britain.

HISTORICAL CHANGES Although the Essex Skipper was only recognised as a British species in 1889 and closely resembles a common species, it appears not to have been recorded from Hampshire before the early 1920s when it was rumoured to have been taken in the New Forest (Fassnidge, 1923). Then, in 1927 and 1928, it was taken "in some plenty" in the New Forest by I.R.P. Heslop (Heslop, 1929; Goater, 1974). However, records for it in the Forest then cease. During World War II, it appeared for the first time on the chalk in the extreme west of the county (Goater, 1974; de Worms, 1950). It seems that during the 1950s and 1960s it was restricted to a few rough downland sites in the extreme west of Hampshire. Richards (1957) does not mention it in his list of butterflies of the Aldershot district. However, in 1976 the butterfly appeared on disturbed grassland in the extreme north-east of the county and during the late 1970s it became moderately widespread along the north-eastern and western borders.

In 1982 the Essex Skipper began a remarkable expansion phase, particularly from its eastern front, which has continued through to the end of the century. In the east, major thrusts of colonisation occurred during the hot summer sequences of 1982–1984 and 1989–1990. However, not all colonisations persisted; thus, it was discovered in a clearing in Pamber Forest in 1980, only to disappear and not be seen again there until 1990. There is also some evidence to suggest that major road corridors, with their associated wide verges, assisted the butterfly's spread.

The butterfly expanded in the Camberley, Farnborough and Aldershot area in 1982 and appeared around Greywell, Hook and Eversley in 1983. 1984 brought a major expansion, with the species colonising Alice Holt Forest, the Alton area and sites in the upper Test valley. The following year saw the start of a sequence of four poor summers, but the Essex Skipper appeared at Basingstoke and Pitt Down and had established a clear front along the foot of the Upper Greensand escarpment in east Hampshire. In 1986, colonies were discovered at Abbotstone Down and Stockbridge Down. In 1987 the butterfly colonised Noar Hill and 1988 saw an expansion in the Andover region. In the good summer of 1989, the species appeared in the Petersfield and Portsmouth districts for the first time and 1990 saw colonisations at Cheriton, Micheldever, the Meon valley, the Magdalen Hill Down and Yew Hill Reserves, and Keyhaven Marshes. The following year it reached Hayling Island. This data gives an idea of the species' spread, but the picture must be far from complete.

Silver-spotted Skipper
Hesperia comma

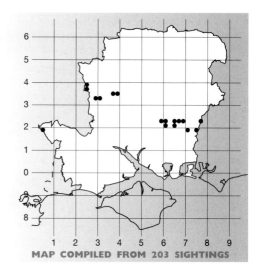

MAP COMPILED FROM 203 SIGHTINGS

DISTRIBUTION 1990–1999 Seven permanent sites are currently known: four in the extreme west (including two distinct colonies at Porton Down), two on the Meon valley NNRs and an introduced population at Queen Elizabeth Country Park NNR. Intermittent small populations occur at two privately-owned Meon valley sites. Apart from Porton Down, the sites are on nature reserves where the management requirements of the Silver-spotted Skipper are taken fully into account. This WNW/ESE spread of records marks the southern edge of the chalk outcrop, where several of the key sites are located. Isolated records at places such as Stockbridge Down, mainly of males, represent strays from the main breeding populations. One of the Meon valley sites was a natural colonisation in 1980.

1999 was an interesting year when records of small numbers came from several sites around the Meon valley away from established colonies. As these were early in the flight season, it would seem that they were not individuals moving out from overpopulated areas; it is more probable that they were the offspring of butterflies that had moved out from the main Meon valley colonies in the highly successful season of 1998. Perhaps, at the close of the 1990s, the species is starting to recover some lost ground. At Beacon Hill–Warnford, Dr Martin Warren found excellent ova counts in September 1998 and very good counts in September 1999.

HABITAT AND FOODPLANTS The species is confined to short-turf calcareous grasslands where the larvae feed exclusively on Sheep's-fescue. In particular, hot dry sites are required with substantial areas of short turf (< 4 cm). Most Hampshire sites are steep, but with aspects ranging from north to south-facing. The white, hemispherical ova are laid singly on small, semi-isolated tussocks of Sheep's-fescue, usually adjacent to bare earth such as paths, hoof prints or Rabbit scrapes, or alongside the rosettes of low broad-leaved plants such as plantains. However, on plants in optimum condition in a particularly favoured location, a number of ova may be found. Indeed, five or more ova on a single small plant is not uncommon. A detailed study at Beacon Hill–Warnford (Warren and Thomas, 2000) established that whilst Rabbits have a role in maintaining optimum turf height, female Silver-spotted Skippers would not select heavily nibbled plants. In common with other skippers, this species will take nectar from a wide range of plants, especially Asteraceae.

MAJOR SITES The major sites are Porton Down, Broughton Down, Old Winchester Hill and Beacon Hill–Warnford.

POPULATION TREND AND SIZE, 1990–1999 *Trend* – Although the transect data below show some seasonal variation, the current situation for the species in Hampshire is reasonably healthy. Throughout the 1990s, the known colonies have remained stable, or if anything strengthened. 1999 was an excellent season, with numbers well up at the introduced site and evidence of colonisation at other Meon valley sites. During the 1990s, the populations on Beacon Hill–Warnford and Old Winchester Hill have increased and expanded well, whilst numbers at Broughton Down in 1998 were described as "phenomenal", Porton Down also having a successful season in that year. Apart from the isolation of our Hampshire centres, and the limited amount of potentially suitable habitat in close proximity, the long-term future at existing sites seems reasonable.

	1990	1991	1992	1993	1994	1995	1996	1997	1998	1999
Beacon Hill–Warnford	132	164	77	121	88	200	227	197	123	173
Martin Down (South)	0	3	6	1	7	12	2	3	1	1
The Mountain	0	0	0	0	0	0	1	0	1	33

Size – In peak season at the larger sites, individual counts are usually in double-figures, commonly above 50 and sometimes exceeding 100. Straddling the Hampshire/Wiltshire border, a count of 243 was made at Porton Down on 15th August 1997; a weekly transect count of 143 was recorded at Beacon Hill–Warnford in August 1996; at Old Winchester Hill, a transect count of 51 was made in August 1995; at Broughton Down, 100+ were seen on 4th August 1990, but recent numbers at this site have been lower until 1998 when around 700 were seen on a systematic count of the entire down, groups of three, four or five males around one female being commonplace.

FLIGHT PERIOD In the west, the species emerges in late July or early August, numbers building to a peak around mid-August and the flight period ending in most years around the first week of September. The flight season is distinctly later at the Meon valley sites, usually peaking in late August and lasting well into September.

EARLIEST/LATEST DATES, 1990–1999 The earliest and latest were at Porton Down, on 13th July 1997 and on 29th September 1990. Prior to the decade, there was a record on the extremely late date of 11th October 1986 from Beacon Hill–Warnford.

INTERESTING OCCURRENCES Although the larval foodplant is exclusively Sheep's-fescue, and in virtually all cases ova are laid individually on leaf blades, an isolated case of ovipositing on Wild Thyme in close-cropped turf was noted on 1st September 1991 at Old Winchester Hill. This plant was immediately adjacent to a Sheep's-fescue plant on which several ova were already present, so the microclimate of this particular spot was especially favourable.

HISTORICAL CHANGES The Victoria County History states that the species "is common in many places on the chalk about Winchester". Fassnidge (1923) described the species as "more or less common on all chalk downs" and Farley Mount was a well known site supporting a large and extensive population (Gaunt, 1937; Goater, 1974). It was also known from the downs around Martin and Damerham (Corbet, 1916, 1921 and 1923), Stockbridge Down, and the Burghclere, Alresford and Meon valley areas, but was probably lost from all but two of these shortly after the onset of myxomatosis in the early 1950s. This decline in Rabbit numbers produced longer turf that was totally unsuitable for Silver-spotted Skippers and other short-turf species such as Adonis Blue. By the 1970s the butterfly was confined to small colonies on Martin Down, Porton Down and Beacon Hill–Warnford with a larger population on Broughton Down.

Since the early 1980s, a widespread recovery of Rabbit populations has greatly increased the extent of suitable habitat in the county; Silver-spotted Skipper numbers at Porton Down have increased considerably. However, the colonisation of Old Winchester Hill was probably due to the introduction of a suitable sheep grazing regime in the late 1970s. On 22nd August 1980, a female was noted on the ramparts of Old Winchester Hill; several more were seen over the next few days and three or four on 3rd September. They had presumably been blown over from Beacon Hill–Warnford by a stiff north-west wind (NCC Event Card data). The initial colonisation was on the south slope, but following an increase in Rabbit numbers the butterfly has expanded to occur over much of the reserve.

Attempted colonisation, sometimes resulting in temporary colonies, has occurred at a few other sites. At The Mountain, the species bred during 1984/85, singletons were seen in 1996 and 1998, and then 33 were recorded on transect in 1999. There have also been sightings at Wheeley Down at the back of Beacon Hill–Warnford and Soberton Down in the mid-1980s, at Stockbridge Down intermittently since 1976, and in 1984 a singleton was seen at Noar Hill.

In August 1990 adults were transferred from Broughton Down to two sites within Queen Elizabeth Country Park by Matthew Oates. He released 28 in the deep coombe at Rake Bottom, where the species occurred in 1924, and 29 on Oxenbourne Down. None was seen at either site the following year, but several were seen at Oxenbourne in 1994 and a small population became established there; this increased greatly in 1999 when 48 were seen on 14th August.

The reputed occurrence of the species in the New Forest is intriguing. The record by Lofthouse (1902) cited in Goater (1974) can be discounted as he was collecting in late June during a poor season. However, the Victoria County History states: "It has been reported from the New Forest, but I have never seen it there", suggesting an element of doubt. Fassnidge (1923) records "occasional specimens", perhaps suggesting wanderers from the chalk downs, whilst Pitman (1963) gives it as "uncommon on the heaths", suggesting residence. Pitman worked the northern Forest at a time when there were sizeable populations close by in the Redlynch area (Fuller, 1995) which could have produced wanderers or even short-lived colonies. If the butterfly were breeding in the Forest, it may well have been utilising Fine-leaved Sheep's-fescue, which is more common on the New Forest heaths than the similar Sheep's-fescue.

CONSERVATION AND MANAGEMENT The long-term future in Hampshire probably requires more sites in the core areas so that a network of sites can be established within close proximity. The natural process of colonisation is slow, but does seem to be occurring in the Meon valley. Even so, it is likely that reintroductions will be needed. In the longer term, it may be beneficial to consider reintroduction to a network of sites around Winchester where a number of sites are currently in a suitable condition for the species.

Large Skipper
Ochlodes venata

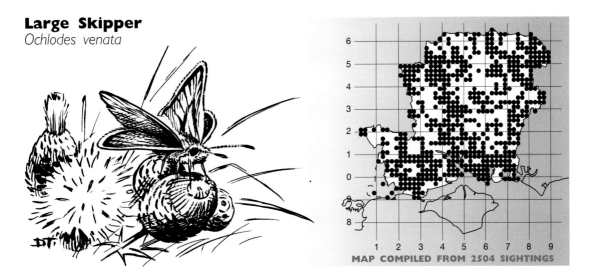

MAP COMPILED FROM 2504 SIGHTINGS

DISTRIBUTION 1990–1999 The Large Skipper occurs throughout Hampshire in a great variety of grassland habitats. The map shows large gaps, but many of these are almost certainly due to under-recording. The butterfly can appear in gardens and on isolated pieces of rough ground from time to time, well away from its usual breeding areas.

HABITAT AND FOODPLANTS This species has a marked preference for grassland with trees or bushes, only occurring in open grassland where there are topographical features providing shelter and raised perching sites. Loose colonies exist in grassy woodland rides and clearings, on rough downland and scrubby wasteland, as well as on moist or damp heathland habitats, old trackways, verges and hedge-lined footpaths. The Large Skipper tends not to be a species of short turf and it is remarkably scarce on dry heaths.

The main foodplants in Hampshire are Cock's-foot and False Brome on downs and in woods and Purple Moor-grass on heaths. Other broad-leaved coarse grasses and a wide range of broad-leaved sedges are also used, especially where the three favoured grasses are scarce or absent, notably False Oat-grass, Common Couch and Wood-sedge. Prominent tussocks are favoured by ovipositing females, usually in semi-shaded situations.

Bramble is a popular source of nectar for the adult butterfly, but on light soils, Viper's-bugloss and large patches of Common Bird's-foot-trefoil are preferred, whilst on moist clay soils, Marsh Thistle and Ragged-Robin are visited. On orchid-rich downland, Fragrant Orchids are attractive nectar sources for Large Skippers, with Bell Heather a favourite on heathland.

MAJOR SITES In hot summers, this species fares better in cool woodland sites than on hotter, more open grassland. Over-activity of adults in exposed hot sites can result in burn-out and a short season, whereas in cooler sheltered sites, the season is generally longer with more adults seen and a greater chance of successful pairings. Major sites fall into these two categories, with either tending to fare well depending on the weather conditions.

The major woodland sites that we have located in Hampshire are Ashford Hangers, Alice Holt Forest, Botley Wood, Crab Wood, Pamber Forest and West Wood. Major downland sites include Portsdown Hill, Stockbridge Down and Wicor Meadows. The damper situation of Winnall Moors also provides an important site for the species. Apart from these, there are many good Large Skipper sites throughout the county.

POPULATION TREND AND SIZE, 1990–1999 *Trend* – In cooler years the flight season can be extended and the butterfly tends to thrive in years of sunshine and showers. Years of abundance have been 1992 and 1995, although in every year in the 1990s the species has excelled at some Hampshire sites, save for 1998 when the picture was universally either mediocre or poor. The transect figures are very interesting in that they illustrate the variation between sites and habitat over the years.

The population dynamics of the Large Skipper are not fully understood. Both drought, overgrazing and excessive wet can affect numbers, having a negative affect on butterfly, foodplant and the related life-cycle.

	1990	1991	1992	1993	1994	1995	1996	1997	1998	1999
Ashford Hangers	25	23	107	68	93	66	87	45	28	37
Botley Wood	*	*	*	*	*	116	**322**	248	199	43
Magdalen Hill Down	32	38	31	24	6	24	7	3	15	8
Noar Hill	37	47	122	67	71	120	64	44	41	31
Pamber Forest	96	31	97	126	241	304	308	174	106	100
Winnall Moors	122	30	38	34	45	46	82	86	53	45

Size – Individual counts of over 100 have been recorded, e.g. Wicor Meadows in 1992, Bentley Wood in 1994, Crab Wood and Westbury Park in 1995 and Hut Wood in 1996. However, there have been very few attempts to estimate a site's population on a particular day and so the above examples of 100+ may be much more commonplace.

FLIGHT PERIOD The main flight period is from June to August, but warmer springs and cooler summers lead to extended flight times. Sometimes, fresh looking individuals have been encountered in late July or early August. It seems likely that these are late emergers rather than a partial second brood.

EARLIEST/LATEST DATES, 1990–1999 Our earliest records were on 10th May 1998 at Rogate and Ashford Hangers. The latest for this period was on 17th September 1993 at Petersfield.

INTERESTING OCCURRENCES Mid-1980s New Forest research into the Wild Gladiolus found that the Large Skipper was the plant's main pollinator (Stokes, 1987).

According to Russwurm (1978), a variety known as ab. *obscura* was not uncommon in the New Forest over the years. This form has an intense dark brown ground colour with the spotting small and indistinct and could well still be encountered.

Males invariably emerge at least a week before the first females, the latter being almost impossible to find until July in some years.

HISTORICAL CHANGES Both the Victoria County History and Fassnidge (1923) list the species as being "common everywhere". In recent times, intensification of agriculture and development of land for new housing and industry has led to the inevitable loss of habitat. These changes have affected numbers over much of Hampshire, but Large Skippers are fairly mobile and can adapt to a variety of grassy situations, so it seems that the species is holding its own. With less herbicide use, the advent of set-aside, conservation headlands, motorway verges and sympathetic garden management, the Large Skipper can claw back some of the past losses away from well established haunts.

Dingy Skipper
Erynnis tages

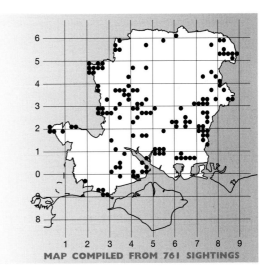

MAP COMPILED FROM 761 SIGHTINGS

DISTRIBUTION 1990–1999 Although the species is by no means confined to the central chalk, the map shows a concentration in that area. The butterfly is likely to be found anywhere from the coast to the extreme north wherever there is suitable habitat, but the largest colonies are on chalk grasslands and it is now rather scarce in woods. It can best be described as widespread but local, usually in colonies of very modest numbers.

HABITAT AND FOODPLANTS This is primarily a butterfly of chalk grassland, unimproved dry meadows, disused railways and woodland clearings, but it is found in some coastal habitats such as the landslipped undercliff at Hordle. Colonies also occur on disturbed dry heathland in north-eastern Hampshire. On chalk grasslands, it favours thin-soil sites which are ungrazed or lightly grazed and where Common Bird's-foot-trefoil, which is the main larval foodplant, abounds. In the west of the county, females readily oviposit on Horseshoe Vetch. The species is adversely affected by heavy summer grazing, particularly by sheep or Rabbits (BUTT, 1986) and requires areas of tall vegetation where butterflies can roost, the dead heads of Common Knapweed being especially favoured. Colonies in woodland clearings tend to be small, simply because such open patches are nearly always restricted in size.

MAJOR SITES As the largest colonies are found on chalk grasslands, it is not surprising that the larger and best preserved downs form the major Dingy Skipper sites. Noar Hill, Martin Down, Beacon Hill–Warnford, The Mountain, Oxenbourne Down, Dean Hill and Broughton Down are good examples, but even these main sites vary with the grazing that takes place and other factors that are not fully understood. For example, Stockbridge Down *has* been subject to controlled grazing and *was* a site of importance, but numbers have suffered a serious decline there in the last few years, probably due to intense Rabbit activity. Colonies away from the chalk can be of reasonable size, Laffans Plain near Farnborough being an example of such a site.

POPULATION TREND AND SIZE, 1990–1999 *Trend* – Numbers have varied much from year to year but over the last decade the species has generally held its own; our spring weather tends to be especially volatile and early butterfly species are prone to frequent fluctuations in numbers as a consequence. The transects shown below have been selected to demonstrate the pattern as a whole.

These figures and other counts show that 1990, 1992, 1995 and 1997 were good years whilst 1991, 1993, 1994, 1998 and 1999 were mediocre at best.

Size – Most colonies are small, even on the downs. An individual count of 30 on any day would be considered good and the highest counts within the period 1990–1999 are 100+ at Noar Hill on 21st May 1992 and 75 at Oxenbourne Down during a 90 minute walk in 1994. Although they are not counts, the species was described as "abundant" on Oxenbourne

Down in 1990 and at Broughton Down in 1992, and present in "large numbers" at Shoulder-of-Mutton, Ashford Hangers, on 1st May 1997.

	1990	1991	1992	1993	1994	1995	1996	1997	1998	1999
Beacon Hill–Warnford	79	22	53	15	13	27	20	115	65	23
Noar Hill	156	90	128	54	47	80	36	134	96	37
Stockbridge Down	34	10	15	5	0	*	9	3	3	2
The Mountain	55	10	23	26	44	34	28	111	63	30
Westbury Park	*	*	*	25	20	56	21	52	70	17

Our highest-ever Annual Index was **210** in 1997 at Oxenbourne Down

FLIGHT PERIOD The last half of May and the first half of June usually see the peak flight period, the precise time depending on whether spring is early or late; in 1992 the peak was in the second half of June. A *very* small second brood is often recorded, mainly on the downs and at large colonies; such an occurrence was seen in 1992, 1993, 1995, 1997 and 1999, always involving just a few individuals. These appear in late July and August. Fassnidge (1923) states that "a more or less numerous second brood often occurs" and so second brood specimens are not new.

EARLIEST/LATEST DATES, 1990–1999 The earliest record was on 12th April 1990 at Noar Hill, but in some years Dingy Skippers will not appear until May. The latest record was on 28th August 1993 at Hordle Cliff, but this was from a second brood. The last first brood individuals are normally seen in late June, but one on 8th July 1990 at Porton Down may be our latest record for the first brood.

PARTICULAR OCCURRENCES One was observed taking salt from pebbles on the shore at Milford on Sea in 1994.

HISTORICAL CHANGES With the continued ploughing of downland and the loss of woodland clearings as coppicing declined, the species must have experienced a major decline throughout the 20th century. Being of sombre appearance, it was not a collector's favourite and does not feature in past literature as much as our more striking species so that the Dingy Skipper's precise status in the past is not well known. The literature simply describes it as common.

The species has declined in Hampshire in recent years, both in numbers and in the number of occupied sites, even if the range is broadly the same. Locally, factors such as overgrazing by Rabbits and/or sheep has had a detrimental effect and was probably the reason why the colony at Dongers, by St Catherine's Hill, disappeared in 1990, although by 1995 the species had re-established itself.

Grizzled Skipper
Pyrgus malvae

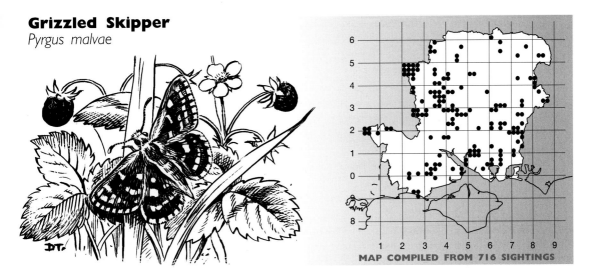

MAP COMPILED FROM 716 SIGHTINGS

DISTRIBUTION 1990–1999 The species is spread diffusely over the central chalk grasslands with a scattering of small colonies across the rest of the county. On the chalk, it is not confined to areas of downland and may be seen in sites such as overgrown roadside verges along minor roads, in young plantations and open areas in woodland. In south Hampshire, including the New Forest, numbers do not reach those of the chalk downs, but the species is nevertheless widely distributed and occurs in many woods in low numbers.

HABITAT AND FOODPLANTS Most colonies are found in sunny, sheltered conditions. Typical sites are amongst sparse scrub, near hedgerows, in unshaded woodland rides, under electricity lines through woods, and on road and railway cuttings or embankments. Requirements are a short sward and broken ground, preferably with taller vegetation where adults can roost and shelter.

A considerable variety of larval foodplants is consumed, of which Wild Strawberry is commonly used on neutral and calcareous soils and is the main foodplant in Hampshire. On acidic soils and neutral clays, Tormentil is used, but only when the plant is growing with sufficient vigour to produce sizeable leaves. Other foodplants that are used less frequently in Hampshire are Common Agrimony, Creeping Cinquefoil and Bramble, whilst Salad Burnet is regularly selected by ovipositing females in west Hampshire and possibly elsewhere. Recent ecological work (Brereton, 1997) found that larvae readily change foodplants in the process of moving from hotter to cooler sites as they develop.

MAJOR SITES The major sites are mostly on the chalk. These include Martin Down, Broughton Down, Stockbridge Down, Pitt Down, Ashford Hangers and Butser Hill. However, off the chalk, the population in Botley Wood has increased dramatically in recent years, so much so that the site now has the highest Annual Index of all Hampshire's transects.

POPULATION TREND AND SIZE, 1990–1999 *Trend* – Over the decade, the species has held its own with reasonably steady numbers, although some sites have seen a decline (At Wendleholme, for example, the Annual Index has fallen from 73 in 1987 to "A critical level" in 1999). 1997 was described as an excellent year, and at worst the other years reported mixed fortunes with successes at some sites.

	1990	1991	1992	1993	1994	1995	1996	1997	1998	1999
Botley Wood	*	*	*	*	*	13	45	150	66	45
Martin Down (South)	28	40	39	*	29	32	36	100	37	27
Stockbridge Down	43	26	16	10	3	*	18	87	33	35
Wendleholme	21	27	26	*	22	14	5	15	9	2

Overall, reports during 1999 suggested a poor year, although the above transect data show Annual Indices to be comparable to the period 1990–1996; the bumper figures of 1997 rather distort the pattern, making 1999 indices seem rather low.

Size – Colonies are generally small and it is unusual at most sites to see more than a dozen well scattered individuals in an afternoon walk. Apart from the diffuse nature of most colonies, the tendency for this species to emerge over a protracted period without an obvious peak flight period means that the size of colonies is not easy to judge. At the main colonies, the population will be into three figures on the best days. In good years, stray individuals appear at new sites, so given favourable conditions, colonisation of new places is still possible.

FLIGHT PERIOD The first are normally seen during the last week of April, but May and early June see the main flight period. A few individuals will be seen in early July, especially if the spring has been cool and wet. Second brood individuals occur rarely, and are given under a later heading.

EARLIEST/LATEST DATES, 1990–1999 The earliest was at The Mountain on 21st April 1990, whilst the latest of the rare second brood was at Monkwood on 2nd August 1992.

OUTSTANDING OCCURRENCES To see over 30 on a single day at one site is unusual and has happened a dozen or so times during this decade. The highest count of all was when Steve Peach counted 150 at Butser Hill and Oxenbourne Down in 1994. The second highest count was of 53 on 10th May 1997, seen by a party from the Hampshire and Isle of Wight Branch of Butterfly Conservation in extremely damp conditions at Stockbridge Down, the butterflies all roosting on top of dead flower heads of Marjoram and knapweeds. As only a tiny portion of the down was covered, a conservative estimate would place the true population at well over 100. Other days may have produced higher counts had numbers been assessed; at Stockbridge Down on 10th May 1998 for instance, Ashley Whitlock reported extraordinary numbers, when "almost every step along the horse runs by the Stockbridge Road produced one".

Other unusual sightings are of presumed second brood butterflies. Two were at Dean Hill on 26th July 1990 and one at Monkwood on 2nd August 1992. Prior to these, the second brood has only been reported during the 20th century in 1933, 1943, 1976 and 1983.

HISTORICAL CHANGES Until quite recently, the Grizzled Skipper occurred commonly throughout Hampshire. Fassnidge (1923/24) dismisses the species as being "common everywhere" and Richards (1957) describes it as being "common in woods and wet pastures in the Aldershot district". The decline of Rabbits in the 1950s, due to myxomatosis, was certainly a major factor in its decline on the downs, whilst loss of habitat through changes in farming methods, the decline of coppicing and the increase of coniferous plantations are others. In eastern Hampshire, Matthew Oates recorded the disappearance of this species from many sites during the 1980s. One encouraging trend for the 1990s has been the discovery of new colonies and the recovery of populations whose numbers had become low in the 1980s.

Clouded Yellow
Colias croceus

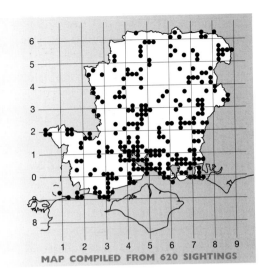

MAP COMPILED FROM 620 SIGHTINGS

DISTRIBUTION 1990–1999 The Clouded Yellow is a migrant from Europe, recorded in Hampshire each year in highly variable numbers. Because 1996 witnessed such a major influx, and 1998 a moderate influx, the distribution map is strongly influenced by those years. A key feature to note from the map is that the Clouded Yellow may be recorded more or less anywhere in the county. However, it is not surprising that the south coast produces the greatest density of records. This is most noticeable in the Hengistbury/Southbourne area and on the coastal stretch from Southampton Water to Hayling Island, although this may partly reflect observer coverage in what is one of the most densely populated parts of Hampshire. The map also indicates a greater number of records along the Itchen and Meon valleys, perhaps suggesting a tendency for species to follow major river valleys northwards from the coast during migration, in a manner similar to migrating birds, as suggested by Oates (1983a).

The species' status was changed in the winter of 1998/99, at least for one season, when overwintering was proved at Southbourne Undercliff (see Records of Interest).

HABITAT AND FOODPLANTS This is not normally considered to be a resident British species as it was thought unable to survive our winter in any stage of its life-cycle, but recent events at Southbourne Undercliff contradict such a statement. However, it is a regular and usually uncommon migrant to our shores. It will occur in a wide range of habitats although there is a preference for open, sunny, flower-rich grasslands, including coastal sites, chalk downland and rough ground. Warm sunny sites are essential and it is rarely reported from woodlands unless they have broad, flower-rich rides.

Common Bird's-foot-trefoil is probably the favoured foodplant in the county, especially on chalk downland, but Hairy Bird's-foot-trefoil was used at Southbourne Undercliff. Red and White Clover are also readily used, particularly in the agricultural leys and in coastal grassland. A variety of other vetches are also readily selected, especially in disturbed ground, notably Hop Trefoil and Black Medick. Females tend to oviposit on small plants growing in bare patches of ground. This may partly explain the absence of county records of oviposition on Lucerne, a reputedly favoured but tall foodplant. Buckler (1877), writing from the Emsworth district, gives a detailed description of what was probably the greatest Clouded Yellow year in entomological history – 1877 – and records females ovipositing *only* on Common Bird's-foot-trefoil.

With regard to nectar sources, the Clouded Yellow utilises a wide range of plants, but is attracted to species such as Wild Basil, Marjoram, Common Fleabane, Hawkweed Ox-tongue and Lucerne. In 1998, detailed observations at Fort Gilkicker by Dr Tindling found the species taking nectar from Autumn Hawkbit, Rough Hawkbit, Cat's-ear, Charlock, Red Clover and Prickly Sow-thistle.

MAJOR SITES As the Clouded Yellow is a migrant species, there are no sites with continuous breeding populations, but many of the major chalk downlands (e.g. Martin Down, Magdalen Hill Down, Old Winchester Hill, Portsdown Hill and

Beacon Hill–Warnford) record the species in most good migrant years. In 1997, over 95% of all late September to late November sightings (3rd brood) were from the meadows of Dibden Bay and Hengistbury Head, and the sheltered Southbourne undercliffs. From late September to mid-October, 10+ Clouded Yellows were seen regularly at Dibden Bay. Since 1997 was a poor Clouded Yellow year, with few records from elsewhere in the region, these high numbers provide strong evidence that the Dibden Bay population represented offspring from ova laid at the site when a small number of second brood migrants had arrived in August and early September.

POPULATION TREND AND SIZE, 1990–1999 *Trend* – Being a south coast county, Hampshire is ideally located to receive a regular influx of this generally uncommon migrant. However, the Isle of Wight undoubtedly intercepts numbers that would otherwise arrive on the Hampshire coast. In the 1990s, all odd-numbered years were poor for the species, 1992 and 1994 were reasonable years, 1998 was good and 1996 was excellent, easily the best year since the great 1983 migration. In 1996, the highest Annual Index for our transects was 40 at Hookheath Meadows and most chalk downland transects recorded indices of 10+. In that year, more than 1,000 Clouded Yellows were recorded from Hampshire and Wight and even this figure represents only a small fraction of the total number of immigrants. Almost every butterfly enthusiast saw Clouded Yellows that year, individual counts of note including 20 at St Catherine's Hill on 18th August, 20 at Peartree Green (Southampton) on 26th August and 20+ around Hengistbury Head on 31st August. A large number of *helice* were also seen in 1996, the majority being sighted in coastal areas. The following graph shows the numbers of Clouded Yellows recorded each year in Hampshire.

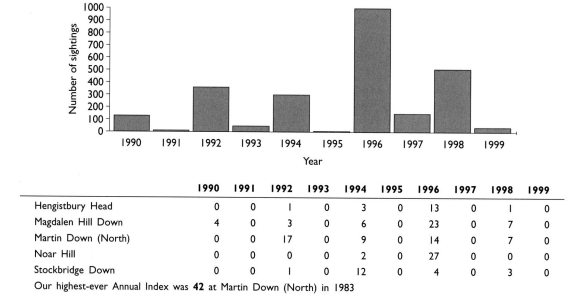

	1990	1991	1992	1993	1994	1995	1996	1997	1998	1999
Hengistbury Head	0	0	1	0	3	0	13	0	1	0
Magdalen Hill Down	4	0	3	0	6	0	23	0	7	0
Martin Down (North)	0	0	17	0	9	0	14	0	7	0
Noar Hill	0	0	0	0	2	0	27	0	0	0
Stockbridge Down	0	0	1	0	12	0	4	0	3	0

Our highest-ever Annual Index was **42** at Martin Down (North) in 1983

FLIGHT PERIOD As a migrant species, the number and timing of sightings in a given year is not only a function of population strength and timing on the continent, but is also related to prevailing weather conditions. In strong migrations, the initial influx is usually in late May and early June and some of these will lay and produce individuals that will breed through in Hampshire. The second brood flight period from late July or early August to early September is usually the strongest and in good years will comprise both individuals that have hatched in Hampshire as well as a new influx of migrants. The final brood commences in late September or early October and can continue well into November and exceptionally into December. This brood is usually small, unless the second brood influx has bred successfully. Whilst this generalised timing was typical of the 1996 season, it can vary greatly (e.g. the peaks in 1992 were about two or three weeks earlier with the main influx in mid to late July). However, the overwintering larvae at Southbourne Undercliff in 1998/99 produced flying adults from 26th March.

EARLIEST/LATEST DATES, 1990–1999 The earliest was on 26th March 1999 at Southbourne Undercliff, hatched naturally from overwintering larvae (see Records of Interest) and this was followed by others through April, but the earliest immigrant was on the 10th May 1994 at RNAD, Dean Hill. The latest was on 4th December 1996 at Southbourne Undercliff.

INTERESTING OCCURRENCES About 10% of female Clouded Yellows are the *helice* form and in strong migrations a good number of *helice* will be recorded (e.g. 25 were seen in Hampshire and Wight in 1996). They are often mistakenly identified as female Pale Clouded Yellows.

The late sighting at Southbourne Undercliff of 4th December 1996 was the last survivor from a group of 5–10 that had established a small colony there from October onwards. Remarkably, a mating pair within this group was recorded as late as 16th November (all Mike Gibbons). Based on these observations, and similar late records by Charlie Morris at Dibden Bay, it was concluded that in relatively frost-free conditions the species can survive very late on our coast.

Successful overwintering by Clouded Yellow larvae in Britain has been suspected but never proved until the winter of 1998/99 when Michael Skelton recorded a fascinating series of events at Southbourne Undercliff (see Plates 25–29, p.28), fully described in *Atropos* (Skelton, 1999). Throughout that winter, larvae were observed on Common Bird's-foot-trefoil and Hairy Bird's-foot-trefoil at three accessible sites on the warm, south-facing cliff face, individual larvae being traced through several instars to the fifth. The first hatched adult was finally seen on 26th March 1999 at Portman's Ravine, followed by several more observations from the Undercliff with a maximum of eight sightings on 29th April. A fresh ovum was then found in May. Michael's sightings may well have been the tip of an iceberg, because his records came from three accessible cliff paths, leaving the remainder of the cliff face uncovered.

HISTORICAL CHANGES The Clouded Yellow is a species that lepidopterists look forward with great expectation to seeing each year. Many seasons disappoint, but most decades produce a few reasonable Clouded Yellow migrations and every so often there is a really exceptional year. Based on Goater (1974), Fassnidge (1923), our detailed Branch records since 1980 and other texts, the outstanding years in Hampshire during the 20th century were 1900, 1903, 1917, 1922, 1924, 1928, 1937, 1941, 1943, 1947, 1949, 1955, 1964, 1969, 1983 and 1996. 1947 was probably the best year of the century; for a Hampshire account, see Antram, 1947. The period 1943–1956 saw many of the most notable immigrations, whereas there were many lean years from the late 1950s to 1983. The 1970s, in particular, saw surprisingly few.

The influx of 1983 is remarkable for its size and the fact that it occurred after a long spell of poor Clouded Yellow years. The invasion in Hampshire is documented by Oates (1983 a and b) and the Hampshire Branch Newsletters for that year. The initial immigration occurred in the wake of thunderstorms which took place during the afternoon and night of 5th June, at the beginning of three hot and sunny months. Further influxes occurred during the second week of June. A sizeable home brood began to emerge during the last days of July and was reinforced by other influxes, which combined to reach a peak around 10th August. Incredibly, the Clouded Yellow was generally more common than Large and Small Whites in Hampshire during that wonderful summer, but the third brood failed in a cold and wet September. There is some evidence of a return migration from the Hampshire coast in the autumn. The remarkable 1983 and 1996 seasons give hope that there will still be excellent Clouded Yellow years in the 21st century.

Brimstone
Gonepteryx rhamni

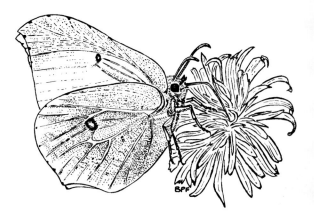

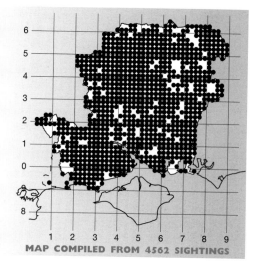

MAP COMPILED FROM 4562 SIGHTINGS

DISTRIBUTION 1990–1999 This harbinger of spring is a determined wanderer, common across the length and breadth of the county and no doubt recorded in every tetrad during the past decade. Naturally, some areas have higher population densities than others and these tend to be where buckthorns abound, though it appears that there are favoured hibernation and spring assembly areas which are not necessarily in districts where the foodplants occur.

HABITAT AND FOODPLANTS After emerging from hibernation, the butterflies seek out warm, sheltered places such as sunny woodland rides, larger gardens and hedgerows. Here they stand the best chance of finding early flowers and the nectar they need to replenish their fuel reserves after their long winter fast, and also to meet and pair. Mated females then disperse in search of buckthorn bushes.

The two native species of buckthorn are commonly used: Buckthorn, which grows mainly on chalk and Alder Buckthorn which grows on acid and neutral soils. Between them, the two buckthorns are widely distributed throughout the county, although there are sizeable gaps where neither occur. Recently coppiced bushes in a dynamic growth state are favoured (Bibby, 1983). Larvae have also been found on exotic varieties of buckthorn grown as ornamental plants in parks and gardens, notably in Hillier's Arboretum near Romsey where *Rhamnus alaternus* 'Argenteo variegata', *R. globosa* and *R. rupestris* are readily used. Larvae are attacked by the parasite *Hypersoter ebinius*, an ichneumonid wasp which is thought to attack only Brimstones in Britain.

Late in the summer, the newly emerged adults seek rich nectar sources, such as stands of Wild Basil, Betony, Devil's-bit Scabious and Small Scabious before finding suitable hibernation sites such as Bramble thickets or dense growths of Common Ivy.

POPULATION TREND AND SIZE, 1990–1999 *Trend* – The Brimstone has not been prone to violent fluctuations in numbers but it is apparent that many larvae perish during wet Junes. In some summers they may seem scarce because they feed up rapidly and hibernate soon after hatching. Many a 'poor' summer has been followed by a spring where high numbers of adults have been reported.

	1990	1991	1992	1993	1994	1995	1996	1997	1998	1999
Magdalen Hill Down	91	52	175	68	85	134	116	96	136	104
Noar Hill	22	88	99	48	33	77	82	77	34	71
Pamber Forest	318	265	304	148	*	184	405	339	*	*
Stockbridge Down	277	**622**	429	271	152	*	*	227	*	196
Yew Hill	39	97	98	72	95	75	120	95	79	90

Size – The species is seldom seen in dense numbers, although driving around for an hour on a spring day of good emergence can easily produce counts of over 50. August counts at one site of more than 30 apparent individuals would be considered 'good' and 100 in a day on any site would be excellent.

FLIGHT PERIOD The first, almost invariably males, are seen in January although it is rare for any numbers to be seen until March, when the first females usually emerge from hibernation. Throughout April and May the adults are a common sight and some battered and faded survivors are still to be seen in late June or early July, when their offspring begin to hatch. After an initial flush, small numbers can be seen throughout late summer and well into the autumn until really cold weather sets in.

EARLIEST/LATEST DATES, 1990–1999 The earliest sighting was at Winchester on 4th January 1994. The latest was at Andover on 29th December 1999. There are no later records in our database; the 1989 record of one on 31st December at Bentley Wood concerned a hibernating individual.

OUTSTANDING OCCURRENCES During some springs, Brimstones have become so common in a particular locality that enormous numbers of ova have been laid, 10 or more per leaf, so that the resulting larvae have stripped the bushes and nearly killed them. On Magdalen Hill Down, Buckthorns planted in October 1996 were found to be hosts to fully grown larvae in June 1997, long before the bushes had managed to grow clear of the protective plastic tubes in which they were planted.

During the early 1990s, aggregations of hibernating adults were found regularly on trunks of Leyland Cypress in a dense plantation at Overton. Observations elsewhere suggest that this tree may be a favoured hibernation site in many gardens and urban situations. Hibernators have also been found hidden amongst luxurious growths of Common Ivy on the trunks of mature deciduous trees.

Various aberrations have been reported. A vivid, orange-coloured Brimstone was at Selborne in August 1994 and another with much enlarged orange spots (ab. *decora*) was seen at Silchester Common on 2nd September 1994. A very small male, less than two thirds the size of a normal male, was seen in Ampfield Wood on 31st July 1993.

HISTORICAL CHANGES Whilst it is clear that the Brimstone has always been a common species in Hampshire, it would appear that it was far more common in the past, though prone to occasional poor years such as 1921 (Fassnidge, 1923). For example, although it is moderately numerous in the New Forest, historical accounts suggest that it was far stronger there before World War II. Symes (1961) describes "one late August in the 1930s, when there were scores, perhaps hundreds, of them sitting on the flowers of Bell Heather along the side road leading from Burley village past Burley Lawn to the Lyndhurst road". He then tells of how Alder Buckthorn was vigorously harvested for fine charcoal used in the munitions factory at Fritham (see also Oates, 1996).

Large White
Pieris brassicae

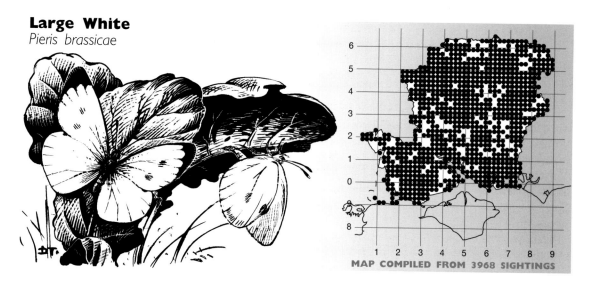

MAP COMPILED FROM 3968 SIGHTINGS

DISTRIBUTION 1990–1999 This is a highly mobile species which undertakes mass migrations from time to time. It has almost certainly been seen in every Hampshire tetrad during the past decade and blank squares on the distribution map are more likely to indicate a lack of observer coverage than the absence of this butterfly.

HABITAT AND FOODPLANTS The original larval foodplant was Wild Cabbage. This has long been domesticated and its many descendants include Broccoli, Brussels' Sprouts, Cauliflower and Kale, as well as cabbages. All are equally acceptable to the Large White, with the exception of red cabbage varieties on which females seldom oviposit (Oates, 1985). It may be that our care in cultivating plots only enhances the quality and quantity of the species' foodplants. Larvae also readily use other foodplants, notably Nasturtiums and occasionally Wild Mignonette and Honesty. All these plants are sources of mustard oils, a group of highly irritant and toxic chemicals that are used by the Large White to make all stages of its life cycle distasteful to vertebrate predators.

POPULATION TREND AND SIZE, 1990–1999 Throughout the decade, the pattern has been for numbers of the first brood to be small with adults seen in ones or twos. The second brood in July and August has tended to be significantly larger, the native population being augmented by migrants from continental Europe. The major migrations were in 1991, 1992, 1997 and 1998; of these, that of 1992 was by far the largest and resulted in considerable numbers being seen throughout the county. On the other hand, in some years the species is decidedly scarce, as in 1996, whilst 1999 saw only a modest increase in numbers during late July and August. The Annual Indices from the selection of transects below show the fortunes of the species through the decade, especially the massive influx of 1992.

	1990	1991	1992	1993	1994	1995	1996	1997	1998	1999
Alresford Farm	26	36	183	39	18	16	11	37	49	29
Hengistbury Head	13	24	77	6	6	41	47	83	21	6
Magdalen Hill Down	62	57	201	56	32	34	28	69	59	38
Noar Hill	48	76	936	136	104	57	16	138	166	187
Pamber Forest	21	10	274	22	23	31	6	60	84	25
The Mountain	97	233	759	143	122	98	38	114	324	138
Yew Hill	32	60	515	31	37	17	15	107	70	76

FLIGHT PERIOD Occasionally appearing in March, it is more usual for numbers to build up slowly throughout April and into May. By late June, the worn and faded survivors of the spring brood are joined by the first of the summer brood. This second brood emerges over a considerable period, and in most years the butterfly is reasonably common well into September with a few being seen in October and even early November. The long flight period of the second brood, coupled with fresh specimens late in the year, suggests that in some years there is a third brood which overlaps with the second. The main summer brood can also be reinforced by immigrants, in some years on an impressive scale.

EARLIEST/LATEST DATES, 1990–1999 The earliest was at Bedhampton on 22nd February 1990 and the latest was at Drayton on 9th November 1991.

OUTSTANDING OCCURRENCES The large influx of July 1992, mentioned above, was the outstanding event of the decade. Some idea of the rapidity of the build-up can be gained from a small number of observations. Thus, on 15th July, 35 were counted at Alice Holt Forest; on 24th July, 153 were seen at Ashford Hangers and 227 at Noar Hill; on 31st July, an estimated 700 were seen at Stockbridge Down. Not until 1997 were similar numbers recorded, when a large immigration took place from late July onwards. The largest 1997 count was 300 at Southbourne Undercliff on 9th September. 1998 saw another large influx and David Green reported the species to be "locally common in almost plague proportions" in north-west Hampshire. In years of such abundance, competition for suitable ovipositing sites is intense. Whilst reports of garden greens being stripped bare in years such as 1992 are only to be expected, seeing butterflies ovipositing on greens in a greengrocer's display at Alresford must surely rate as one of the most unusual reports ever. Females ovipositing on Nasturtiums in second floor window boxes in 1989 must also rank amongst the unusual records (Hoskins, Ed, 1989). In 1992, an enterprising Magpie in Alton discovered that Large Whites *were* edible and was seen picking the butterflies off the lower branches of a *buddleia*. Later, large numbers of Large White wings were seen scattered on the grass below.

The only report of an aberration comes from 1990, generally reported as a poor year for the species. At Gallows Hill, near Fordingbridge, one was found without any black markings. The aberration is known as ab. *albinensis* and had previously been known only from specimens bred in captivity.

HISTORICAL CHANGES Whilst the above descriptions indicate that the Large White can still occur in large numbers, entomological literature indicates that in the past the species was much more abundant (see Williams, 1958 and Thomas, 1991). Evidence suggests that the abundance of the species has been significantly lower since 1955 when a granulosis virus which kills larvae *en masse* reached Britain. Fraser (1946), writing from Bournemouth, indicates the scale of abundance in 1945, when there was a massive immigration: "Many (larvae) perished from sheer hunger after all available food had been consumed, but in spite of this, the sides, walls and eaves of my house were literally encrusted with the resulting pupae. They even invaded the windows, and pupae may still be seen on the walls and ceilings of several bedrooms". He then adds: "Certainly not less than 90 per cent were infested with Braconids" (parasites). Similar accounts exist for other years of abundance, notably 1887, 1924, 1935 and 1939.

Small White
Pieris rapae

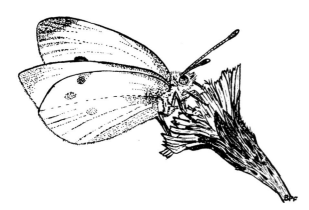

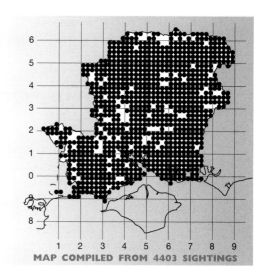

MAP COMPILED FROM 4403 SIGHTINGS

DISTRIBUTION 1990–1999 This common and mobile wanderer, which has such a catholic taste in choice of habitat, must have appeared in every Hampshire tetrad in the past decade. In those areas that have been mapped systematically and thoroughly, the map has no blank tetrads and the blanks that show on the accompanying map must be due to a lack of observer coverage.

HABITAT AND FOODPLANTS The Small White is found in a wide variety of habitats, from gardens, allotments, farm fields and downland to disused cress-beds. Being a wanderer and immigrant, it takes advantage of any suitable habitat from the coast to all parts of the county boundary. Ova are deposited on Brassicas and wild Crucifers, the larvae doing considerable damage to garden crops. Brassica crops grown as Pheasant cover are readily utilised and are of considerable advantage to the species in that they are not sprayed with insecticides, and the presence of Pheasant feed strips can often explain local abundances of Small Whites. Wild Mignonette is regularly used as a foodplant on the Hampshire chalk and goosefoots have also been used. Females also readily oviposit on garden plants such as Aubretia, Nasturtium and Dame's Violet.

MAJOR SITES In view of what has been said in the previous paragraph, this common wanderer is liable to appear at a considerable number of sites in large numbers and one cannot name a few localities within the county that are regular 'major sites'. It has been seen in numbers on fields of Rape, and there are no doubt many vegetable growers in Hampshire who remember hordes of Small Whites descending on their crops, though the use of pesticides ensures that Rape fields are not major breeding grounds. The species does breed on Rape growing on road verges and other cultivated lands. Where Brassicas and Crucifers are abundant, Small Whites are likely to congregate, often in the company of Large and Green-veined Whites. In many summers, and particularly late in the season, numbers are strongest in and around towns and villages, indicating the degree of hostility of commercial farmland.

POPULATION TREND AND SIZE, 1990–1999 *Trend* – Most years within the period have been successful for the Small White, although numbers were well down at most sites in 1998. A typical pattern which has occurred in several years is for the season to start with poor or modest numbers which then pick up later in the year, often due partly or mainly to large-scale immigration from the continent. 1993 was the only relatively poor year, although the following transects show that even that year was reasonable at some sites. The other years were described either as good or very good. Transect data are much influenced by what is growing in neighbouring fields.

Size – Counts in excess of 100 at a site are quite frequent at the right time of year, which is generally mid-July to mid-September, when the species gathers at good sources of nectar or larval foodplants, although in 1998 observers only sent in two counts of 100+. Two examples of the species gathering at good nectar sources were 400 seen at Sutton Down Farm in north-west Hampshire on 19th July 1997 and 200+ over Kale at Cheesefoot Head on 11th September 1997. However, apart from these counts, observers have used such terms as 'prolific', 'very abundant', 'plague proportions' and 'I have never seen so many', without specifying what these mean, and so these records *may* refer to counts that dwarf the numbers given at the start of this paragraph.

	1990	1991	1992	1993	1994	1995	1996	1997	1998	1999
Alresford Farm	234	101	225	231	222	514	81	230	72	115
Farlington Marshes	88	94	143	24	144	148	117	110	28	58
Hengistbury Head	76	35	106	28	110	185	122	6	63	14
Magdalen Hill Down	239	32	122	136	282	434	114	157	154	113
Noar Hill	85	69	342	95	409	277	100	193	51	199
Stockbridge Down	108	82	455	97	245	*	5	257	158	106
Yew Hill	217	103	300	51	101	225	107	213	51	184

Our highest-ever Annual Index was **592** at Alresford Farm in 1983

FLIGHT PERIOD The last half of March has typically seen the first of the year, but in 1993 and 1996 the first records were not until April. This first generation typically peaks in late May and carries on until the last days of June or the first week of July. 1990 and 1992 were the only years of the decade when a large spring immigration from Europe was witnessed to swell these early numbers. The second generation often begins to emerge just as the first generation is ending, in early July. This generation has been boosted by large numbers of immigrants in most years of the 1990s. Numbers peak in August, but can still be high in early September, the peak of this second generation usually being much greater than the peak of the first. Only a remnant remains in October and only three years in the 1990s have produced November records.

EARLIEST/LATEST DATES, 1990–1999 In the period 1990–1999, the earliest records were on 12th March, at Ropley in 1995 and Southampton in 1997. Our latest record was on 16th November 1999 on the Southbourne Undercliff.

HISTORICAL CHANGES Although the Small White is still a *fairly* common butterfly in Hampshire, it is clear from the entomological literature that its numbers are nothing like as strong as in the days before pesticides and when Brassicas were grown more extensively as fodder crops. Goater (1974) writes: "Dixon (pers. Comm) has attributed the decline in abundance which he has noticed to the disappearance of charlock from cultivated fields, but other factors such as the delicate balance with the parasitic *Apanteles*, crop spraying and possibly climate change, have undoubtedly contributed". The latter point was made during a sequence of poor butterfly summers and does not refer to global warming – rather the reverse. It may be that our better years are comparable to average years before 1950 and that years of relatively scarcity are a modern phenomenon. Descriptions *in litt.* of the massive invasions of 1887, 1891, 1928, 1933, 1939 and the early 1940s suggest orders of magnitude of difference in terms of the scale of abundance in Hampshire. There is a detailed description of the massive Large White and Small White invasion of 1887 in *Entomologists' Monthly Magazine 24: 84–5.*

Green-veined White
Pieris napi

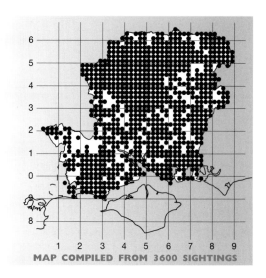

MAP COMPILED FROM 3600 SIGHTINGS

DISTRIBUTION 1990–1999 This is a very much overlooked species, partly because it has not excited the interest of many collectors and breeders and partly because it is frequently confused with the Small White. Unlike the Small White, it exists in distinct colonies, although it *is* a great wanderer and in all probability it has occurred in every Hampshire tetrad during this period. It is perhaps strongest in damp woods and meadows on clay soils, and in and around peaty meadows in the main Hampshire river valleys, but it is also quite common in chalk woods, especially where Clay-with-flints supports Garlic Mustard. It is scarce in New Forest Inclosures where grazing has eliminated its foodplants and it only occurs on heathland and brackish coastal marshes in its wanderings. It has been seen in numbers wandering on chalk downs and in woods on the chalk, and is one of the main species along roadside verges in chalk areas where expanses of weed-free cereals give little scope for butterflies. It occasionally swarms over fields of Rape.

HABITAT AND FOODPLANTS Cuckooflower and Garlic Mustard are the main foodplants over much of Hampshire, with Hedge Mustard also being much used. This is similar to the Orange Tip but the present species lays on the lower leaves of well-shaded plants, especially seedlings and non-flowering first year plants, and not on flower heads.

Both broods use the standard foodplants but the summer brood is more catholic and has a stronger affinity with watercress species and allied plants. Lesser Marshwort, an umbellifer, is readily used along the edges of water courses in the river valleys, with females often laying on plants growing in flowing water. In effect, the species is the nearest thing in Hampshire to an aquatic butterfly. Conversely, Wild Mignonette is regularly used as a foodplant on the chalk.

In gardens, where the species regularly breeds, it lays readily on Horse-radish and Dame's-violet, with Alyssum, Aubretia and Arabis also in use (Oates, 1985). It does not lay on cabbages.

MAJOR SITES Although populations tend to be modest, it is fair to say that unimproved meadowland systems in river valleys, such as the Hampshire Wildlife Trust's reserves at Lower Test Valley and Winnall Moors, and The Moors at Bishop's Waltham, consistently support the strongest populations. Sizeable populations also exist in areas of coastal grazing marshes which are strongly influenced by freshwater, such as Farlington and Keyhaven Marshes and along the Hamble estuary. There are also sizeable populations in wooded valleys on the Gault Clay of east Hampshire and in remnant acidic meadows in the Fleet and Farnborough areas.

POPULATION TREND AND SIZE, 1990–1999 *Trend* – The decade has seen both good and bad seasons. 1991, 1992, 1995, 1997 and 1998 were clearly good years, although even in such years some sites did not perform well. The following transects are typical of the county pattern.

	1990	1991	1992	1993	1994	1995	1996	1997	1998	1999
Alresford Farm	117	230	253	177	73	154	105	257	124	118
Bishop's Waltham	*	210	258	*	139	**412**	114	*	*	*
Farlington Marshes	58	44	103	105	205	203	98	216	211	110
Lower Test Marshes	*	196	111	37	14	143	127	170	179	141
Noar Hill	59	60	77	47	43	77	25	89	42	52
Pamber Forest	66	41	201	71	102	158	156	219	156	84
Winnall Moors	38	70	134	61	123	184	59	134	144	89

Size – There are very few counts estimating population size, but a concentration of 300 taking nectar from Rape at Watership Down on 22nd July 1995 gives an indication of how many can be in one small area.

FLIGHT PERIOD There are two main broods, in spring and late summer. Strong colonies may produce a partial third brood in early autumn in all but the worst years, but colonies are not synchronous. Typically, males emerge in mid-April, numbers peak in the first half of May and this first brood disappears before mid-June. The summer brood generally starts around the second week of July, lasting into early September, but in hot summers can commence as early as mid-June. This may merge with the third brood which emerges sporadically and may last into October and even beyond.

EARLIEST/LATEST DATES, 1990–1999 Within the period 1990–1999, our earliest and latest dates are at Alton on 24th March 1997 and at Fort Gilkicker on 27th and 28th October 1999. This last specimen was a very fresh male, seen at very close range by Dr David Tinling as it basked and fed on Black Mustard, giving excellent views of both upper and underwing patterns. However, the earliest record in our database was on the remarkable date of 3rd March 1989 at Hook, whilst the latest was on 3rd November 1975.

PARTICULAR OCCURRENCES This is not a species where one might expect too many outstanding events. In the past decade, the most notable comments have been how it was the only butterfly left in numbers on the chalk downs in late summer 1997 when so many species of butterfly and flower finished early in the hot, dry conditions, and how widespread it is by roadside verges amongst the prairie-like fields of cereals that cover so much of the chalk.

In the autumns of 1997 and 1998, David Green observed larvae ascending the walls of a cottage to pupate. Pupae were either hidden under eaves or in clear view on the white-painted walls at heights of between 2 m and 3.5 m from the ground. At least some of these overwintering pupae produced adults. Both Large and Small Whites are known for such behaviour, but the Green-veined White more usually pupates hidden amongst dense ground vegetation.

HISTORICAL CHANGES As stated above, this is another butterfly that was not much noted by earlier collectors. Both Goss (Goss, Fletcher and Reid in Doubleday, 1900) and Fassnidge (Fassnidge, 1923), when commenting on the Large, Small and Green-veined Whites, merely noted that they were all common throughout Hampshire. Interestingly, Goss contrasted the respective habitat preferences: "The Common White Butterflies (*Pieris brassicae, P. rapae* and *P. napi)* are plentiful throughout the district, but with the exception of the latter species, which is found in the woods, they are most abundant in and about gardens, fields, and other cultivated places". The Green-veined White is certainly not restricted to woods today. Perhaps this reflects the increased shadiness of Hampshire woodlands as coppicing declined.

Goater, (1974) considered that the species was probably found in "every parish" in Hampshire but that it was nearly always less common than the Small White; this is generally true today. He was the first Hampshire commentator to note the species' preference for damp habitats and listed particularly favoured sites as being water meadows and rides in woods.

It is probable that the Green-veined White declined greatly in Hampshire during the 20th century, due primarily to the loss of extensively grazed unimproved meadows, urban development and changes in woodland management. Nonetheless, it has not declined as severely as many other so-called *common* species and now fits into the 'Widespread and locally common' category. It is scarcely mentioned in entomological literature, though it is clear that it was regarded as common and ubiquitous, perhaps especially in woods.

Orange Tip
Anthocharis cardamines

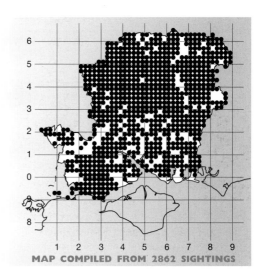

DISTRIBUTION 1990–1999 The Orange Tip is still widespread and quite common but less numerous than of old. Being a wanderer, with the ability to utilise a range of habitats, it has occurred in most Hampshire tetrads. It is absent only from heaths, urban centres, dense coniferous woodland and New Forest Inclosures where ride-side vegetation has been destroyed.

HABITAT AND FOODPLANTS This is a versatile species, breeding in a range of habitats and on a variety of foodplants. Damp meadows, silted-up ditch systems, uncut verges, waste land, bridle paths, footpaths, hedgerows, woodland rides and glades, and gardens are all used.

Garlic Mustard and Cuckooflower are far and away the most important foodplants, depending on what part of the county is being considered. On chalkland above the river valleys, Garlic Mustard grows along roads and lanes in profusion where Cuckooflower is absent. In damper areas, the reverse is true so that the main Orange Tip foodplants change across Hampshire.

Hedge Mustard, Charlock and Rape that has spread from fields are used frequently. Wavy Bitter-cress, Thale Cress and Hoary Cress are used occasionally. In gardens, Dame's-violet and Honesty are favourites whilst Hairy Rock-cress is used on the downs. In 1989, George Else found a larva near Tidworth on Wild Mignonette.

MAJOR SITES The species is so widespread that it is difficult to pick individual major sites. It spreads itself out along suitable lanes or over suitable meadows, seldom appearing *en masse* but met with frequently along the most favoured areas. Moreover, sizeable populations can develop for a few years in ephemeral habitats, such as damp woodland clearings. Generally, it would be fair to say that some of the best Hampshire populations are to be found in and around large unimproved meadow systems in the river valleys, such as The Moors at Bishop's Waltham and Winnall Moors. There are also areas on chalk farmland where hedgerows lining the mosaic of footpaths can hold very healthy numbers, strung out over a considerable area.

POPULATION TREND AND SIZE, 1990–1999 *Trend* – Overall, the species performed well during the 1990s. The best year was 1991, with 1990, 1992, 1993 and 1997 all being described generally as good seasons, although fortunes varied considerably from site to site. The worst year was 1996, but even that was not positively poor, whilst the four other years can be best summarised as being mediocre or moderate.

Size – The Orange Tip does not occur in distinct colonies. However, as both sexes aggregate over stands of the main foodplants and nectar sources, notably Cuckooflower and Garlic Mustard, it is possible to see over 20 in the best localities. Over much of the county however, it is unusual to see more than 10 adults in any one place.

	1990	1991	1992	1993	1994	1995	1996	1997	1998	1999
Alresford Farm	66	115	66	48	37	24	32	63	43	36
Farlington Marshes	31	26	16	12	14	16	21	39	19	15
Hookheath Meadows	*	*	19	39	28	63	44	83	37	24
Lower Test Marshes	*	87	41	40	26	23	14	21	10	12
Noar Hill	35	54	19	41	20	40	24	25	30	27
Pamber Forest	26	41	23	27	13	39	34	29	32	20
Stockbridge Down	41	10	30	56	23	*	8	13	13	24

FLIGHT PERIOD Typically, butterflies emerge in mid-April, peak in early May and linger to mid-June. However, being a spring species and subject to the vagaries of our spring weather, such a programme may be earlier or later. During the 1990s there was a distinct trend towards earlier flight seasons, the first appearing during March in six years of the 1990s, with few being recorded during June in some years. In 1990 for example, the butterfly emerged in some numbers and oviposited during the last days of March. On the other hand, in late years individuals can linger into early or even mid-July, as happened widely in 1979.

Occasionally, very late individuals are seen. It is thought that these are attributable to a second brood, though it is possible that they are simply late developers. The majority of these records come from urban areas during the second half of August. In the 1990s, such records occurred in 1991 (two in mid and late August), 1994 (one in mid-August), 1995 (two on 3rd August) and possibly in 1996 (one in mid-July). Curiously, not one of these late individuals was recorded in 1984, 1989 and 1990, three exceptional years when Orange Tips fared particularly well.

EARLIEST/LATEST DATES, 1990–1999 The earliest Hampshire record was on the surprising date of 10th March 1990, at Totton. March records have occurred subsequently and also in the past, for example at Alton on 31st March 1920 (Stowell, 1920), though Dale (1900) records no sightings earlier than 2nd April during the 19th century. The latest, one of the apparent second brood, was at Vernham Dean on 28th August 1991.

PARTICULAR OCCURRENCES It has been noted that adults are distinctly dwarfed in east Hampshire, especially during the first half of the season. This was first documented by Haworth (1973) and seemed to be largely a feature of Gault Clay where the species is almost wholly associated with Cuckooflower which itself seems to be dwarfed in that district. The majority of early season Orange Tips in east Hampshire are little larger than a Purple Hairstreak and Matthew Oates caught a female at Oakhanger in 1978 that was the size of a Common Blue. Recently, although it is not a majority that is involved, John Taverner has noticed a marked size difference in Orange Tips on chalk around Winchester, where Garlic Mustard is the main foodplant. Some of these have been as small as those described above so that a normal Orange Tip seen nearby looks like a giant. It would seem that dwarf Orange Tips are not confined to the Gault of east Hampshire, merely that they are prevalent there.

HISTORICAL CHANGES Although it is still a widespread and reasonably common butterfly, its preference for 'waste' land must have resulted in a steady decrease in numbers through the century as various pressures have led to such land being developed for agriculture, building and the many uses we find for land today. The Victoria County History states that "The Orange Tip is common both in the woods and lanes, and in the cultivated parts of the county". The former description still applies, but the latter does not.

We really need quantitative data from the past in order to judge the extent of this butterfly's decline, but in the case of Hampshire's butterflies, such data really belong to the last two decades so that accurate comparisons of loss or gain are only possible over that period.

Green Hairstreak
Callophrys rubi

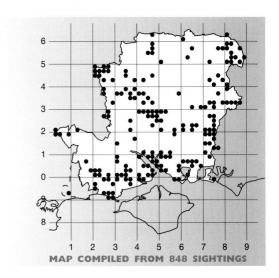

MAP COMPILED FROM 848 SIGHTINGS

DISTRIBUTION 1990–1999 Because the species has successfully colonised a variety of habitats, its distribution is widespread over the central chalk and the younger rocks of northern and southern Hampshire, although the strongest colonies are on downland with few sizeable populations on heathland. The species tends to form discrete colonies, generally small and typically consisting of fewer than 50 individuals. As the males are strongly territorial, they are well spaced within these colonies. However, at some sites the species appears in ones and twos over large areas, suggesting diffuse and possibly more mobile populations. This is also indicated by its ability to appear on a transect after many years of absence.

HABITAT AND FOODPLANTS No British butterfly has a wider range of foodplants, with the possible exception of some grass-feeding species (Thomas, 1991). On Hampshire's downland, Common Rock-rose and Common Bird's-foot-trefoil are the preferred foodplants, with the strongest colonies based on Common Rock-rose, but Dogwood, Buckthorn and a variety of other flowers and shrubs are used. On acid soils, Gorse is the main foodplant, with Bramble, Dyer's Greenweed and Broom occasionally used. Curiously, there are no records in Hampshire of the species breeding on Cranberry or Bilberry; the former supports large colonies on raised bogs in northern Britain and is plentiful in some bogs in the Woolmer Forest area, yet searches have failed to find the butterfly.

The species' habitat includes chalk down, heath, woodland rides, meadows and tumbled cliffs such as those at Hordle. It is now scarce in Hampshire woodland, although this has not always been the case. Areas with scrub and scattered bushes are especially favoured and many of the colonies are on slopes. Warmth and shelter seem important so that south-facing downs with bush cover, such as Magdalen Hill Down and Stockbridge Down, hold strong colonies.

MAJOR SITES With a species where colonies are usually small, it is perhaps erroneous to write of major sites. Hampshire has a number of strong colonies, amongst which would be Ashford Hangers, Chilbolton Down, Danebury, the Farley Mount area, Hordle Cliff, Magdalen Hill Down, Martin Down, Oxenbourne Down, Porton Down, Portsdown Hill and Stockbridge Down. The preferred foodplant is Common Rock-rose at nearly all these sites.

POPULATION TREND AND SIZE, 1990–1999 *Trend* – Over this period, there have been good, bad and mediocre years depending on the weather. On the whole, the species has fared well.

Sites in the table below are all chalk downland with scrub. It can be seen that 1990, 1992, 1993 and 1994 were good years and most reports from 1997 and 1998 also spoke of success. 1991 and 1996 were poor, although the last-named saw Hampshire's highest-ever Annual Index at Magdalen Hill Down, this probably being due to the conservation work carried out on this Branch Reserve. 1995 and 1999 were mediocre. In both 1998 and 1999, reports varied considerably from site to site, ranging from poor to very good.

	1990	1991	1992	1993	1994	1995	1996	1997	1998	1999
Ashford Hangers	1	3	3	8	23	5	8	15	10	*
Beacon Hill–Warnford	25	18	21	18	10	34	5	13	20	27
Magdalen Hill Down	34	4	63	44	85	47	110	62	56	83
Noar Hill	27	7	16	10	21	35	4	12	5	7
Stockbridge Down	53	13	11	9	2	*	13	22	1	10

Size – Twenty would be a good day's count at any Hampshire site, although on 13th May 1998, Coulter's Dean was said to be "awash with them"! Andy Barker recorded 38 on a single transect count on 30th April at Magdalen Hill Down, mostly males that had established territorial perches on Hawthorn. The butterfly is well camouflaged, so it is not surprising that specific counts have been modest.

FLIGHT PERIOD The first appear in April, usually around the middle of the month. Peak flight time is in late May and early June, a few then lasting until late June with occasional stragglers lingering into July, especially on New Forest heaths where the flight season is later than on warm downland sites. The 1989 Hampshire Butterfly Report stated that one on 16th July was possibly from a second brood, but there have been July records since then, in 1990, 1991, 1993 and 1996 and these are almost certainly individuals that have emerged late.

EARLIEST/LATEST DATES, 1990–1999 The earliest was on 1st April 1997 at Magdalen Hill Down and the latest on 17th July 1997, in the New Forest coastal belt, at Norley Farm, East End.

HISTORICAL CHANGES From year to year, it is probably the vagaries of our English spring that cause populations to rise or fall. For example, in 1981 the species emerged unusually early due to good April weather, only to be decimated by a late fall of snow. Much more important are colonies that are lost through land development. Over Britain as a whole the species has certainly decreased in status with countless colonies lost through reclamation of rough land, urban growth and a general tidying up of the environment (Thomas, 1986). This pattern must also apply to Hampshire. Much of this loss has been in the last half of this century when population pressures have led to urban areas expanding into surrounding countryside and farmland taking over areas that were unused. The few accounts of this species in Hampshire's entomological literature suggest that it has declined noticeably in woodland. For example, Fassnidge (1923) records it as being "Generally distributed and common", referring to woods and downs.

The Green Hairstreak colonies on the chalk are usually well separated from each other and since these colonies are small and the species rather sedentary in character, loss of one may be permanent, although recolonisation from wanderers mentioned in the above text is a possibility. There is apparently suitable but unoccupied habitat on the chalk, particularly along old railway lines.

Brown Hairstreak
Thecla betulae

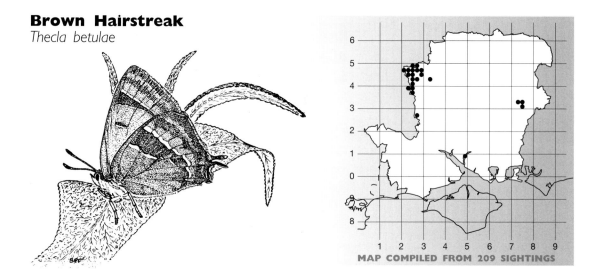

MAP COMPILED FROM 209 SIGHTINGS

DISTRIBUTION 1990–1999 Despite apparently suitable habitat in several areas and historical evidence that the Brown Hairstreak was formerly widespread, only two populations are known today and the butterfly can be considered an endangered species within the county. A relatively strong colony exists at Selborne, though it has contracted in range over the last 25 years and is now based almost wholly on the 10 ha nature reserve at Noar Hill. Fortunately, it has recently reappeared at nearby Selborne Common following Blackthorn coppicing work by the National Trust. The second area involves a weak population that ranges over countryside to the west and south west of Andover which is becoming increasingly fragmented as a result of modern farming and forestry practices. Here, the butterfly is heavily dependent on green lanes near Kimpton and Quarley, on MoD land to the south and east of Tidworth, on a large area of mixed scrub west of Shipton Bellinger, and in the Cholderton area where it occurs on land farmed by Mr Henry Edmunds, a keen entomologist who manages hedges specifically for this species. This population overspills into Wiltshire (Fuller, 1995).

Extensive searches for ova in the 1980s in other parts of Hampshire failed to find new populations, though it is certainly possible that one or two small and discrete colonies still await discovery in the county. For example, the butterfly could be found on sites close to the West Sussex border on the South Downs, for a sizeable population exists just over the border on Harting Downs. Interestingly, this species may have been seen in the Queen Elizabeth Country Park in 1999. Claims of a new population in the Lymington area (Taverner, Ed, 1995) have not been substantiated.

HABITAT AND FOODPLANTS The species ranges diffusely over areas where Blackthorn abounds, this being the larval foodplant, with small concentrations of adults occurring in favoured places. It is primarily a species of Blackthorn landscapes where the shrub is a dominant species in hedges and where entanglements occur in woodland clearings, along wood edges, in neglected corners and along lane verges. Tight, definable colonies are rare.

Males congregate on Ash and oak trees growing near Blackthorn stands, individual trees being seldom favoured from year to year. Ova are laid, both high up and low down, in forks or at the base of spines, on prominent leaders or side shoots on stands in a vigorous state of growth. Advancing edges of Blackthorn are favoured, and over-mature growths and heavily browsed stands, such as those in the New Forest, are unsuitable.

The butterfly can be indolent and elusive and is often inexplicably inactive on warm, sunny August days. However, adults will descend to take nectar from a narrow range of flowers, notably Bramble and Hemp-agrimony, where they occasionally linger for lengthy periods on one flower-head.

MAJOR SITES Although there is nowhere in Hampshire where one can guarantee seeing the species, one *can* expect to see it at Noar Hill, at least in good seasons, when the butterfly is moderately plentiful there. Indeed, the reserve is probably the best known Brown Hairstreak site in Britain at present. At Noar Hill, the butterflies are particularly attracted to Hemp-agrimony flowers, a plant which has increased considerably there in recent years.

In north-west Hampshire, a group of Ash trees favoured by male Brown Hairstreaks was discovered to the west of Shipton Bellinger in 1993. The main habitat types in this north-western area are outlined in the opening section.

POPULATION TREND AND SIZE, 1990–1999 *Trend* – At Noar Hill, the population has been closely monitored since 1975, initially by Matthew Oates and latterly by Tony James. During the 1990s the population fared reasonably well, partly because the decade has been notable for much good August weather. The most memorable season was 1995, when the Brown Hairstreak was numerous at Noar Hill, but numbers were also quite high during 1990, 1991, 1994 and 1999, the last of these years being the second best of the decade. Only in 1997 did the butterfly experience one of its periodic bad years, when few adults were seen. Transect data reflects the fortunes of the Brown Hairstreak at Noar Hill over the last 17 years.

	1983	1984	1985	1986	1987	1988	1989
Noar Hill	5	19	15	14	10	12	15

	1990	1991	1992	1993	1994	1995	1996	1997	1998	1999
Noar Hill	26	25	11	10	18	98	21	8	21	36

Size – It is almost impossible to gauge the size of a Brown Hairstreak population, especially in an area such as the north-west of Hampshire where the population is so diffuse. Ova counts give some indication of numbers. In December 1997, Tony James found 50 ova in 90 minutes at Noar Hill and 50+ were found in north-west Hampshire on 9th March 1997 by Tim Bernhard, whilst Glynn Evans and Dr John Moon found a total of 122 ova at three sites in the north-west in 1995. As for adult counts, Matthew Oates counted 41 in two hours at Noar Hill in the record year of 1995, which is easily the highest count for the decade.

FLIGHT PERIOD The Brown Hairstreak can have a flight season in excess of eight weeks, though much depends on September weather. In an average year the first males appear at Noar Hill on or around 7th August, with peak season occurring during the period 18th–25th August. Males disappear at the end of August with females straggling on through much of September. In Indian Summers, females can last into October, though in contrast, poor weather in early September can bring a premature end to the flight season. The Selborne and Andover flight seasons seem to be synchronised.

EARLIEST/LATEST DATES, 1990–1999 Both come from Noar Hill. The earliest was on 24th July 1992 and the latest on 11th October 1991, although outside the decade it was seen at Noar Hill on 16th October 1986.

INTERESTING OCCURRENCES Strays sometimes appear along the county boundary, presumably coming from neighbouring counties. One was at Liphook, near the Surrey border, in 1992 and another was seen in 1994 at Martin Down, close to the Wiltshire border.

HISTORICAL CHANGES The Victoria County History records the Brown Hairstreak as being "common locally in many parts of the county". However, the butterfly was poorly recorded as entomologists tended to visit a small number of well known sites, notably Selborne Common, Balmer Lawn in the New Forest, and Botley Wood.

Selborne Common was renowned for the species. Stowell (1924) provides a useful description: "This consists of charming glades set with clumps of fine beeches and a few oaks, and immense blackthorn bushes ... Larvae of *Z.betulae* may always be obtained at the beginning of June, and with luck the indolent imagines may be seen sitting on bramble or hemp agrimony in August and September". Curiously, Noar Hill did not gain a reputation for this butterfly until the 1950s. During the mid-1970s, the butterfly occurred along the East Hampshire Gault Clay belt from Bentley to Hawkley. Matthew Oates found ova in 17 kilometre squares during this period and identified strongholds on the south-western edge of Alice

Holt Forest and at Green Street and Binswood below East Worldham. However, by the early 1980s the butterfly had become confined to Noar Hill due to the hammer and anvil combination of agricultural intensification and neglect.

The Brown Hairstreak was always local in the New Forest. C.B. Antram (1952) describes the Balmer Lawn site: "The locality comprises of several hundred acres of blackthorn, very densely grown and impenetrable ... Every year many collectors visit this spot to beat for larvae". In August, adults could be seen on heather flowers. However, during the late 1950s, large areas of Blackthorn were bulldozed away to create more grazing land and then browsing by rising numbers of deer and Commoners' stock rendered the surviving thickets unsuitable for the butterfly. Linford Bottom, near Ringwood, was the other renowned Forest locality, but here too the surviving Blackthorn bushes are too heavily browsed for the butterfly. The Forestry Commission prohibited the collecting of Brown Hairstreaks in the Forest at the beginning of the 1960s, following concern about declining numbers, but to no avail. In all probability, the Brown Hairstreak died out in the Forest during the early 1970s.

Baron de Worms was one of many collectors who used to visit the Botley Wood area for Brown Hairstreaks. In 1942 he wrote: "I have never seen so many larvae of *Thecla betulae*". The butterfly thrived here into the 1970s, but was forced out of the wood itself as fellings ceased and young plantations grew, when it became dependent on Blackthorn stands outside the forest fence. These were either grubbed up or heavily flail-cut by farmers, or neglected so that they became unsuitably over-mature. The butterfly was last recorded at Botley Wood in 1979 by Dr C.J. Luckens. Extensive searches by Matthew Oates for ova in 1984 and 1988 were unsuccessful. The Whiteley Pastures development then destroyed much suitable habitat.

It is probable that the butterfly occurred at a number of other sites into the second half of the 20th century, notably around Faccombe, Burghclere, Heath End and Odiham in the north of the county, between Hursley and Chilbolton in mid-west Hampshire, and around Bishop's Waltham and Southwick in the south-east. The evidence provided by an analysis of historic records – Goater (1974) lists some 26 localities – and by the presence of fragments of surviving habitat, suggest that the Brown Hairstreak is one of the butterflies to have declined most in Hampshire during the 20th century.

Purple Hairstreak
Neozephyrus quercus

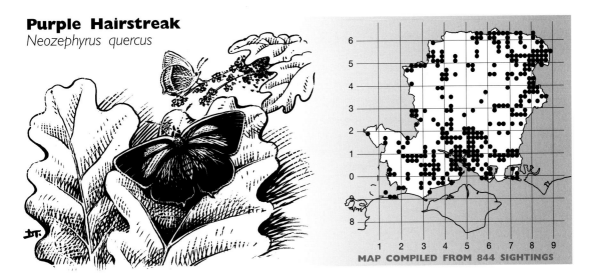

MAP COMPILED FROM 844 SIGHTINGS

DISTRIBUTION 1990–1999 Being a butterfly of the tree canopy and one which is most active in the evenings, the Purple Hairstreak is often overlooked and the map no doubt under-records the species. It is common wherever oaks are the predominant trees, with Pedunculate Oak the most favoured. Just a few oaks can support a population, or even an isolated oak if it is not exposed. Along the coast, good numbers of Purple Hairstreaks can be found at suitable sites, such as Hamble Common. Even in towns and cities the species can thrive; Southampton Common and the 'greenways' of Southampton still support good populations (Barker and Budd, 1997).

HABITAT AND FOODPLANTS Oak is almost exclusively the required foodplant, although the species has been seen to lay on Ash and may breed on Holm Oak as it does at Ventnor on the Isle of Wight. It seems to be especially strong in oak woods on clay where it can be by far the most numerous butterfly. Trees with broad crowns are favoured and populations are weak in pole-stage oak woods.

Adrian Hoskins discovered valuable data on ova-density by examining oaks blown down in the Great Storm of October 1987. He found the highest ova counts – 30 per 15 minute search – on broad-crowned Pedunculate Oaks spaced about 20 m apart in coppiced woods. At the same site, 50% of Sessile Oaks produced no ova at all whilst the remainder held only two or three per tree. A small number of Turkey Oak hybrids produced an average of 10 ova per 15 minutes. Pedunculate Oaks in more exposed habitats had significantly lower ova counts than those in coppiced woods. Altogether, 342 ova were located, of which 60 were found to have been parasitised by Chalcid Wasps *Trichgramma* spp. (Hoskins, Ed, 1988).

Adults are said to rarely visit flowers, but they may do so in anticyclonic weather when Hemp-agrimony and Bramble have been chosen. At Whitely Pastures on 19th July 1997, Mike Gibbons saw the species use a variety of flowers such as Creeping Thistle and Hedge-bedstraw, and very small Scots Pines. The same observer also recorded the species on an umbellifer near Ringwood. Honey-dew is the adults' main source of sustenance, obtained mainly from oaks and Ash, although other broad-leaved trees are utilised. In very hot weather, adults will descend to seek moisture from the ground, especially along open rides.

MAJOR SITES There are probably a number of major woodland sites in Hampshire, but our knowledge of the species is too slight to give a list. Certainly Alice Holt Forest, Botley Wood, Crab Wood, Harewood Forest, Pamber Forest and West Wood hold vast populations, as do many Inclosures and woods in the New Forest. Probably any wood containing oaks has a considerable population.

POPULATION TREND AND SIZE, 1990–1999 *Trend* – Enormous fluctuations are known to occur from year to year in response to weather in late May and June (Thomas, 1974). The best summers of the decade were 1990,

1992, 1995, 1997 and 1998. It is not a species that can be monitored by transects, but the following figures may be of some value, Pamber Forest being one of the county's top Purple Hairstreak sites.

	1990	1991	1992	1993	1994	1995	1996	1997	1998	1999
Bartley Heath	*	*	*	*	*	*	64	92	61	41
Pamber Forest	11	13	20	7	6	41	18	27	45	28

Size – Very little is known about numbers due to its tree-top life style, but there are sufficient records to suggest that it is abundant in a number of places. Castle Russell netted 100 adults in two sweeps over Silver Birch saplings near Aldershot in 1887 (Castle Russell, 1955), but modern reports also suggest impressive counts. At Pamber Forest in 1988, the species was reported as 'cascading out of tall oaks onto a carpet of ferns' (Hoskins, Ed, 1988). David Green sampled 50 oaks in Harewood Forest in 1995 and found the butterfly in every tree. He thought that adult Purple Hairstreaks were possibly on *all* the oaks at Harewood. David also found the species on Beech, Silver Birch, Aspen, Wayfaring-tree and Dogwood, but thought that they were simply seeking shade.

FLIGHT PERIOD The flight season lasts about six weeks. At most sites the first adults appear around 7th July with the peak flight time during the third week of July. In exceptionally hot summers the species may start before Midsummer Day and finish before the third week of August, as was the case in 1976 and 1989. In most years of the decade, a few late individuals were seen during the first days of September.

EARLIEST/LATEST DATES, 1990–1999 Our earliest records were both on 20th June and both at Woolston, one in 1993 and one in 1995. The latest record was on 19th September 1998 at Wildhern, near Andover. Previous decades have produced sightings outside this range. The earliest on our database was a single adult in Botley Wood on 13th June 1989 whilst the last was a very late individual on 21st September 1977 at Alice Holt Forest.

PARTICULAR OCCURRENCES One of the most attractive sights in the world of British butterflies is the evening dance of Purple Hairstreaks. Peak activity is between 1730 hrs and 1930 hrs, but on really warm evenings during the first half of July the flight may go on until 2100 hrs. Males dart above the tree canopy searching for females. When two males meet they chase each other about at great speed, often encouraging other males in the process. Groups of 10 or so may be seen in mad chases along sunny wood edges. The special feature is the spiral dance where individuals circle round each other, drifting slowly up and away before returning to the canopy. David Green recorded 150+ displaying around the top of a single oak in Harewood Forest on 3rd July 1993, around 2015 hrs, but although the same tree has been visited regularly since that date, it has not been used for evening flights. Matthew Oates once netted a group of five which consisted of four males and one female. Evenings have to be warm and fairly still and the flights are mostly along south or west facing wood edges. It appears that most females emerge during late afternoon so that most courtship is in the evening.

HISTORICAL CHANGES The Purple Hairstreak has undoubtedly declined in Hampshire during the 20th century, one major factor being the replacement of oaks by plantations of conifers and Beech. It has also suffered from the decline in coppicing, Adrian Hoskins' work on ova counts in the previous text showing the highest densities in coppiced woodland. However, it has without doubt suffered less than many woodland species because areas of oaks are still present in many Hampshire woods. In the New Forest the species was not dependent on ride-side vegetation, the loss of which was such a disaster to White Admirals, Silver-washed Fritillaries, Pearl-bordered Fritillaries and other species. It is probable that this species has declined greatly in the countryside generally during the 20th century as a result of the removal of small copses and trees in fields and hedgerows. The present paucity of young oaks in the county poses a very real long term threat. However, on the plus side, native species such as oaks are increasingly being planted in urban areas such as Southampton.

White-letter Hairstreak
Satyrium w-album

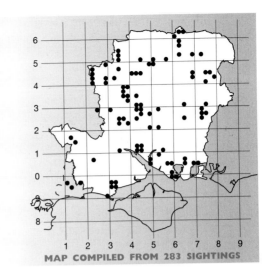

MAP COMPILED FROM 283 SIGHTINGS

DISTRIBUTION 1990–1999 This is another species where, in all probability, the distribution map underestimates the species' range in Hampshire. It is probably one of the most under-recorded butterflies in the county. The species is clearly widespread in districts where elms are frequent and has been recorded from 101 named localities in 93 tetrads during the 1990s. The number of individual colonies would be fewer than this since some localities may have spanned the same colony.

The White-letter Hairstreak is a specialist, living in colonies on flowering elms in sunny but sheltered positions, and it is possible that the majority of such trees in Hampshire support a colony. Indeed, a single isolated tree may hold a small population. Most colonies are small, though the species *can* occur in profusion and is prone to great fluctuations in adult numbers. The majority of known colonies are in roadside hedges or along wood edges and some are in suburban situations. There are some areas of Hampshire where elms do not occur, notably large areas of the New Forest, with a resulting absence of White-letter Hairstreaks.

As the adult is so small and elusive, spending much of its time in the canopy, often inactive, it is very easy to overlook and much more fieldwork needs to be carried out to ascertain the insect's true status. Fortunately, ova are quite easy to find on the lower branches of flowering Wych Elm and many of the Hampshire colonies have been discovered through ova-searches, or even looking for larvae and pupae.

New colonies are discovered every year, at least 15 in 1996 for example. In the Southampton area, a number of new colonies have been discovered since 1993 (Barker and Budd, 1997). The butterfly's ability to seek out and colonise young elms as they become suitable is quite remarkable, suggesting that this is a highly mobile species with considerable powers of colonisation and recovery. It will need such powers if it is to survive periodic outbreaks of Dutch Elm Disease.

HABITAT AND FOODPLANTS The larvae depend entirely on elms. It is clear that Wych Elm and Wych Elm hybrids are preferred and tend to support the largest colonies. Furthermore, they are less vulnerable to Dutch Elm Disease than English Elm, although the 1990s have seen groups of Wych Elms succumb to the disease with the resulting loss of White-letter colonies. It is probable that tall English Elms were much used prior to the main onslaught of Dutch Elm Disease in the mid-1970s, but only a handful of such trees now survive, most of which are English Elm hybrids. Indeed, most of the tall hybrids which survived the disease fell during the great storms of 1987 and 1990. It is ironic that young English Elms are colonised by White-letter Hairstreaks when they become tall enough to produce flowers, which is precisely the time when they become susceptible to the disease. Thus, many of the colonies that have developed on the new generation of English Elms appear destined to be short-lived. A small number of colonies are known to use other elm species, subspecies and hybrids, whilst some colonies utilise two or even three types of elm.

Adults spend much of their time high in the canopy, basking or sipping honeydew, particularly from Ash. They sometimes visit flowers in numbers, perhaps when there is a shortage of honeydew in the canopy. Bramble and Creeping Thistle are particularly favoured whilst those at a Braishfield colony came regularly to Hogweed. Visits are often confined to specific patches or clumps.

MAJOR SITES As colonies are so small, it is difficult to talk of major sites, but some areas have a number of small colonies and so can be considered important. For example, 12 colonies were discovered in 1993 at Ashford Hangers, Stoner Hill being of particular importance. Indeed, the East Hampshire Hangers have been the butterfly's county stronghold since the 1970s. The Cholderton area in north-west Hampshire and the Avon valley around Fordingbridge have also produced a number of colonies.

Strong colonies have been found throughout the county at places such as Abbotts Ann, Crab Wood, Hook-with-Warsash, Hursley, Redenham Park, Timsbury, Wendleholme and Whiteley Pastures, but this is by no means an exhaustive list and towns such as Southampton hold colonies of importance. Sometimes a colony fails as Dutch elm disease strikes, but this is an adaptable species which will recolonise nearby younger flowering elms as old trees die.

POPULATION TREND AND SIZE, 1990–1999 *Trend* – We have no reliable data from transects and so trends have to be judged by observers' comments from year to year. What is clear is that adult numbers are prone to considerable fluctuations from year to year and that there are occasional years of abundance. The decade started with a "poor to average" 1990, but five of the next six years were described as "excellent" and the sixth year as "very good", so that by 1996 the species had experienced a run of success. 1997 was a poor year with the bad weather at that time a possible but unproven cause and this was followed by a disappointing season in 1998. However, the 1990s ended with reasonable success for the species in 1999, although considerable losses of Wych Elms continued due to disease.

Size – Populations are almost impossible to measure; a count of 20 seen in flight may mean there are around 100 in the canopy. Our highest actual counts during the decade are 36 at a Fordingbridge site on 10th July 1995, 23 at Redenham Park on 18th July 1996 and 20+ at Crab Wood on 2nd July 1993.

FLIGHT PERIOD Apart from 1998, in each year of the 1990s the first sighting has been between 13th–25th June and the last between 10th–18th August, both of which are narrow time bands. Peak flight time is typically in mid-July.

EARLIEST/LATEST DATES, 1990–1999 The earliest date was on 13th June 1992 at Timsbury, the earliest Hampshire record since 1976. The latest was on 18th August 1996 at Milford on Sea.

HISTORICAL CHANGES There is remarkably little reference to this species in Hampshire's historical literature and what little there is suggests that most entomologists regarded it as a rare butterfly in the county. The lack of records is partly due to the fact that elms have always been rare in the New Forest, an area to which the bulk of Hampshire's butterfly literature relates. It may also be that both the butterfly and its immature stages are far easier to find on today's relatively young and low trees than on the giant elms of yesteryear. The insect is not mentioned in the Victoria County History, though the author was primarily a man of the New Forest. Fassnidge (1923) describes the butterfly as "Rare in Hants" and could list only three localities. However, Goater (1974) listed 20 localities, these being mainly old sites which suggests that some previous authors had been unaware of such colonies. An element of confusion is caused by South (1906) who states that "It is rare in Hampshire", only to quote Barrett's (1893) statement that it is "found more or less plentifully" in the county. Either the species was severely under-recorded in the past or it has increased dramatically in recent years.

We cannot say for certain which of these two possibilities is correct, but the evidence suggests that the former is the more likely, particularly as elms occurred profusely in large areas of the county (Brewis, Bowman and Rose, 1996). Also, as the species is not prone to variation, it was not a main target for collectors, who tended to pay sufficient visits to a known locality to take a good series and then neglect this small, elusive and rather difficult species. Despite the paucity of records in past literature, the butterfly appears in all old Hampshire butterfly collections of importance and so was probably not as rare as the literature suggests.

It may well be that nothing approximating to a systematic search had taken place in Hampshire prior to 1975, when Matthew Oates arrived in the county and found the butterfly to be common in the east Hampshire hangers. Indeed, the butterfly abounded around the dying elms in the hangers during the hot summers of 1975 and 1976. It may well be that the White-letter Hairstreak was a common but overlooked butterfly in large areas of Hampshire prior to the ravages of Dutch Elm Disease in the mid and late 1970s. Certainly, there was a massive disease-induced collapse during and immediately after the summer of 1976 and very few colonies were known in Hampshire during the late 1970s and early 1980s. Fortunately, the species did survive in greatly reduced numbers at a scatter of sites such as Crab Wood and some of the Upper Greensand hangers in east Hampshire. The first signs of revival occurred during the hot summer of 1984. As the insect's new-found conservation significance developed alongside new generations of elms during the 1980s, and as the band of informed butterfly enthusiasts grew, so new colonies were found, supporting the view that the White-letter Hairstreak may have been much under-recorded in the past. Nevertheless, the possibility of a recent increase in Hampshire cannot be ruled out; as stated in the preceding text, there has certainly been an increase in the number of colonies in the Southampton area (Barker and Budd, 1997).

Small Copper
Lycaena phlaeas

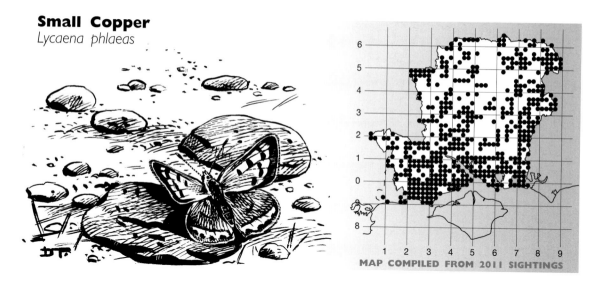

MAP COMPILED FROM 2011 SIGHTINGS

DISTRIBUTION 1990–1999 The Small Copper is widespread but thinly distributed throughout Hampshire. It is rarely abundant, but the species may be found almost anywhere within the county, particularly along the coast, on dry heaths and in unimproved meadows. The butterfly is fairly mobile and individuals are often found away from their normal breeding areas, visiting nectar sources such as gardens.

HABITAT AND FOODPLANTS Being so widespread, it is not surprising that a wide variety of habitats is used. These include woodland rides, chalk downland, rough grassland, waste ground, urban areas, roadside verges and particularly dry heathland and coastal grasslands. The larval foodplants are almost exclusively Common Sorrel and Sheep's Sorrel, the former on chalk downland and neutral meadows and the latter on non-calcareous soils such as coastal shingle. The majority of the strongest colonies are based on Sheep's Sorrel.

MAJOR SITES At Needs Ore, areas of old compacted shingle have become carpeted with Sheep's Sorrel and a considerable colony has become established. In 1998, John Taverner counted 20 per 30 m of shoreline, the adults taking nectar especially from Smith's Pepperwort, but also from Springbeauty, Sea Campion, Sea Mouse-ear and Gorse. The Small Copper can be similarly abundant on areas of dry heathland in the New Forest and north-east Hampshire. Sizeable colonies also occur at a number of other coastal sites such as Dibden Bay, Hook-with-Warsash, Hythe, Brownwich and Hayling Island, on unimproved grassland such as Chilworth Manor, in old meadows in the major river valleys and on some chalk downs, notably Broughton and Stockbridge Downs.

POPULATION TREND AND SIZE, 1990–1999 *Trend* – There was a significant decline throughout Hampshire during the early 1990s and the species was all but lost from the majority of sites, reaching a very low ebb in 1993. There was then a marked recovery from 1994 to 1997, well illustrated by the following transect figures.

	1990	1991	1992	1993	1994	1995	1996	1997	1998	1999
Beacon Hill–Warnford	90	32	16	1	3	6	13	43	5	3
Farlington Marshes	30	12	5	0	0	13	4	2	7	1
Hookheath Meadows	*	*	*	*	3	94	49	72	13	9
Noar Hill	42	16	14	0	6	18	14	9	5	3
Stockbridge Down	72	98	20	4	18	180	44	89	56	13
Wendleholme	89	75	60	0	13	26	59	50	32	9

Our highest-ever Annual Index was **194** in 1989 at Oxenbourne Down

The 1998 picture was very mixed with reports varying from excellent to very poor, but this was followed by a very poor season in 1999.

Size – Colonies usually consist of modest numbers and Small Coppers are typically seen in twos and threes at most inland Hampshire sites. Over a whole down, such as Stockbridge Down, and at favourable coastal sites, it is not unusual to record upwards of 40 on an August visit. At Needs Ore in 1998, (see Habitat and Foodplants) the population on one day was well in excess of 100 whilst at Stockbridge Down in 1998, Ashley Whitlock found the species to be "everywhere" on 16th May, "rising at almost every step and perching on the very small bushes".

FLIGHT PERIOD There are normally three generations in Hampshire. The first Small Coppers typically emerge during late April or early May and individuals of this brood continue until the end of June. This spring generation is often partial in that some do not emerge until the second brood. The second and invariably stronger generation appears in early July and flies until the end of August. There is then a third generation during September and October. If the season is late, this often strong brood is largely missed on transect counts, which end on 30th September, so that transect trends are not entirely reliable for this species. It is thought that in particularly favourable seasons there may be four broods (Thomas and Lewington, 1991). This is believed to have occurred during 1992, for example.

EARLIEST/LATEST DATES, 1990–1999 The earliest sighting was from Boscombe Undercliff on 16th March 1998, eight days earlier than the next in our database. The first three months of 1998 were *very* mild and as the south-facing Undercliff at Bournemouth/Boscombe is a considerable sun-trap, this early record is not surprising. The finder, Michael Skelton, counted 34 Small Coppers along the Undercliff on 12th April in that year, one day earlier than the next site in Hampshire recorded its first. The latest was from the same site, on 16th November 1999.

INTERESTING OCCURRENCES Specimens with a row of blue spots on the margin of the upper hindwing, conforming to ab. *caeruleopuncata*, have been reported from several localities. This form is more common in northern parts of Britain. An unusual specimen with the ground colour of the left forewing almost white was seen at Noar Hill on 29th August 1991.

HISTORICAL CHANGES Although the Small Copper remains widespread in Hampshire, it is generally believed to be far less numerous than it was in the past. For example, Fassnidge (1923) considered it to be abundant everywhere, which is certainly not the case today. Goater (1974) was able to note a steady decline which first became noticeable in the early 1940s. There seems to have been a partial recovery during the mid-1970s, for it was very common in 1975 and 1976. However, a massive decline took place away from the dry heathland and coastal strongholds in the late 1970s and throughout much of the 1980s, with many observers expressing concern over the butterfly's increasing scarcity. There was a further recovery in 1989 and 1990 when many populations were considered to have returned to their mid-1970s levels. In general, the Small Copper appears to have become more scarce in several habitats during recent decades, notably on downland, in woodland other than that on dry acidic soils, and especially on roadside verges.

Small Blue
Cupido minimus

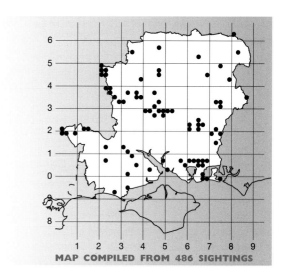

MAP COMPILED FROM 486 SIGHTINGS

DISTRIBUTION 1990–1999 The map illustrates a thin scattering of locations and yet, with the exception of the Common Blue, it is nationally the most widely distributed Blue butterfly. Branch records show that the species has been present in 82 tetrads during the 1990s. Reliance on just one larval foodplant naturally restricts colonies to those areas where Kidney Vetch grows strongly, that mainly being on chalk grassland, so it is largely absent from the New Forest and only rarely sighted in north-east Hampshire. The butterfly is strongest on the western and central chalk and is surprisingly local on the northern downs and in east Hampshire. Given that it is Britain's smallest butterfly and not a 'wanderer' by nature, it is possible that one or two discrete colonies may exist in these two areas. Even across the South Downs, where several colonies are found, it is considered to be relatively scarce despite its widespread but sporadic national distribution.

HABITAT AND FOODPLANTS It cannot be assumed that Small Blues are found wherever Kidney Vetch grows. The plant is widespread though rather local on the Hampshire chalk and also occurs sporadically on clay cliff systems and shingle along the New Forest shore and on imported rubble in the New Forest (Brewis, Bowman and Rose, 1996). Kidney Vetch is a pioneer coloniser of bare ground, as indicated by the frequency of its occurrence in chalk quarries and along road cuttings and embankments. It was sown along the Alresford by-pass in the early 1980s, though the Small Blue has not colonised. It is a sensitive plant which requires moderate grazing pressures; it is sensitive to heavy grazing, especially by sheep and Rabbits, but becomes rare and disappears altogether if swamped by tall and coarse grasses. Rabbits and sheep eat the flowerheads on which Small Blues oviposit and where larvae develop. The abundance of flowering Kidney Vetch varies greatly from year to year, a phenomenon that has been studied at Noar Hill where the plant can be restricted to a few flowering individuals in two or three chalk pits in some years, whereas in other years it can be common in several pits.

On the chalk, old pits and quarries, warm sunny coombes, sheltered hollows, south-facing slopes and well-worn or cut tracks through long grassland sites are favoured Small Blue habitats. Also, there are a few covered reservoir and road cutting sites. The adults may be seen taking nectar on Horseshoe Vetch, Kidney Vetch and Common Bird's-foot-trefoil.

MAJOR SITES Martin Down is one of Hampshire's two largest areas of unimproved or semi-improved chalk grassland, the southern part being botanically rich owing to the reintroduction of sheep grazing in 1979. The northern part was ploughed in the Second World War and so provides an ideal habitat for Kidney Vetch, whilst the ancient Bokerley Dyke forms steep and sheltered hollows much favoured by Small Blues.

In north Hampshire, Old Burghclere Lime Quarry has been an isolated haven for the Small Blue, but numbers have declined in the last few years. It is a steep-sided, sheltered hollow where the once disturbed ground is now almost totally covered with thin turf and heavily grazed by Rabbits. Kidney Vetch has colonised the uneven ground, especially on the sheltered slopes by the banks and spoil heaps. In 1993 and 1994, good numbers were recorded, but numbers have been disappointing in the last few years.

The Mountain is a downland site which has not been grazed by livestock since 1982; it is grazed by Rabbits but not overrun by the animals. Kidney Vetch grows abundantly on the east-facing slope whilst tall grasses at the foot of the slope provide perfect perching sites for adult butterflies. With a highest-ever Annual Index for Hampshire of 728 in 1986, this is undoubtedly the county's best site, though it was not known from there until stock grazing ceased.

Portsdown Hill has a precipitous south-facing slope with thin turf, which is ideal habitat for foodplant and butterfly. The butterfly abounded along the slope during the 1970s and 1980s, particularly along the new M27 cutting and in areas grazed by tethered gipsy ponies, until the practice was stopped by Portsmouth City Council in the mid-1980s. Numbers of Small Blues were high in 1993 and 1994, then dwindled to a mere handful towards the end of the 1990s but showed signs of recovery in 1999.

Recently, the small reservoir at Weeke Down has been added to the list of major sites. Smaller than a football pitch, the area has been set aside by Southern Water as a wild flower reserve and Kidney Vetch carpets parts of the enclosure.

Grass verges at the Percy Hobbs roundabout, on the outskirts of Winchester, have also held good numbers. During the 1990s, the species has also been recorded in good numbers at Drayton Down, Noar Hill, Old Winchester Hill, Oxenbourne Down, Pitt Down, Porton Down, Stockbridge Down and the West Meon disused railway.

POPULATION TREND AND SIZE, 1990–1999

Trend — Generally, after what was considered to be a 'recovery' in the late 1980s, the 1990s started with low numbers. Signs of improvement were noted in 1992 and this trend was more or less maintained to 1994. 1995 and 1996 saw declines at most sites, but most Annual Indices showed promising signs in 1997, Portsdown Hill being a sad exception, whilst 1998 and 1999 were encouraging for the number of sites recorded but generally disappointing for numbers. At some sites, the butterfly declined with the resurgence of high Rabbit numbers, but the 1990s ended on an optimistic note with records of improved numbers.

	1990	1991	1992	1993	1994	1995	1996	1997	1998	1999
Martin Down (Kitts)	30	8	7	6	12	49	23	37	*	13
Martin Down (North)	19	2	37	24	39	10	32	33	29	18
Noar Hill	8	2	16	22	24	34	4	29	20	12
Portsdown Hill (West)	*	*	*	55	43	12	1	0	2	9
Stockbridge Down	29	12	16	9	6	*	1	7	0	12
The Mountain	78	259	625	531	509	75	53	138	313	457

Our highest-ever Annual Index was **728** in 1986 at The Mountain

Size — A typical colony consists of approximately 30 butterflies and our records show only five tetrads where larger or multiple colonies have been recorded, but counts on one day can exceed 100 at the best sites as the following examples show: early on 31st May 1994, at Martin Down's Bokerley Dyke, Peter Stannard and Pete Owens found over 100 roosting along the northern part of the dyke and Brian Fletcher found 110 there on 29th May 1997; on 29th May 1999, Sue Ellis recorded 146 at The Mountain; at Winchester's Weeke Down reservoir, Small Blue counts have exceeded 100 on individual days in 1997, 1998 and 1999, a careful systematic census of the entire site in fine weather by John Taverner on 1st June 1999 producing a count of 108, with males heavily outnumbering females.

Even when numbers are generally low, one or two localities will report high numbers. 1996, for instance, was a poor year when the massive decline in 1995 at The Mountain continued, yet 21 were seen at the Percy Hobbs roundabout, this being a good count for a small site.

FLIGHT PERIOD

The first brood emerges around mid-May and peaks in early to mid-June. It will continue until early July and often overlaps with the second generation. This second brood is nearly always much smaller and peaks about mid-August, continuing to the end of the month. In favourable weather, it may linger into September.

EARLIEST/LATEST DATES, 1990–1999 The earliest was at Noar Hill in 1990 on the exceptionally early date of 30th April. The last of the second brood was at The Mountain on 21st September 1991.

INTERESTING OCCURRENCES It is encouraging when new colonies are discovered. The colony at Weeke Down reservoir, mentioned previously, was discovered in 1997 when John Taverner found numbers in excess of 100. As the reservoir is surrounded by farmland and a Winchester suburb, with only one tiny Small Blue colony close by, it is amazing that this colony exists, the density of adults probably being the highest in Hampshire.

During the late 1980s, a colony existed on a roundabout along the Basingstoke ring-road system, miles from the nearest known site, but was destroyed during road improvement work.

HISTORICAL CHANGES The entomological literature indicates that the Small Blue was widespread and locally common on the Hampshire chalk until about World War II. However, there were few sites in the north and east. Fassnidge (1923) lists the Small Blue as being "Very common on all chalk downs". This is a curious situation given the species' poor tolerance of sheep grazing. Presumably the insect fared well in ungrazed pockets and on lightly grazed or winter grazed downs. The Small Blue must have increased steadily with the decline of sheep grazing during the depression of the 1920s and some spectacular expansions were recorded following the loss of the Rabbit in the early 1950s.

Fassnidge also lists some interesting colonies off the chalk on the edge of the New Forest, at Everton, Hinton Admiral and Ringwood. Strangely, he does not mention the Barton-on-Sea cliff system, which he knew well and which had been a renowned locality for a large and unusually blue variation, ab. *alsoides*, for decades (Pifford, 1902). The headquarters was around Beckton Bunny, which is now part of a golf course. The butterfly seems to have died out along these cliffs, possibly as a result of cliff stabilisation works.

Silver-studded Blue
Plebeius argus

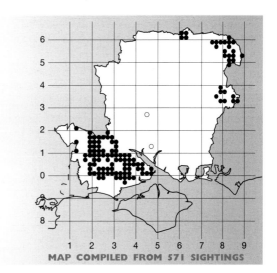

MAP COMPILED FROM 571 SIGHTINGS

DISTRIBUTION 1990–1999 The Silver-studded Blue is largely confined to three regions. These are the New Forest, the eastern heaths around Bordon and the north-eastern heaths, although in the northern heathlands, Silchester Common is the only remaining site in a once more extensive heathland area. It is poorly recorded in all three areas but the butterfly can be abundant on some heaths. There have also been records from heathland pockets in the south-east, so it is well worth searching for this species on any heath. Branch records show the species present in 116 tetrads. It no longer occurs on the Hampshire chalk.

The heathlands of Hampshire and Dorset support nationally important populations of this high priority species. Indeed, they may account for 40% of the total United Kingdom resource.

HABITAT AND FOODPLANTS In Hampshire today, this butterfly breeds exclusively on heathland, including the edges of wet heaths and pockets of heathland in coniferous plantations. It forms discrete colonies in areas sheltered by dykes, the local relief, or clumps of trees and bushes. Its foodplants have not been studied in Hampshire, and little can be discovered by following ovipositing females as ova are regularly laid on debris. There may be an association with Bell Heather on the east Hampshire heaths, whereas it appears that the butterfly uses Heather and Cross-leaved Heath in the New Forest, and possibly Bell Heather.

In recent years the ecology of the heathland subspecies of the Silver-studded Blue has been well studied, though not in Hampshire. It is clear that the species requires managed heathland and that colonies die out on neglected heaths as mature heathers are unsuitable. Grazing, rotational burning or periodic disturbance are essential. Joy (1995) summarises the butterfly's requirements, *viz:* a) Flat or gently sloping land; b) A warm microclimate; c) Heathers in the pioneer or early building stages; d) A continuous supply of pioneer heathland within one kilometre of a colony so that the species can move should conditions on the site deteriorate; e) A flight area containing varied age structures; f) The correct species of ant – more work needs to be carried out on this in the Hampshire heaths, but pupae are attractive to ants of the genus *Lasius* with which larvae and pupae are strongly associated.

MAJOR SITES The extensive heathland tracts of the New Forest hold the largest populations, the numerous sites including Beaulieu Heath, Acres Down, Bishop's Dyke, Dibden Bottom, Fair Cross Heath and Upper Crockford. Substantial populations also occur in the north and north-east at Silchester Common, Yateley Country Park, the heathland in the triangle between Aldershot, Farnborough and Fleet, and at Broxhead Common on the Bordon heaths.

POPULATION TREND AND SIZE, 1990–1999 *Trend* – The New Forest colonies which are managed only by grazing are fairly stable, threatened only by the short-term effects of uncontrolled fires and long term problems such as Silver Birch and Scots Pine invasion. However, colonies on New Forest heaths which are managed by rotational burning do fluctuate greatly. The butterfly is reasonably mobile in the Forest and so can readily colonise new habitat as and when it develops.

Some colonies in east and north-east Hampshire have also remained generally stable over the past decade, although the general trend in these districts has been one of steady decline. In the north-east, sites have been lost to neglect, forestry, urban development and fragmentation. The recent ending of the Hampshire Heathlands Project, which successfully reintroduced grazing to a number of neglected sites, means that other colonies are likely to die out. The population on Broxhead Common LNR, Bordon, has increased well following the adoption of patchy burning management by Hampshire County Council.

	1990	1991	1992	1993	1994	1995	1996	1997	1998	1999
Badminston Common	*	*	*	17	2	5	23	2	4	2
Bourley Road	188	136	161	113	71	38	*	*	*	*
Ludshott Common	*	*	*	*	21	25	57	48	20	11
Pig Bush	*	*	*	*	*	*	*	*	183	204
Roydon, Woodhouse	18	2	10	12	5	5	10	3	0	0
Silchester Common	*	*	*	*	140	186	**319**	230	144	293

The above transects give no idea of population size (see below), simply of annual trends.

Size – New Forest colonies can produce thousands of adults in a season. Counts of several hundred can be amassed on a single day, as on 7th July 1997 when 618 were counted on Fair Cross Heath and 30th June 1995 when 1,000+ were seen in one small area at Upper Crockford. Many colonies are measured in hundreds, including Yateley Country Park, Silchester Common and Pamber Heath in the north-east, and Setley Plain, Dibden Bottom, Pig Bush and Acres Down in the New Forest. Even the smallest colonies may produce 100+ adults in a season.

FLIGHT PERIOD   Emergence is not strongly affected by seasonal weather. New Forest and north-east populations both usually begin to emerge in mid to late June, peak in early July and disappear by mid-August.

EARLIEST/LATEST DATES, 1990–1999   The earliest date we have is 30th May 1997 at Rowbarrow, in the New Forest. The latest was also in the Forest, on 2nd September 1995 at Pig Bush. Fassnidge (1923) records a specimen in the New Forest on 30th October 1921 and attributes this and another New Forest specimen on 3rd October 1926 (Fassnidge, 1926) to a second brood.

INTERESTING OCCURRENCES   There are a number of interesting records of adventive specimens miles from heaths, which occur in exceptionally hot weather; at the height of the 1976 drought, the species could be seen in fair numbers on downs and in woods throughout east and north-east Hampshire. One was seen at our Yew Hill Reserve by Brian Fletcher on 15th July 1995, which is a considerable distance from any heathland. On 2nd August 1996, two males were seen at the Hawthorn's Centre (Southampton Common) by Andy Welch and Andy Barker.

At Upper Crockford, on 30th June 1995, John Taverner saw 1,000+ at 0830 hrs on what was to become a day of scorching heat. Most were males, hovering an inch or two above the heath in a living carpet of blue, presumably searching for females. They were in a very small area of a large heath, so the total population could have been vast (Taverner and Butler, 1997 and Taverner, Ed, 1995).

HISTORICAL CHANGES   The Victoria County History records the Silver-studded Blue as being "abundant on heaths throughout the county, especially in the New Forest". Lister (1918) gives a delightful description which could apply to the New Forest today: "*Plebeius aegon* swarmed on the heathery plain between Beaulieu Road Station and Denny Lodge; males and females in perfect condition. They rose about us in scores as we walked, and many sat paired on the herbage, on a showery day they hung, like little flags at half-mast, on the bents and heather". The difference between then and now, of course, is the extent of heather-clad heathland in the county, for outside the New Forest there have been extensive losses of this habitat (see Part 2, Landscape and Geology). The butterfly has ebbed and flowed in some districts; for example, Richards (1957) records its status in the Aldershot district as being "abundant on heaths in the 20s and 30s, now local". It disappeared during the mid-20th century from the Burghclere heaths.

Fassnidge (1923) lists the butterfly as being "Locally common on heaths" and adds "and on downs". Indeed, the calcareous grassland subspecies *cretaceus*, which breeds of Common Bird's-foot-trefoil, occurred on downs in the west and south-east of the county but died out following the loss of Rabbits to myxomatosis. It was known from the Damerham downs, the Farley Mount area, the Meon valley downs and intermittently from Portsdown Hill. It lasted into the early 1960s on Stephen's Castle Down and on Portsdown Hill (Goater, 1974).

Brown Argus
Aricia agestis

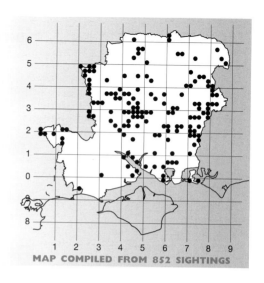

MAP COMPILED FROM 852 SIGHTINGS

DISTRIBUTION 1990–1999 In the 1980s, the Brown Argus was largely confined to chalk downland, but the map for the 1990s accurately reflects the expansion of the species to habitats off the chalk, especially in south Hampshire. Most unimproved chalk downlands support a small colony and some hold very large colonies. By contrast, the Tertiary sands and gravels of the New Forest are generally unsuitable for the species. Colonies off the chalk tend to be low density breeding populations, such as those in rough grassland habitats within and near Southampton. On Hayling Island, Sandy Point supports a 'permanent' population.

HABITAT AND FOODPLANTS The Brown Argus is found in three habitat types in Hampshire. The first, and undoubtedly the most important, is unimproved chalk downlands where the primary foodplant grows, this being Common Rock-rose. South-facing downlands with short to medium turf and patches of bare ground, typically produced by Rabbit scrapes and burrowing, are especially favoured, but other aspects are also used. BUTT (1986) suggested that the species favours turf height of <5 cm. This was confirmed in a detailed study at Magdalen Hill Down in 1991, where it was shown that whilst ova were not laid exclusively in areas with turf height <5 cm, such habitat is greatly favoured. Indeed, the Common Rock-rose plants usually selected for oviposition are typically small and often young plants adjacent to areas of bare earth. Marginal leaf spikes are greatly favoured and the Magdalen Hill study found that oviposition occurred on both leaf undersides and uppersides in approximately equal proportions, and less commonly on leaf bracts. It is certainly not confined to leaf undersides as reported in several texts. Common Rock-rose on ant-hills, or lush plants in taller grassland with little or no bare earth, are rarely selected for oviposition at Magdalen Hill Down, but this need not be true of all Brown Argus sites, since undoubtedly aspect and other local factors will have an influence. In the Yew Hill/Whiteshute Ridge area, a colony has been recorded throughout the decade, although there is no Common Rock-rose present. Indeed, there have been a number of instances of mostly short-lived populations occurring on Hampshire downs where Common Rock-rose does not occur. The foodplant(s) of such colonies is/are unknown, though oviposition has been observed on Black Medick in Hampshire (BUTT, 1986).

The second breeding habitat is sandy grassland at Hayling Island, most notably at Sandy Point, where the principal foodplant is Common Stork's-bill. The final breeding habitat is open grassland in meadows, woodland rides, rough ground and lawns, both on and off the chalk. Low-density populations exist in a few areas of south Hampshire and less commonly elsewhere in the county, but it is quite likely that many small colonies of this type may have been overlooked. Ovipositing on Dove's-foot Crane's-bill has been confirmed at several sites and this would seem to be the main larval foodplant in this habitat type. However, it is quite possible that other related species such as Cut-leaved Crane's-bill are also used. It may be that this third habitat type only supports transient colonies and it has yet to be proved whether any of the recorded sites have sustained colonies over more than a few years.

MAJOR SITES Most chalk downland sites support small to moderate populations, but a few sites such as Magdalen Hill Down, St Catherine's Hill, Broughton Down and Martin Down support substantial populations.

POPULATION TREND AND SIZE, 1990-1999 *Trend* – After a series of poor summers in the late 1980s, when the species was at a low ebb throughout the county, the 1990s saw a resurgence. Several good years in the early and mid-1990s produced significant population increases at most sites, with small populations being recorded at many others, including some that were new. This trend was reversed with a weak second brood in 1997 and a very poor season in 1998; for many sites, transects showed a 70–80% decline from 1996 to 1998. In 1999 numbers were still generally low, but they had improved in comparison with 1998. Whilst the general outlook is good, the continuation and almost unnoticed loss of small fragments of unimproved chalk grassland has undoubtedly given rise to the loss of a number of small colonies over recent years, thus further isolating sites in an already fragmented mosaic of once very extensive chalk downland. Transect data emphasise the strength of some sites. They also show the good numbers recorded in the mid-1990s, especially in 1995 and 1996, and the decline in the late 1990s due in part to a succession of wet Junes.

	1990	1991	1992	1993	1994	1995	1996	1997	1998	1999
Beacon Hill–Warnford	48	33	35	43	66	56	52	43	31	54
Magdalen Hill Down	390	388	350	514	406	921	875	727	258	248
Martin Down (North)	55	12	30	31	31	75	285	62	15	31
St Catherine's Hill	58	54	32	18	326	304	307	136	62	50

Size – At the larger colonies, individual counts can be impressive, especially for the second brood which is usually stronger than the first. A weekly transect count of 211 at Magdalen Hill Down on 30th April 1997 represented a massive first brood emergence at a very strong colony. At St Catherine's Hill, a 30-minute visit on 8th May 1995 produced a count of 210. In good years, second brood counts commonly run into the hundreds at the strongest sites. On 12th August 1995, 271 were recorded on a single butterfly transect at Magdalen Hill Down. Whilst such figures are impressive, very few sites record such numbers, and more characteristically the butterfly is recorded at other sites in single figures and not often in numbers exceeding 20 on a single visit.

FLIGHT PERIOD The first brood typically emerges in the first week of May and continues to mid-June. First emergence varies greatly from site to site, with strong populations on south-facing slopes such as Magdalen Hill Down often having the species on the wing a week or more earlier than smaller sites with less favourable aspects. In early seasons, the Brown Argus is often on the wing from late April but in poor years it may be mid-May before the first is seen. Peak numbers are usually around the third week of May. The second brood is on the wing from mid-July to late September or early October, with peak numbers usually in mid-August. In 1997, ovipositing females were recorded as late as 4th October at Magdalen Hill Down, and in mild frost-free autumn weather close to Southampton Water, the species has been recorded into late October.

EARLIEST/LATEST DATES, 1990-1999 The earliest was at Magdalen Hill Down on 24th April 1997. The latest record was from Dibden Bay on 25th October 1997, but this was highly unusual and records after the first week of October are very rare.

INTERESTING OCCURRENCES A detailed study of ovipositing at Magdalen Hill Down in 1991 (Barker, 1992), contradicting other published texts, is described under the section 'Habitat and Foodplants'.

A specimen with white discoidal spot was seen and photographed at Magdalen Hill Down on 2nd September 1996 by Rev and Mrs Kelsey. It is probable that it was an aberrant Brown Argus, possibly ab. *snelleni*. Apparently, some individuals in southern England may have some of the visual characteristics of Northern Brown Argus (*Aricia artaxerxes*).

HISTORICAL CHANGES Goater (1974) described the Brown Argus as "common on chalk, though decreased through loss of habitat; very local, and usually uncommon, away from calcareous soil". Since this time, the range in

Hampshire has changed little; indeed, it has probably stayed much the same throughout the 20th century. It does, though, appear to have been lost from the New Forest, where it was always very local. Over recent decades, the loss of small colonies by scrub encroachment on isolated fragments of unimproved chalk downland has given rise to a gradual but progressive decline in the number of sites supporting the species. A sizeable colony at Sinah Common, Hayling Island, appears to have died out as a result of golf course developments.

CONSERVATION Where sites are overgrown, the reintroduction of appropriate grazing could restore habitat to a suitable condition for the Brown Argus to return and evidence of dispersal in the 1990s would suggest that natural recolonisation may still be feasible. In the late 1990s, the situation remains positive, with virtually all remaining unimproved chalk downlands where Common Rock-rose grows supporting at least a small population.

Common Blue
Polyommatus icarus

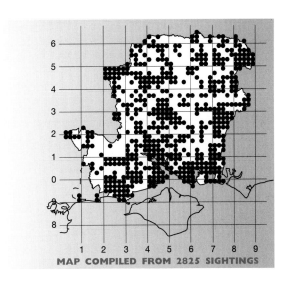

MAP COMPILED FROM 2825 SIGHTINGS

DISTRIBUTION 1990–1999 This is the most widespread of our Blues and as indicated on the map, it can be seen almost anywhere in Hampshire with perhaps the exception of large areas of heathland in the New Forest. It enjoys a variety of habitats ranging from heathlands in north Hampshire to the southern coastline, although the preferred habitat is chalk downland where the majority of the larger colonies are found.

HABITAT AND FOODPLANTS This species occurs in chalk downland, wasteland, road cuttings, verges, embankments of disused railways and unimproved dry meadows. The principal foodplant in Hampshire is Common Bird's-foot-trefoil, particularly on short chalk grassland turf, whilst White Clover is readily used, especially in semi-improved grassland, at inland quarry sites such as Old Burghclere Lime Quarry and along some coastal stretches. Black Medick is also favoured and is the principal foodplant at some sites, Magdalen Hill Down being an example. Greater Bird's-foot-trefoil is used in clay woodland and damp meadows along river valleys. When these valleys dry out during prolonged hot weather, they provide an ideal habitat for the Common Blue. However, colonies raised on this foodplant tend to be rather local and short-lived, as do those based in woods and on heathland.

MAJOR SITES The Hampshire Downs play host to many large colonies. The butterfly is common on downs such as Magdalen Hill Down, Old Winchester Hill, Portsdown Hill, Shipton Bellinger and Stockbridge Down. Sizeable populations also exist in both traditional and semi-improved meadows in the major river valleys, Stockbridge Common Marsh being an example. There are also good populations on heathland-edge habitats at Eelmoor Marsh, Heath Warren and Silchester Common in north-east Hampshire. In the south, coastal grazing levels such as those at Farlington and Keyhaven Marshes, the Hayling Island sand dune systems and coastal heaths such as those at Brownwich provide fine habitats for this species.

Conservation work at the Magdalen Hill Down extension has produced ideal breeding habitat for the Common Blue. Within two years of seeding the site, Common Blue numbers increased to the point where the Annual Index was the highest for any transect in the Branch database.

POPULATION TREND AND SIZE, 1990–1999 *Trend* – Both population size and the frequency of colonies in secondary habitats fluctuate greatly in response to summer weather. Although no obvious trend was apparent at major transect sites during the 1990s, the first three years produced good counts. Numbers dropped slightly in 1993, but started to pick up in the following year. By 1996 numbers were generally higher than at the start of the decade and this level was maintained in 1997 when Noar Hill achieved what *was* the highest-ever Annual Index of 555. However, 1998 saw numbers falling again, especially so in the second brood, to resemble those of 1993. The trend in 1999 was difficult to identify because there was such contradiction in reports from various sites; some observers spoke of abysmal numbers whilst others reported excellent counts. Individual sites have had poor years not following the general trend, such as Stockbridge Down in 1996, but the variety of reports in 1999 was quite remarkable.

The Annual Indices from Magdalen Hill Down extension demonstrate what can happen when a piece of habitat experiences restoration.

	1990	1991	1992	1993	1994	1995	1996	1997	1998	1999
Farlington Marshes	66	72	240	102	301	88	203	224	131	290
Magdalen Hill Down	278	292	368	256	315	312	262	331	175	269
Magdalen Hill Down (extension)	*	*	*	*	*	*	50	77	99	**575**
Martin Down (south)	337	140	213	129	111	219	419	237	61	59
Noar Hill	482	429	259	81	237	483	492	555	356	240
Stockbridge Down	101	68	114	56	129	313	25	176	66	99
Yew Hill	187	107	110	79	86	158	215	209	89	149

Size – In 1990 at Noar Hill, more Common Blues were recorded on transect than any other species whilst Sandy Point attained record numbers in 1992. On the Magdalen Hill Down extension, an hour's transect walk on 12th August 1999 produced a count of 188. Other than transects, which show trends rather than numbers, there have been few attempts to count populations, but counts of 100+ have been made, such as 100+ at Heath Warren on 4th August 1994, 100+ at Broughton Down in August 1996, 114 at Eelmoor Marsh on 7th August 1996, 139 at Martin Down on 25th August 1998 and 160 at the Magdalen Hill Down extension on 21st August 1999. Some colonies must have populations of several hundred and data is needed on colony size.

FLIGHT PERIOD The first of the two broods emerges around the beginning of May, peaks in late May/early June and finishes in early July. The second and larger of the two broods emerges in late July, peaks in mid-August and will continue regularly through to mid or late October.

EARLIEST/LATEST DATES, 1990–1999 The earliest of the first brood came from Bentley Station Meadow on 23rd April 1990 and the latest was at Yew Hill on 28th July 1991. The earliest of the second brood was seen at Basingstoke on 15th July 1992 and the latest sighting came from Southbourne Undercliff on 12th November 1999.

INTERESTING OCCURRENCES Several very small specimens, particularly females, were recorded in August 1995 which was a drought month. Indeed, most second brood specimens on Hampshire downs during the 1976 drought were dwarfed. A 'half-sized' individual was seen during August 1996 at Noar Hill, where a rare male aberration *pallida* was recorded on 14th August 1995. Females were prevalent on Portsdown Hill in 1993, over 50% of which were the blue form. In some years the blue females do appear to be more common than the normal brown form and this was evident at several sites in 1994, in particular at The Mountain.

On 12th August 1999 at Magdalen Hill Down, Andy Barker observed 85 males aggregated on slightly moist ash marking the remains of a bonfire. They were clearly probing for fluids and/or mineral salts. Such aggregations are now a great rarity amongst British butterflies.

HISTORICAL CHANGES It is probable that the Common Blue is one of the butterflies that has declined most in Hampshire during the 20th century, primarily as a result of the improvement of old pasture. At the beginning of the century it must have been a common species in dry meadows, which is certainly not the case today. The Victoria County History, for example, describes it as being as much a species of meadows as of downs.

The success of the Common Blue lies not only in its adaptability to different habitats but also in its apparent dependence on successive long, hot summers. During such periods, it expands to colonise areas that are otherwise too cool to support colonies of any significance. When this sequence is broken by poor summers, it retreats to its former strongholds. This pattern was observed throughout the 1970s and 1980s. By 1988, numbers had fallen to an all-time low since our records began, but recovered dramatically the following year. By 1990, second brood figures had already exceeded those of the great summer of 1976.

Chalkhill Blue
Polyommatus coridon

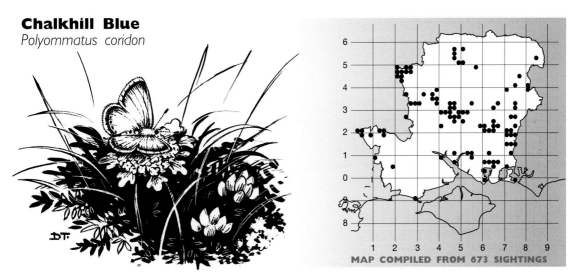

MAP COMPILED FROM 673 SIGHTINGS

DISTRIBUTION 1990–1999 The butterfly is confined to unimproved chalk grasslands. It is widespread and locally common on the chalk, particularly in western and central Hampshire, but in east Hampshire there are few colonies away from the South Downs. Occasional wanderers appear several miles from any major colony, such records being usually linked to periods of high temperatures when butterflies become unusually active and some may stray from their colonies. There are, for instance, frequent references in entomological literature of stray specimens in the New Forest. Nearly all records of strays refer to males.

HABITAT AND FOODPLANTS The Chalkhill Blue is a species of short and medium height downland turf where there is an abundance of the foodplant, Horseshoe Vetch. The species fares best in short turf of less than 3 cm, but unlike the Adonis Blue, it can breed in turf up to 15 cm in height, albeit less successfully than in very short turf. It is not restricted to especially warm aspects, though colonies on north-facing escarpments tend to be centred around pits or banks that are sun-traps. All Hampshire colonies are in old downland, such as land in and around Scheduled Ancient Monuments. This is because the foodplant is a rather poor coloniser of new grassland, following ploughing or other disturbance. Consequently, the prospects of this butterfly in downland restoration schemes are not good in the short term.

MAJOR SITES The best sites are the remaining areas of unimproved chalk grassland, many of which are managed nature reserves or country parks. Amongst the best are Beacon Hill-Warnford, Broughton Down, Farley Mount Country Park (Pitt Down), Magdalen Hill Down, Martin Down, Old Winchester Hill, St Catherine's Hill, Stockbridge Down and Yew Hill. The last-named is a small site and high population densities can occur in such places, Danebury Hill and The Dongas being other examples.

POPULATION TREND AND SIZE, 1990–1999 *Trend –* As can be seen from the following transect data, numbers may vary considerably at a particular site over the course of a few years, sometimes by a factor of ten. Implementing appropriate management plans can cause impressive results, well illustrated at Magdalen Hill Down which the local Branch of Butterfly Conservation took over in 1990. Since the reintroduction of grazing there in 1991, Chalkhill Blue numbers have steadily risen.

Furthermore, in any one year, some sites might do well whilst others are below par. It is generally recognised that this butterfly is very sensitive to weather conditions, Rabbit pressure and grazing regimes, and the last two of this trio may not change in the same way from year to year at all major sites resulting in different degrees of success. This apparent contradiction between sites in any one year, with large populations at some colonies and a marked decline at others, has been a feature of Hampshire in the last decade. At many sites, numbers fluctuate in cyclical fashion and past collectors were aware of this pattern, though it is not clear from only one decade's data.

The influence of Rabbits is demonstrated by St Catherine's Hill. The 1990 population there was measured in hundreds, rather than the thousands found there in the 1980s, because of overgrazing by Rabbits.

	1990	1991	1992	1993	1994	1995	1996	1997	1998	1999
Beacon Hill–Warnford	484	236	194	170	140	299	241	446	262	716
Magdalen Hill Down	437	317	466	555	765	963	1345	1487	1898	1931
Martin Down (North)	226	667	1352	550	207	143	153	130	326	596
St Catherine's Hill	268	198	237	64	145	106	123	305	133	445
Stockbridge Down	1747	1096	1160	436	256	127	381	522	243	832
Yew Hill	1787	2787	810	718	417	433	433	265	503	1144

Our highest-ever Annual Index was **3737** in 1995 at Old Winchester Hill

Size – Whilst they are invaluable for showing trends, transect counts do not indicate the size of the population on any one day. The major colonies will contain a few thousand individuals at any one time (see Outstanding Occurrences).

FLIGHT PERIOD There is a considerable difference in the timing of the flight season and its peak period from site to site; there are also 'early' and 'late' sites. This lack of synchrony has been a feature of Hampshire in the 1990s so that the following is a generalisation. The first are usually seen at 'early' sites at the beginning of July, with mid-July the norm at 'late' sites. Numbers build up to a peak in late July or early August, depending on the site and weather, and remain high throughout August unless the season is curtailed by foul weather, and the species can usually be seen somewhere well into September.

EARLIEST/LATEST DATES, 1990–1999 The earliest, by a margin of nearly a fortnight, was at Stockbridge Down on 17th June 1990, with the latest at both Beacon Hill–Warnford and Yew Hill on 26th September 1990.

OUTSTANDING OCCURRENCES From time to time, vast numbers of Chalkhill Blues congregate in a small area and turn the downland turf blue with their outstretched wings. On two occasions, a few thousand males have been seen at Stockbridge Down by John Taverner, a regular visitor to this site. These were on 4th and 5th August 1996. On the latter occasion, at 0730 hrs with temperatures already high and set to soar considerably higher, at least 3,000 males were seen in a fairly small clearing surrounded by bushes, sitting with open wings or fluttering low over the ground in search of females so that the area looked as though a mass of light blue petals were gently blowing in the wind. All the females in the area were already in the company of one or several males. A similar sight was witnessed at Old Winchester Hill in 1999, where Andy and Linda Barker estimated 3,000+ on 7th August. Such numbers present considerable problems to transect recorders; at Yew Hill on 8th August 1991, it took most of the morning to count the 728 Chalkhill Blues with up to five on a single knapweed head being a common sight.

For a relatively sedentary species, the appearance of individuals miles from their nearest colonies is unusual, but in the warm years of the 1990s it became increasingly common. In 1991 a solitary male was found on Hayling Island. In 1995, individuals were seen at The Moors (Bishop's Waltham), Waltham Chase, Brockishill in the New Forest and at Sandy Point (Hayling Island). At this last site, two males were found, one during a moth-trapping evening. Individual males were seen at Noar Hill in all warm summers of the decade, this being five miles from the nearest Horseshoe Vetch. Such sightings often represent dispersal from sites with large populations, which in the above cases are five miles or more from where these wanderers were observed.

HISTORICAL CHANGES The entomological literature indicates that this butterfly was very widespread on the Hampshire downs until a large but unquantifiable number of sites were destroyed during agricultural intensifications in the Second World War. However, it was scarce along northern downs and has never been other than rare in eastern Hampshire where there are few sites for the foodplant. Stowell (1924), writing about the Alton district, states "I have never detected any *Hippocrepis comoca* [sic]" and adds, interestingly, that the Chalkhill Blue "appears to make shift with *Lotus*", suggesting that there were colonies based on Common Bird's-foot-trefoil. The Chalkhill Blue suffered far less than the Adonis Blue from the impact of myxomatosis, owing to its ability to breed in longer turf.

The best documented Chalkhill Blue site in Hampshire is St Catherine's Hill. The literature indicates that the population there has fluctuated greatly in size over the years, largely on account of variations in grazing pressure by stock and Rabbits. There has been a tendency for the site to be heavily overgrazed during drought summers resulting in a population collapse. Castle Russell (1944) recalls: "I never saw, or heard of, one at St Catherine's Down". It quickly recovered, for Goater (1974) states: "Abundant in late 1940s, then decreasing and becoming very local". Luckens (1977) describes how cattle were left on the down until early July during the great drought of 1976 and adds: "When the livestock were finally removed the down had been ruined for Lepidoptera, for probably several seasons to come, the surviving butterflies being confined to a strip of fenced grassland by the path at one end of the hill" (The Dongas, now separated from St Catherine's by the new M3). See also 'Population Trend' above.

Finally, there is an interesting tale of an introduced population along the railway line at Woodfidley in the New Forest (see Goater, 1974 and Snell, 1925). Rear Admiral Torlesse (pers. comm. to Matthew Oates) recalls this as an introduction which persisted for several years, breeding on Common Bird's-foot-trefoil.

Adonis Blue
Polyommatus bellargus

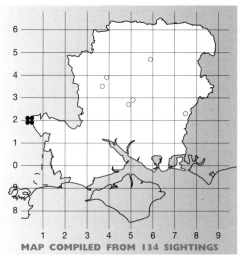

MAP COMPILED FROM 134 SIGHTINGS

DISTRIBUTION 1990–1999 Since the loss of the introduced colony from Old Winchester Hill in 1989, the species has been restricted to a single site, that being Martin Down NNR on the border with Wiltshire and Dorset. The occasional records from central Hampshire probably represent stray individuals from sites such as Porton Down.

HABITAT AND FOODPLANTS Southern England is right at the northern limit of the Adonis Blue's European range. In Hampshire, it is restricted to calcareous grassland sites where its larval foodplant, Horseshoe Vetch, grows in short turf (<4 cm) on hot, usually south-facing slopes. Only in such situations in Hampshire are its breeding requirements met.

At Martin Down, the Adonis Blue breeds in a restricted area along and adjacent to Bokerley Dyke, an ancient archaeological feature comprising a ridge and gully. The habitat is maintained for the Adonis Blue by a carefully managed regime of sheep grazing, which is no easy task as the Marsh Fritillary also occurs there and requires slightly longer turf. The area is also common land, which makes management more difficult. A smaller colony occurs in the Kitt's Grave area on the other side of the A354 from Bokerley Dyke, though this may die out during poor summer sequences.

MAJOR SITES As stated above, Martin Down is the only remaining site in Hampshire.

POPULATION TREND AND SIZE, 1990–1999 *Trend* – Intense Rabbit activity and a series of dry summers in the early 1990s ensured that the species fared well at Martin Down. Then, following a catastrophic year in 1993, the species recovered well with a major population increase over the period 1994–1997. Indeed, the 1997 population reached impressive proportions and was the strongest since detailed transect recording started at the site in the early 1980s. The species survived quite well in 1998, despite evidence of poor numbers from the transect count; "hundreds" of freshly emerged adults were seen on 30th May. In 1999 the first brood was disappointing, and although the species was seen in reduced numbers compared with 1998, a count of 186 was made on 30th August. The pattern of several good years followed by a dramatic crash in population has been a feature of the Adonis Blue throughout the 1980s and 1990s, and no doubt will continue in the future. The key point to ensure the survival of the species is that sites must have large enough populations and enough breeding habitat to survive the crashes. Martin Down has good areas of breeding habitat; indeed, management

	1990	1991	1992	1993	1994	1995	1996	1997	1998	1999
Martin Down (North)	247	197	214	5	49	84	309	**672**	281	121
Martin Down (South)	32	50	30	19	23	18	117	277	122	77
Martin Down (Kitt's)	25	27	22	9	15	22	12	54	*	*

at the site probably increased the area of suitable habitat in the 1990s, especially in the more northerly part (Kitt's Grave) on the border with both Dorset and Wiltshire.

Size – In 1997, the impressive numbers at Martin Down made this the most numerous butterfly at the site in peak season. A weekly transect count of 128 was recorded there during the first brood peak in late May 1997 and "hundreds" of newly hatched adults were seen on 30th May on a non-transect visit, confirming what an excellent emergence took place in that spring following the hot summers of 1994–1996. On 30th August 1997, 308 were recorded on another non-transect count. In 1998, hundreds of freshly hatched adults were again seen in late May and 446 were counted on 25th August. Usually, the second brood is the stronger of the two in Hampshire.

FLIGHT PERIOD The first brood usually commences around mid to late May, peaks in late May or early June and finishes in mid to late June, depending on the season. The second brood typically emerges in mid-August, peaks in late August and usually ends by the second week of September. Although mid to late September records are rare at Martin Down, on the nearby Isle of Wight it is not uncommon in late seasons to find a few on the wing in late September, and rarely into October.

EARLIEST/LATEST DATES, 1990–1999 The earliest was at Martin Down on 6th May 1990. The latest records are from the now extinct Old Winchester Hill colony. The Adonis Blue always emerged much later there compared to Martin Down, and in 1987 was on the wing as late as 17th September. In 1986, with good weather, the second brood at Old Winchester Hill lasted well into October.

INTERESTING OCCURRENCES Adonis Blue males often congregate on the ground imbibing from animal faeces (especially dog faeces), a well-known habit of several Blue species. In dry weather at peak season, it is common to see up to 10–20 males aggregated in such a way.

HISTORICAL CHANGES It appears that the Adonis Blue was always more restricted than the Chalkhill Blue in Hampshire, but was nonetheless widespread and locally common throughout the chalkland until the 1940s and 1950s, when there was a massive decline due to the ploughing of the downs and vegetation changes resultant from myxomatosis. The butterfly had strongholds on the downs around Martin, on the mid-west downs (especially Stockbridge and Danebury), in the Winchester area, around the Meon valley and on Portsdown Hill. Scattered colonies were known from the north of the county. The only significant downland system from where there are no records is the Butser Hill area. However, few sites maintained colonies after the late 1950s. Indeed, Martin Down apart, only a few short-lived colonies have existed in Hampshire since the late 1950s and the last sites to support natural colonies were Magdalen Hill Down and Stockbridge Down.

On many downs it tended to come and go, probably in response to fluctuations in grazing pressure and good or poor summer sequences. For example, its fortunes at St Catherine's Hill are quite well documented. Fassnidge (1923) states that it was abundant there, following a reappearance in 1920. Goater (1974) reports it as sometimes common during the 1940s, but last seen on 12th May 1949. However, Holloway (1952) lists it as "abundant" there during 1952, but it died out during the late 1950s following myxomatosis. There are no records from St Catherine's from the mid-late 1960s (Goater, 1974), but Luckens (1977) saw a few specimens in 1976. The following year it may well have been lost due to heavy cattle grazing. Luckens (1978) bemoans this happening: "When the livestock were finally removed (in July) the down had been ruined for Lepidoptera for probably several seasons".

The butterfly was almost lost from Hampshire in the late 1970s when the foodplant was adversely affected by the drought of 1976. Then, during the poor summers of 1977–1979, the population at Martin Down dwindled almost to the point of extinction, mercifully to be rescued by the hot spring of 1980 and a sensitive grazing regime organised by Paul Toynton who was warden at that time.

In June 1981, the Adonis Blue was reintroduced to Old Winchester Hill NNR by Jeremy Thomas, 65 adults being brought in from Purbeck. The butterfly bred very successfully during the hot summers of 1982–1984, reaching a peak of some 5,000 adults during the second brood of 1984. However, 1985 brought a very wet summer and there was a major population crash. The species lingered in low numbers during the ensuing poor summers, but the hot summers of 1989 and 1990 arrived too late to save it. The last adult was seen in early 1989 (see Oates and Warren, 1990, for a full account). The following transect counts depict this train of events.

	1980	1981	1982	1983	1984	1985	1986	1987	1988	1989
Old Winchester Hill	0	16	85	135	141	17	42	5	6	0

CONSERVATION AND MANAGEMENT With just a single site, the future of the Adonis Blue in Hampshire remains precarious. It requires a carefully managed grazing regime to ensure short turf with bare earth patches and an abundance of Horseshoe Vetch in appropriate condition. A rotational regime of sheep-grazing of different, temporarily fenced compartments in the key breeding areas at Martin Down, has maintained a flourishing colony in the late 1990s.

Holly Blue
Celastrina argiolus

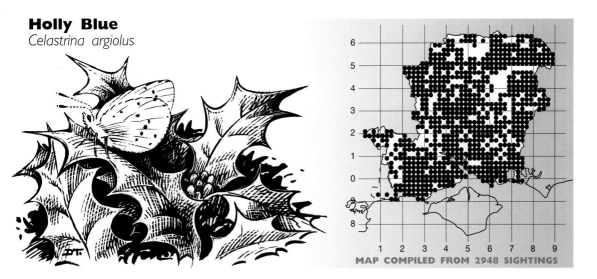

MAP COMPILED FROM 2948 SIGHTINGS

DISTRIBUTION 1990–1999 The Holly Blue is widespread and occasionally common throughout Hampshire, probably occurring at some time or another in most tetrads. Only in exceptionally good years, however, would they occur in hostile habitats such as arable fields, although they are seen in roadside hedgerows that traverse cereal areas. This is most likely in the often stronger second brood, when nomadic females locate relatively insular patches of the larval foodplant – Common Ivy in the second brood – particularly where it is clambering vertically up the sunny side of sparsely foliaged trees or flowering amongst remnant hedgerows, old barns and other, perhaps isolated, farm buildings.

It is a notorious species for expanding its range, usually during short periods of high population density and then rapidly contracting, often due to a series of cold, dull Aprils and Mays or simultaneously increased populations of its host-specific parasite.

HABITAT AND FOODPLANTS This species can be found in a wide variety of habitats, but the best areas are those with good concentrated stands of its most commonly utilised larval foodplants, Holly and Common Ivy. The Holly Blue is unique amongst British butterflies in utilising different foodplants in the spring and summer broods, as there are no Holly flower buds available for the ovipositing second brood females in July. First brood females deposit ova below the unopened flower bud of Holly, on the protective green sheath which does not fall to the ground as the flower dies. Second brood females oviposit on the unopened flower bud of Common Ivy.

One of the main factors why the Holly Blue can be so common and widespread is the wide variety of plants selected by ovipositing females, especially during years of abundance such as the early 1990s. They do not confine themselves to Holly and Common Ivy, although some 'core' populations, particularly in urban areas, seem to survive purely on these plants, especially in years of low populations when migration from such sites is minimal. Females have been observed ovipositing on garden plants as diverse as *Pyracantha, Hebe, Buddleia,* currants and Wild Privet and in the wider countryside on plants such as Bramble, Gorse, Heather, Rowan and a host of other species. In the great Holly Blue years of 1989–1991, first brood females were readily seen ovipositing on Alder Buckthorn, Buckthorn, Dogwood, Wild Privet and Spindle in Hampshire (Hoskins, Ed, 1990)

MAJOR SITES It is difficult to select strong Holly Blue populations in Hampshire because the species is renowned for its fluctuating numbers, but the New Forest, with its array of suitable larval foodplants, has always been a heralded area (see S.G. Castle Russell's comment in 'Historical changes'). In recent years of high populations, it was not unusual to see ten butterflies per Holly tree on Hayling Island. Noar Hill, where the larval foodplant is also well represented, can be a good site (see transect data below). Almost anywhere where the two major foodplants grow in profusion can expect to become a major site in good Holly Blue years.

POPULATION TREND AND SIZE, 1990–1999 *Trend* – Periods of north-easterly winds in April and early May inhibit the breeding success of this species, as only the thermoregulating males become active during the middle of the day in sheltered parts of their habitat. Adult emergence from pupae is also delayed by the clear, cold nights typical of this weather pattern. There are fewer successful pairings and limited oviposition. Population fluctuation is also thought to be correlated with its host-specific parasitic wasp *Listrodomus nycthemerus*. As Holly Blue populations increase, so do those of the parasite, thus eventually sending numbers of the butterfly tumbling as first instar larvae, which are injected by the wasp, become far easier to locate so that few escape parasitisation (see Revels, 1994).

Transect data from six selected sites showing fluctuations in Holly Blue populations from 1980–1999.

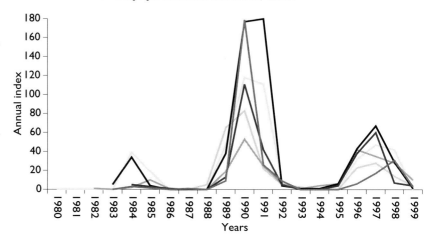

The 1990s started with some of the highest populations ever recorded, but from 1992 through to 1994, they crashed. From 1995, a less dramatic but steady recovery in numbers began and numbers were still quite high in 1998, although there were reports of a faltering second brood. 1999 saw a reasonable but weaker first brood, and a poor second brood suggests that the 1990s ended with the start of another downswing in the cycle. There is good transect data which clearly show the dramatic fluctuations elucidated in this account, shown by the above graph and the following table (the six transects in the graph are not all the same as those in the table.

	1990	1991	1992	1993	1994	1995	1996	1997	1998	1999
Alresford Farm	118	111	9	0	0	1	32	47	42	0
Magdalen Hill Down	33	23	20	0	0	3	16	45	34	11
Noar Hill	177	**180**	4	1	1	6	43	67	29	1
Pamber Forest	111	42	5	0	0	4	38	60	7	4
Portsdown Hill, West	*	*	*	0	1	28	105	115	29	*
Wendleholme	83	22	5	*	0	0	23	28	14	4

Size – Because of the ubiquitous nature of this species, such estimates can be difficult. In poor years some observers can fail to find the species at all, unless they visit a 'core' site where larval foodplants are abundant and condensed. From such 'core' sites of annually occurring populations, large numbers build up in good years and many migrate to formerly uninhabited surrounding districts.

FLIGHT PERIOD The Holly Blue is double brooded in Hampshire, each brood flying for a period of approximately six weeks, varying according to weather patterns. In most years, emergence begins in mid-April; 1997 was an exceptionally early year, when there were numerous observations throughout March and several were seen in 1998 during mid-March. Global warming *may* make this a more frequent occurrence. The peak of the spring flight period is usually the first week in May. The second summer brood usually begins to appear during the first half of July and flies throughout August, with some old females still on the wing in early September. There is evidence of a very small autumn brood in some years in

October, but a percentage of these may well be summer stragglers from ova laid late in the spring brood, especially when early summer weather is poor. Descriptions of the conditions of October examples are rarely forthcoming. An "old" female was seen as late as 11th October 1986 on Old Winchester Hill and a late first brood was recorded near Odiham on 1st July 1986, thus illustrating the above possibilities.

EARLIEST/LATEST DATES, 1990–1999 The earliest and latest were both in 1997, at Tadley on the exceptionally early date of 10th March and at an unstated locality on 1st November.

INTERESTING OCCURRENCES A fine female aberration ab. *aquilina* taken in a hot summer drought at Pamber Forest on 8th July 1976 by R.L. Harvey and figured in *Aberrations of British Butterflies* by A.D.A. Russwurm, is heavily suffused with black scales with only the mid-section of the forewings retaining the azure blue colour. In general, aberration is rare in this species, being confined to the blue spots on the undersides of the wings being obsolete or elongate and variation in the blue colour on the uppersides which can, in the extreme, appear almost grey.

HISTORICAL CHANGES The erratic nature of Holly Blue populations has long been known and famous past authors such as F.W. Frohawk, Rev F.O. Morris and Richard South have been aware of the phenomenon. The last-named author writes in his *Butterflies of the British Isles*, first published in 1906: "For a few years in succession the species may become increasingly numerous, and then suddenly become quite scarce for a year or two. Most probably this is the result of favourable or unfavourable weather conditions". F.W. Frohawk writes: "From 1900 it gradually became more abundant each successive year, until it appeared in profusion, especially in suburban gardens, and remained in undiminished numbers until 1931, after which time it rapidly decreased and became comparatively scarce ... but during the year 1934, it again became plentiful in all its usual haunts".

In Hampshire, several periods of abundance and scarcity are documented. Castle Russell (1952) recalls the butterfly swarming "around the holly trees literally in thousands" in the New Forest during the 1890s, and recalls another period of abundance around 1920. Conversely, the butterfly was relatively scarce for much of the 1940s and 1950s. In recent times, the periods of relative abundance have been 1969 (second brood) to 1971, 1975–1977, 1982–1984 and most notably, 1989–1991.

Duke of Burgundy
Hamearis lucina

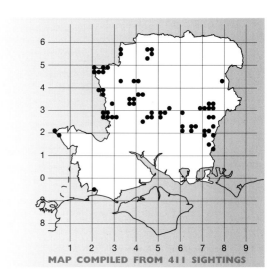

MAP COMPILED FROM 411 SIGHTINGS

DISTRIBUTION 1990–1999 Hampshire is one of the species' three English county strongholds, alongside Wiltshire and Gloucestershire. However, it is very local in Hampshire and most recent colonies have been small. Moreover, many colonies are short-lived, especially in woods, and have occupied areas of less than one hectare, with some based on a few clumps of primulas. Between 30–40 colonies have existed at any one time during the 1990s, the majority in pockets of rough chalk grassland. Colonies are found throughout the chalk, with minor concentrations around Butser Hill, the Meon valley, the Winchester area and in particular along the Wiltshire border. It appears to be extinct in New Forest Inclosures; the only recent records from the Forest area are of a small colony near Exbury in 1991 and a singleton near Hinton Admiral in 1994, both sites outside the New Forest perambulation. Its status in Hampshire is decidedly vulnerable.

HABITAT AND FOODPLANTS The Duke of Burgundy is now primarily a species of poorly-grazed, scrub-invaded, sheltered downland where Cowslips grow. Typical Hampshire chalk downland sites are neglected pockets on steep banks, old chalk pits, railway cuttings and embankments, ailing plantations and unplanted fragments in or on the edge of woodland. Research conducted in the 1980s by Matthew Oates, mainly at Noar Hill, established the basic ecology of the species on chalk grassland. Essentially, it is a species of sheltered grassland where Cowslips occur in longish turf in the 10–20 cm height range. The Cowslip roots *must* be in shade so that plants maintain green leaves until larvae pupate. Cowslip leaves in exposed situations turn yellow before July and are unsuitable for larvae. Consequently, the butterfly is intolerant of summer grazing and early summer drought, and tends to occupy downland sites which are reverting to woodland, but such transitional sites are difficult to maintain. Additionally, the species is intolerant of wind and requires sheltered flight areas (see Oates in Heath and Emmet, 1989, Bourne and Warren, 1998 and Oates, 2000).

Although most recent colonies in woods have been based on Cowslips in trapped pockets of old chalk grassland, the butterfly was formerly associated with clearings and young plantations in woodland where it bred primarily on Primrose. Such colonies have become increasingly rare in Hampshire with few woodland systems supporting the species in the last two decades. The species was breeding in Spearywell Wood in the early 1990s and Andy Barker saw two in Holbury Wood in 1997, so the woods around Mottisfont and Tytherley are still occupied. The coppice system to the east of Stockbridge also supports the butterfly, which breeds there on Primrose in actively managed Hazel-coppice. At Harewood Forest, the butterfly is dependent on chalk fragments.

MAJOR SITES During the 1980s and for much of the 1990s, Noar Hill supported the largest known colony in Britain. Until the late 1990s, the reserve had remained in good condition for the butterfly, apart from a spell of heavy Rabbit grazing in the mid-1980s. However, there are signs that the reserve is now deteriorating significantly for the butterfly, with fewer areas of abundant Cowslip growth and much scrub invasion on the banks and edges of the pits which are the important breeding sites (Oates, 2000).

Porton Down holds a large population, made up of several colonies centred on the Hampshire sector, whilst in the late 1980s, another sizeable population existed at Vernham Dean, but this has since waned. Numbers were also high periodically in Winterdown Copse, Stockbridge, notably in the early 1980s, and the butterfly was quite common in part of Harewood Forest in 1990 and 1996.

Another large colony developed at The Mountain; it appeared in 1985, three years after monitoring began and two years after summer grazing ceased, and since 1990 the site has held one of Hampshire's strongest colonies. Indeed, the Annual Index at The Mountain exceeded that at Noar Hill in both 1998 and 1999.

POPULATION TREND AND SIZE, 1990–1999 *Trend* – Where habitat conditions remain relatively stable, flight season weather appears to be the main factor influencing adult numbers. Weather during the previous June and July may also have an influence. However, by far the greatest current threat to the species on chalk grassland is the Rabbit resurgence. The 1986 crash at Noar Hill was almost entirely due to a short-lived increase in Rabbit numbers and several Hampshire colonies appear to have died out or declined during the 1990s as a result of heavy Rabbit grazing. 1990 was exceptional in Hampshire; it produced the highest Weekly Count at Noar Hill in 17 years of recording, when 96 were recorded along the one-hour route on 7th May. 1991 and 1992 were also extremely good, but since then numbers have declined due to poor springs. By the time a good spell of May weather came in 1998, populations had been somewhat reduced at some sites. Numbers that year were disappointing at Noar Hill, for instance, but at other sites the species fared well, this being especially true at The Mountain. The record low tally at Noar Hill in 1999 was due to a complexity of reasons, many of which have already been alluded to, but in addition the steady growth of scrub in traditional male territories along the transect route was identified as a key factor (see 1999 Hampshire and Isle of Wight Butterfly and Moth Report). Elsewhere in 1999, the species had a modest season.

	1982	1983	1984	1985	1986	1987	1988	1989
Beacon Hill–Warnford	3	8	9	7	I	17	19	12
The Mountain	0	0	0	11	7	14	56	51
Noar Hill	*	157	224	134	67	150	122	137

	1990	1991	1992	1993	1994	1995	1996	1997	1998	1999
Beacon Hill–Warnford	41	21	36	11	20	11	7	12	13	I
The Mountain	123	178	172	57	104	75	56	112	138	127
Noar Hill	237	242	190	139	112	158	88	129	82	50
Westbury Park	*	*	*	48	7	17	19	21	38	14

Size – At Noar Hill and The Mountain, in calm, hazy sunshine in late morning, one can expect to see over 50 in two hours at peak season in an average year, upwards of 100 during a good year and 30 during a poor spring. At most sites it is unusual to see more than 10 adults in a visit and at some sites one will struggle to find the species at all.

FLIGHT PERIOD On chalk grassland, the first adults tend to appear in late April, peak in mid-May and finish in early June. At Noar Hill, where the flight season has been monitored closely since 1977, there was an April emergence in every year in the 1990s, in contrast to only five in the 1980s. Indeed, the flight season there seems to begin, peak and end progressively earlier year by year. The flight season in woodland is distinctly later; in 1990, for example, peak season in Harewood Forest was around 25th May, nearly three weeks later than Noar Hill.

EARLIEST/LATEST DATES, 1990–1999 Noar Hill has produced the earliest sightings in entomological history on three occasions: 14th April, 1993; 13th April, 1995; 10th April 1997. The latest record was on 29th June 1991 at The Mountain.

INTERESTING OCCURRENCES The Duke of Burgundy is a great wanderer, individuals of both sexes appearing in surprising places. The singleton at Pamber Forest in 1992 may have come from just south of Kingsclere, 10 km distant.

HISTORICAL CHANGES Although the species is now strongly associated with downland and is rare in woodland, the reverse was the case in the 1950s when myxomatosis greatly increased the amount of suitable downland habitat at a time when the butterfly was declining in its woodland haunts. But for myxomatosis, this might now be one of Britain's rarest butterflies; nationally, it underwent a 98% decline in woodland between 1950–1990 (Bourne and Warren, 1998).

The Victoria County History describes the species as "Common in woods in many parts of the county". Fassnidge (1924) expresses surprise at an atypical downland colony. There *were* chalk grassland colonies prior to 1953; indeed, several formed during agricultural depression in the 1930s and some existed before then. Stowell (1924) states that on Selborne Common "*N. lucina* is in some seasons commoner than I have seen it anywhere else and also occurs on Nore Hill [sic]", and Sir Robert Saundby (1948) writes of a large downs colony about three miles from Burghclere.

In woods, the butterfly initially benefited from post-war fellings, breeding in young conifer plantations; around Aldershot, for example, it was described as "fairly common" in Alice Holt and other woods (Richards, 1957). However, once the supply of clearings from broad-leaved woodland began to decline, the species disappeared rapidly from many woods. For instance, it last occurred in Alice Holt in 1976.

The Victoria County History describes its New Forest status as "local, but common in one or two enclosures in the extreme east and also in Stubby Copse, New Copse and elsewhere in the south east". Always restricted to the more neutral clays, Stubby Copse was the best known locality and Wells (1898) expresses concern about it being collected out there. Fraser (1961) berates the impact of the Forestry Commission's policies on the butterfly: "thirty years ago I knew of five flourishing colonies of this gem, but today I do not know of any ... All have been smothered by the ubiquitous spruce". The species became dependent on broad ride edges, but the shading over of rides and the increase in grazing animals in the Inclosures during the late 1960s and the 1970s steadily reduced this habitat. The species' last stand was in New Copse Inclosure, where it bred on Primroses growing along ditch sides. The habitat was pulverised by forestry machinery in 1981 and today there are few Primroses evident in the New Forest.

White Admiral
Limenitis camilla

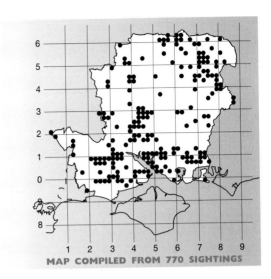

MAP COMPILED FROM 770 SIGHTINGS

DISTRIBUTION 1990–1999 The White Admiral is widespread throughout Hampshire, although there are few large populations and its presence in many woods is diffuse and intermittent. It has periods of expansion and contraction, when small or marginally suitable woods are colonised temporarily and then deserted due to poor weather or habitat deterioration. For example, a small colony persisted at Hengistbury Head from 1982 to 1991.

The butterfly is surprisingly scarce and local in the New Forest. There are few areas where it occurs in any numbers and in many Inclosures it is merely adventive. Suitable growths of the foodplant are rare or absent in large parts of the Forest crownland woods.

Evidence suggests a decline in suitable habitat during the decade, associated primarily with maturing conifer plantations, the thinning of oak and conifer stands and the neglect of small broad-leaved woods. Fragmentation and isolation of surviving habitat, such as recent developments at Whiteley Pastures, is a growing threat, whilst heavy thinning of oak stands by the Forestry Commission in Alice Holt Forest during the 1990s has greatly reduced the White Admiral population.

HABITAT AND FOODPLANTS It is worth looking for this species in any wood where tangles of Honeysuckle are frequent amongst dappled shade and where there are rides or glades lined with Brambles. Females lay on Honeysuckle growths along shaded ride edges and far under the tree canopy, both high up and low down. Dangling, unhealthy-looking strands are favoured, but luxuriant growths in full sunlight and strands trailing over the ground are avoided.

Colonies occur in various types of woodland, particularly oak woodland from the pole stage onwards, moist Ash woods, derelict Hazel-coppice with standards, Silver Birch woods on former heathland, damp Alder woods and middle-aged and mature conifer plantations. The strongest populations are in broad-leaved woods on clay soils.

Both butterfly and foodplant are absent from some woodlands, notably Beech woods and dense conifer plantations on dry, acidic soils. This, plus browsing of Honeysuckle by Fallow Deer, is partly responsible for the insect's restricted distribution in the New Forest.

MAJOR SITES Pamber Forest held the strongest Hampshire population during the 1980s and 1990s, although numbers at that site fluctuated wildly. Large populations also occur in Botley Wood, Crab Wood and Harewood Forest, with sizeable numbers at Butterwood, the Hartley Maudit woods, at Great Copse on the National Trust's Mottisfont Estate, in some private woods outside the New Forest perambulation and in a few small and isolated woods such as Johnson's Copse at Havant. The strongest New Forest populations are in the Inclosures to the south and east of Lyndhurst, notably at Churchplace and Pondhead Inclosures.

POPULATION TREND AND SIZE, 1990–1999 *Trend* – June weather is crucial in determining adult numbers as mortality is high when the pupal stage is prolonged by poor weather (Pollard, 1979). During the 1990s, White Admiral numbers fluctuated largely in accordance with this theory, with other factors such as woodland management and Honeysuckle's vulnerability to drought playing a part. The species began the decade in low numbers due to atrocious weather in July 1988. An even more dramatic collapse occurred in 1990, caused by a long pupal stage and poor flight-season weather. 1992 was highly favourable, with most populations recovering, and moderate numbers were found at most sites during the mid-1990s due to good July weather. A cold and wet June in 1997 brought about another collapse. Populations recovered to some extent in 1998, despite poor flight season weather, but fell again badly during another poor season in 1999.

The only major site with good transect data is Pamber Forest, where the butterfly underwent a major collapse in 1993 that was not replicated elsewhere in Hampshire. This was probably due to heavy thinning and clearance work in 10 ha of forest at that time.

	1990	1991	1992	1993	1994	1995	1996	1997	1998	1999
Pamber Forest	106	141	**361**	24	45	78	128	59	83	31

Size – At most Hampshire sites it is difficult to see more than a dozen individuals in two hours in peak season. During good White Admiral years numbers can be considerably higher and hard work may produce more than 100 in a day at a top site. In a bad year, one can struggle to find the species even in the better sites and in 1990 and 1997 many observers failed to see the butterfly. Many small colonies appear to consist of a mere handful of adults.

FLIGHT PERIOD The White Admiral usually flies for some five weeks, with a short and pronounced peak that can be curtailed by extreme heat, followed by a lengthy tail with low numbers. Appearance and peak are not well synchronised throughout the county; indeed, there is often more than a week's difference in the timings from site to site. Furthermore, there is no consistent pattern from year to year, although some sites are known for their early emergences. At such sites, the first White Admirals occur around or soon after 21st June, although in other woods the first males emerge during the last days of June. Peak season is typically between 4th–12th July, but in late years it may be in the second half of July.

Exceptionally hot summers can generate a small second brood in late September/early October. This weak brood has only been documented six times in Hampshire: in the New Forest in 1893, 1911 and 1947; at Leckford in 1935; at Pamber Forest and Warsash in 1989. On 25th July 1989, Matthew Oates found larvae going into the third instar at Pamber Forest. Then, on 29th September, Martyn Davey saw a freshly emerged White Admiral on Bramble. A few days later, Richard Levett saw one in a small copse near Warsash, this sighting suggesting that a second brood is not restricted to sites with large populations.

EARLIEST/LATEST DATES, 1990–1999 Our earliest record for the decade was on 10th June 1992 at Pamber Forest, although a fully grown larva was found in Harewood Forest by Matthew Oates on 3rd May 1990. Our latest record for the decade was on 5th September 1991 in Bentley Wood. However, Hampshire has earlier records outside the 1990s; in the exceptionally fine 1893 summer, *numbers* emerged in the New Forest in late May.

INTERESTING OCCURRENCES 'Black Admirals' (ab. *nigrina* and ab. *obliterae* or *semi-nigrina*) usually occur after hot summer sequences when White Admiral numbers are high. 1896, 1918, 1919, 1932, 1934, 1941 and 1942 were the great 'Black Admiral' years in the New Forest, Frohawk capturing 25 in the Forest during 1919.

In the mid-1970s a number of Black Admirals were recorded in Hampshire, notably in Pamber Forest and Straits Inclosure (Alice Holt Forest). Seven were collected in Straits Inclosure in 1976 and 15 ab. *obliterae* and two full ab. *nigrina* were seen or taken there in 1977. Strangely, none was seen in 1978 when White Admiral numbers at the wood were higher, but Black Admirals were again seen there in 1979, 1981, 1982 and 1983. Since then, the severe tree-thinning has reduced the White Admiral population with a single ab. *obliterae* in 1994 the only record. No Black Admirals were recorded in Hampshire during the period 1985–1991 and only six during the 1990s, three of which were in 1992.

HISTORICAL CHANGES Hampshire, and in particular the New Forest, was traditionally the national stronghold of the White Admiral. Indeed, it is only since 1930 that the species has expanded its national range to become a familiar woodland butterfly throughout southern England (Pollard, 1979) and the species increased strongly in Hampshire before this national expansion began. Fassnidge (1924) lists the White Admiral as being "Locally common in all larger oak woods". Goater (1974) suggests that the butterfly underwent a period of retraction during the 1940s, a decline that was probably precipitated by extensive fellings in World War II and exacerbated by clear-fellings of the 1950s and a series of poor summers. The butterfly has enjoyed a relatively stable status in the county, outside of the New Forest, since the early 1960s.

Numerous descriptions speak of the White Admiral's past abundance in the New Forest. Frazer (1961), writing of the 1920s, recalls seeing "as many as a score at a single glance up-and-down a riding in Woodfidley; the bramble blossoms were attracting them in dozens ... the hibernacula could be found with the greatest of ease". Herbert Goss, in the Victoria County History for Hampshire, states that in the New Forest the species "may in some seasons be seen in thousands floating gracefully up and down the rides ... I have counted upwards of thirty on one bramble bush". This abundance was, however, localised; for example, H.P. Jones (1920) recalls how in 1919 *"Limenitis sibylla* was uncommon in many woods (e.g. Queen's Bower), but I found it in extraordinary numbers in a damp and rather gloomy part of the Forest a stone's throw from the Lymington River, where females, basking in the sun on the bracken fronds, attracted as many as a dozen males at a time".

In the New Forest, the species began to decline during World War I, due to massive clear-fellings. Subsequent forestry policy radically reduced the extent and quality of habitat, as outlined in a previous chapter, particularly after World War II. By the 1960s the White Admiral had become a local butterfly in the New Forest and its fortunes there plummeted further during the 1970s and 1980s when a rising Fallow Deer population severely depleted, and in places eradicated, the Honeysuckle in many Inclosures.

Purple Emperor
Apatura iris

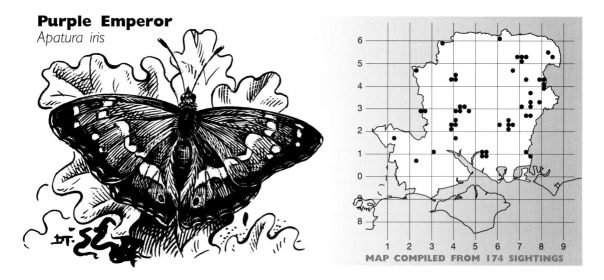

MAP COMPILED FROM 174 SIGHTINGS

DISTRIBUTION 1990–1999 This majestic butterfly occurs in most wooded areas of Hampshire, with the notable exception of the New Forest where suitable sallows are rare. It is probably more widespread than the map suggests, but it is under-recorded largely because it is an elusive, rather indolent, arboreal species which tends to occur at low population levels and which has a short and unpredictable flight season. Also, it is probable that many butterfly enthusiasts do not know how to search for it and there is, and always has been, a strong tendency for people to visit a few well known localities. It is a highly mobile species and individuals can appear almost anywhere.

HABITAT AND FOODPLANTS The Purple Emperor breeds in and around woods where sallows abound. Its reputed association with oaks is more a part of the insect's mythology than fact, for where oaks grow, so too will sallows. Moreover, many of today's Purple Emperor woods are not oak woods. Prior to the mid-1970s it is probable that pole-stage oak plantations were particularly important, but little such habitat remains in Hampshire. Research carried out in Alice Holt Forest and the Oakhanger woods by Matthew Oates in the late 1970s and early 1980s found the species breeding almost exclusively on Great Sallow. As suggested by I.R.P. Heslop (Heslop, Hyde and Stockley, 1964) most ova were laid on female sallows, particularly in semi-shaded positions on well established bushes with somewhat grubby leaves.

The majority of late 20th century breeding grounds in Hampshire have been in unweeded, thicket-stage conifer plantations which remain suitable for 10–15 years. Obviously, plantations of broad-leaved trees can also hold high sallow densities and retain the butterfly for longer, but these have become relatively scarce in Hampshire. Ride-side sallows are particularly important, but there have been many instances of these being felled just as they become ideal for the butterfly. The species also regularly breeds on sallows protruding through the canopy of derelict coppice woodland and on sallows invading woodland clearings and derelict land, notably on neglected damp heathland and along road verges.

MAJOR SITES The best known sites are Alice Holt Forest, Botley Wood, Crab Wood, Pamber Forest and the small Hampshire section of Bentley Wood, although concentrations are highly localised within these woodland systems and breeding grounds shift periodically. These are not necessarily the best sites in the county, for smaller woods can support relatively high densities, at least for a few years. Indeed, there are only weak populations at Crab Wood, Pamber Forest and Harewood Forest. Conversely, Coxmoor Wood, Odiham, and parts of the East Hampshire Hangers are highly suitable.

Butterfly enthusiasts assembled in numbers at the Lodge Inclosure of Alice Holt Forest between the 1930s and the early 1990s. The Straits Inclosure, at the southern end of Alice Holt, was an even better Emperor site, particularly during the 1960s and 1970s, but the population plummeted after thinning work began in the early 1980s.

POPULATION TREND AND SIZE, 1990–1999 It is difficult to assess numbers of such an elusive species and no methodology exists for monitoring populations. At most Hampshire localities one would do well to see the butterfly in any one visit. On a good day at one of the better sites one may have 10–20 sightings, which may consist of one or two individuals. Only exceptionally will more be seen, suggesting that the species is not currently common anywhere in Hampshire, although it was certainly so at sites such as Straits Inclosure as recently as 1983.

Adult numbers and activity are greatly affected by weather. Poor June weather probably reduces adult numbers and it may be that high larval mortality occurs in mild wet winters and cold snaps in early spring. Certainly, adult numbers appeared low following poor June weather in 1990, 1991 and 1996. The butterfly is most active in sunshine and showers on westerly airstreams and is only fitfully active in strong anticyclonic weather. Therefore July 1998, which was dominated by low pressure, was far more suitable for viewing Purple Emperors than the hot sunny July months of 1994–1997.

Starting at a low ebb in 1990/1991, largely as a result of a series of poor Junes, numbers increased in 1992 and 1993. 1994 was the best season of the decade, although it did not compare with great *iris* years such as 1976 and 1983. 1996 and 1997 saw a return to very low numbers, but the butterfly was reasonably prominent again in 1998 and 1999, the last of these probably being the second best season of the 1990s.

The decade saw a significant decrease in the occurrence of sallow-infested young plantations due to fewer conifer plantings and the regular thinning and weeding of plantations. There has also been a steady loss of sallows from neglected coppice woodland. These important breeding habitats have not been replaced by new forms of breeding grounds. Roadside sallows are now probably of considerable importance for the species in the county and it would seem that the Purple Emperor enters the new millennium in a state of decline in Hampshire.

The elusiveness and increasing scarcity of the Purple Emperor is illustrated by the paucity of records submitted by observers during the 1990s. Over 120 observers submitted records annually during this period, yet the yearly total of Purple Emperor records never exceeded 31 and was usually around 15–25. Comparable observer coverage during the 1970s may well have added a naught to all these figures.

FLIGHT PERIOD The flight period is variable and hard to predict. In the 1990s, the first recorded dates have varied between 24th June and 20th July and the last dates between 25th July and 20th August. In most years, the butterfly is on the wing for some four weeks, numbers quickly reaching a peak that lasts for some seven to ten days, after which numbers are low and the butterfly exceedingly hard to find. As a rule of thumb, look for Purple Emperors when White Admirals are emerging strongly and stop when Silver-washed Fritillaries are becoming worn, and concentrate on the first week of the Emperor season when the butterfly is most active.

EARLIEST/LATEST DATES, 1990–1999 Our earliest dates for the decade were the 24th June 1992 and 1997, at Crab Wood and Ashford Hangers respectively, and the latest was the 20th August 1991 at Alton.

INTERESTING OCCURRENCES The species is a great wanderer. One was taken on the piles of Bournemouth pier in late July 1916 (Entomologist 49:214). Three years later, one was seen two miles out to sea, coming from the direction of France (Bramwell, 1919). More recently, a male was rescued from Boots the Chemist in Petersfield in 1977, one was seen at a Nursling gravel pit in 1979, a female was seen in Alton town gardens in 1991 and one was seen flying over Kilmeston Down in 1998. Males are seen regularly around, or even in, the park centre at Queen Elizabeth Country Park.

A female ab. *semi-iole* was in Bentley Wood on 15th July 1990. Similar aberrations have also been recorded from Alice Holt in recent years.

HISTORICAL CHANGES The Victoria County History (1900), Fassnidge (1924 and 1930) and Goater (1974) list a large number of Hampshire sites, many of which retain the species today, though in greatly reduced numbers.

There are some amazing accounts of the pursuit of this butterfly in entomological literature, many of which are set in Hampshire – including the most bizarre: "In August 1877, whilst driving in a dog-cart from Christchurch, I saw *Apatura iris* flying along the hedge of a bare roadside. I immediately gave the reins to a friend ... and pursued it with dog-cart whip, and through a piece of luck I managed to hit the under wing above the upper, and so disable it enough to capture it. It was fine male and not in the least damaged" (Heseltine, 1888). Another memorable Victorian capture in the New Forest runs thus: "of *Apatura iris*, one was captured, two more seen. My brother and I had a long chase after one — including a climb up two trees; but to no purpose. The one caught we disturbed as it was drinking at a stream, it flew up and pitched in a tall ash nearby, so we sat down and enjoyed a smoke, and in about ten minutes were gratified to see 'His Majesty' come down and, after several circles, alight on a stone, just in shallow water. We allowed him to get comfortable, and my brother managed to get the net over" (Buckell, 1892). Another collector had mixed fortunes: "one day I saw three *Apatura iris*, one of which sat on the ground within three yards of me, but when I tried to reach it, it successfully pleaded a previous engagement ... but on another day I got a nice male which an old woman had caught in her hands sitting on a flower in her garden" (Woodforde, 1904).

The Purple Emperor's occurrence in the New Forest was always enigmatic, its headquarters being in the south and east. The entomological literature gives a confusing picture of periodic localised abundance, disappearance, and much contradiction. Rear Admiral A.D. Torlesse, one of the last of the old New Forest collectors, provides the clearest insight: "Up to the middle nineteen-twenties it was still to be found in some numbers by those who knew where to look for it ... There is little doubt that even before the turn of the century its habitats in the Forest were becoming ever more restricted. After 1922 the widespread destruction of its habitats through the woodland management policy of the Forestry Commission steadily reduced the butterfly, but it did not become finally extinct (so far as is known) until after the second war. It is pertinent that in many of the remaining deciduous areas of the Forest it is hardly possible today to find even a single well-grown bush of the foodplant" (Torlesse, 1983). Indeed, the removal of underwood and ride-side shrubs by the Forestry Commission and high levels of browsing by deer and Commoners' stock has ensured that Great Sallow is rare in the Forest today. The tree is restricted to the verges of main roads where fencing has precluded browsing animals. Rusty Sallow occurs in many wet woods but the leaves are unsuitably small. There are some recent records of the Purple Emperor in the New Forest and it is probable that the butterfly is continually trying to recolonise the area. Fortunately, parts of some Inclosures are becoming suitable, notably Pondhead Inclosure.

Red Admiral
Vanessa atalanta

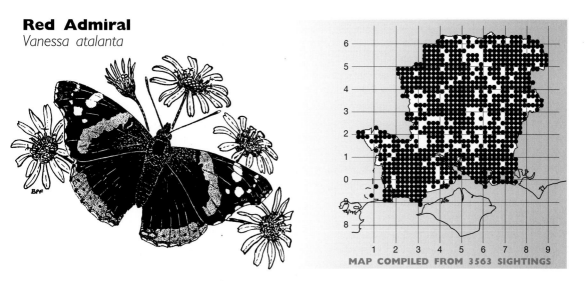

MAP COMPILED FROM 3563 SIGHTINGS

DISTRIBUTION 1990–1999 Like the Painted Lady, this mobile immigrant must have occurred in every Hampshire tetrad. It is unpredictable in abundance and there is nowhere in Hampshire where one can guarantee seeing the species, although it is likely to be seen almost anywhere in town or country.

HABITAT AND FOODPLANTS The species uses a great diversity of habitats. Recently arrived males can be seen seeking mates on exposed hill-tops and this frenetic 'hill-topping' can be witnessed following Red Admiral immigrations at places such as Burghclere Beacon, Butser Hill and Old Winchester Hill. In late June and July, the species is usually most prominent in woods and tree-lined lanes, where males establish territories in sun traps.

Only Common Nettle has been recorded as a larval foodplant in Hampshire, females utilising nettles growing in a variety of situations, apart from heavily shaded patches. Early arrivals are therefore likely to be found in or near to rough ground where such nettles grow, but since the butterflies are moving through, they occur almost anywhere, especially where there is shelter with nectar sources. The peak numbers of late summer gather where adults can find food in plenty. They are very fond of rotting fruit, hundreds being seen on such food in the autumn of 1976 in Selborne orchards. At this time of year, *Buddleia* bushes are great attractions, along with the fruit of Strawberry Trees (see below). As they are migrants, coastal sites are favoured in both spring and autumn.

MAJOR SITES Only in late summer and autumn are numbers sufficiently high to speak of major sites and there are so many places where *Buddleias* and other nectar plants grow in abundance that favoured sites are too many to list, but towns and their environs clearly afford ample supplies of nectar plants from cultivated flowers.

POPULATION TREND AND SIZE, 1990–1999 *Trend* – Over this decade, there has not been a poor Red Admiral year, although the species faded somewhat in 1998 after a most promising start. Each year has been good or

	1990	1991	1992	1993	1994	1995	1996	1997	1998	1999
Alresford Farm	19	28	71	38	34	57	166	42	31	59
Farlington Marshes	48	39	40	13	37	48	117	60	35	59
Hengistbury Head	7	36	31	11	12	29	263	8	21	18
Magdalen Hill Down	8	13	18	10	9	33	40	6	9	39
Noar Hill	30	18	51	20	19	28	172	12	25	65
Pamber Forest	24	2	44	18	10	16	51	10	7	20

better than good, but 1996 was quite outstanding as the above transects show. In late summer and autumn 1996, the species even outdid Painted Ladies in places.

Size – Apart from gatherings in late summer and autumn at nectar sources, the species is usually seen singly. In normal years, a dozen at one bush in August or September would be a notable count but in an outstanding year such as 1996, 100 or more can be seen in one very limited area or even on one patch of *Buddleia*. During the 1980s however, Matthew Oates' diaries indicate that he regularly saw less than 100 Red Admirals in Hampshire in a season; in 1981 and 1984 he recorded 18 and 25 respectively.

FLIGHT PERIOD Until quite recently a matter of controversy, overwintering is now proven for Britain; Matthew Oates has records of Hampshire hibernators in sheds and houses and in the past few years, observers have found others. A few isolated January records have become the norm in the past decade with singletons in 1991, 1992 and 1994, two apiece in 1995 and 1996, a quite widespread scattering in the very mild weather of January 1998 and a handful in 1999. In the winter of 1997/98, the species was recorded up to 31st December and then from 9th/10th January, which were the first warm and sunny days of the year; indeed, they were more like good April days. Individuals were then seen on dates following the 10th whenever the weather was suitable, several days in mid-February being more like summer than winter, and reports came from widespread localities. The Admirals appeared on such days with other hibernating species. On nearby Wight, Brian Warne recorded the species flying throughout December 1997 and January/February 1998 whenever days were warm and sunny whilst at Hengistbury Head, Mike Gibbons considers that records show the species as an all-year-round flier, semi-hibernating in winter when days are cold and wet and coming to life with sunshine.

After the January records, a few may be seen in February and March and some of these are known to be early migrants because coastal bird-watchers have often seen Red Admirals flying in off the English Channel in the early months. Nearly all Hampshire's Red Admirals are migrants of that year or their offspring, the migrants apparently emanating from North Africa (Emmet and Heath, 1989). Migrants usually begin to appear in small numbers in the second half of May. These early movements nearly always involve small numbers, but they produce a native brood in late June and early July which is typically augmented by a much larger wave of migrants from the continent, this being especially marked in 1996. As a consequence, late summer usually produces a strong showing and this is when observers expect to find numbers at their peak. Up to this late summer peak, Red Admirals are seldom present in large numbers.

The late summer population embarks on a return migration south, but there is sometimes a late influx in September and October and the two opposite migrations may cross. In 1991, Red Admirals were streaming out to sea on 7th September at Hengistbury Head but on the previous day, the species had been seen coming in off the sea in numbers from the south on the Isle of Wight. On 27th September 1992, again at Hengistbury Head, visible migration to both north and south was observed. This simultaneous north and south migration late in the season has been seen in other counties. In late September and early October 1987, Red Admirals were also seen streaming out to sea at Hengistbury Head and along Southampton Water, a Red-footed Falcon taking them on the wing at Hengistbury.

Hampshire's peak migration dates concerning incoming butterflies are much affected by the Isle of Wight which *captures* many individuals that would normally reach Hampshire so that there have been years when Wight has had impressive early influxes and breeding that are not mirrored on the mainland.

EARLIEST/LATEST DATES, 1990–1999 The earliest we have is of one on 3rd January 1996 at Winchester, although just before the decade there was one on 1st January 1989 at Fawley. The latest was on 31st December 1997 at Boldre.

PARTICULAR OCCURRENCES An interesting record was of over 50 resting on a tree trunk at Shedfield golf course on 5th August 1996, the observer's attention being attracted to the expanse of red, whilst in the same year, 150 were resting on a Pedunculate Oak at Emsworth in early August. In the latter case, Red Admirals had behaved in a similar way on the same tree in previous years. It has been suggested that the tree might have been used for moth-sugaring, but the butterflies may have simply been attracted by sap runs.

1996 saw the most impressive numbers of recent years. On 17th August, over 1,000 were seen at Mockbeggar Hill, rising in swarms as the observer walked through deep heather. Over 100 were seen feeding on a small *Buddleia* patch by the

Winchester Canal on 5th August, outnumbering Painted Ladies that were such a feature of that year and a similar number was recorded at Noar Hill on 16th/17th August. Counts of over 50 in August were commonplace, report after report mentioning *Buddleia* bushes packed with the species.

On 4th August 1986, dozens were seen flying around a Strawberry Tree at Lee-on-Solent, presumably feeding on the fruit. If this species of tree grew more widely, it could be an important food source in autumn.

HISTORICAL CHANGES Anecdotal evidence suggests that the species was formerly far more numerous, accounts in both Victorian and Edwardian literature speaking of both adults and larvae in abundance. The journals of the Hampshire Entomological Society indicate that the species was stronger during the 1920s and 1930s than it is today. The 1940s also produced some great Red Admiral seasons, other years of note before the present decade being 1950, 1952, 1955, 1964, 1969, 1973, 1976, 1982 and 1987.

Painted Lady
Vanessa cardui

MAP COMPILED FROM 1906 SIGHTINGS

DISTRIBUTION 1990–1999 In the 1996 invasion, Painted Ladies must have appeared in every Hampshire tetrad as they swarmed across the county in their tens of thousands so that the accompanying map must be inaccurate and should be read as showing the areas where the species is most likely to be seen in more normal times. During the 1996 influx, the butterflies appeared over every conceivable type of habitat, from Southampton docks and city centres to chalk downs and New Forest Inclosures.

HABITAT AND FOODPLANTS The taller, more leafy thistles are the main larval foodplant, Creeping Thistle perhaps being especially favoured. Slender Thistle is much used in coastal sites where that species mainly grows, but the common Marsh Thistle, which is rather leafless, is seldom used. When thistles are in short supply the females lay readily on Common Nettle. In 1991, a female was seen laying on Marsh Cudweed at Exbury and in 1996, Common Mallow was used at Southbourne Undercliff. The love of thistles means that rough ground is a main habitat for laying and thistles near the coast are used avidly by early arrivals as these are the first ones that such immigrants would meet. After laying, adults are likely to be found in any habitat where flowers provide nectar. *Buddleia* is especially attractive, as is Hemp-agrimony, but the species uses a wide variety of flowers. Warm and sheltered locations seem to attract the species, although like Red Admirals, males of this species can be seen sparring for mates on hill-tops during good immigration summers.

MAJOR SITES This is another of those species where it is difficult to name major sites as there are so many. In 1996 for example, any *Buddleia* in town or country was likely to hold numbers of Painted Ladies (see section on Outstanding Occurrences). With such a wanderer, it is possible to find gatherings at any site where thistles or other sources of nectar are available.

POPULATION TREND AND SIZE, 1990–1999 *Trend* – Taking the period back to 1988, the trend has been markedly one where a good year is followed by a poor season and the better the year, the worse the one that follows. This pattern was broken by three bad years in succession in 1997, 1998 and 1999. The pattern has been: 1988, good; 1989, a dearth of records; 1990, quite good; 1991, poor; 1992, moderate; 1993, very poor; 1994, excellent; 1995, poor; 1996, an unprecedented invasion; 1997, very poor; 1998, poor; 1999, poor. This pattern is shown by the following transects where 1996 stands out as an event of the century in the butterfly world.

Before 1996, the largest Annual Index for the county was 34 at Noar Hill in 1988. In 1996, over 20 transects had Annual Indices above 100 and most beat the previous record of 34.

Size – In 1996, over 700 were counted at St Catherine's Hill on one day. This single count would be greater than the total number of records received for Hampshire in a moderately good year, so that the size of the population can only be considered on a yearly basis.

	1990	1991	1992	1993	1994	1995	1996	1997	1998	1999
Alresford Farm	13	1	1	0	2	1	78	0	0	1
Farlington Marshes	11	15	14	0	18	4	194	0	3	0
Hengistbury Head	5	14	9	1	11	4	**826**	0	24	3
Hookheath Meadows	*	*	*	*	16	2	818	3	16	24
Magdalen Hill Down	15	11	7	0	7	8	165	0	4	2
Noar Hill	26	4	12	0	26	2	405	1	0	8
Portsdown Hill, East	*	*	*	*	*	3	784	1	0	0
Stockbridge Down	5	2	2	0	5	*	103	0	9	4
Yew Hill	9	4	8	0	7	1	132	2	3	2

FLIGHT PERIOD Isolated individuals might appear in February, March or April but it is late May before numbers can be expected. The 1996 invasion took place first in late May, mainly consisting of worn individuals, followed in the first days of June by a further wave of mainly fresh adults. The main initial influx arrived in southern Britain on 30th May, a day of strong southerly winds which deposited dust from the Sahara. Many arrived on nearby Wight overnight on the 1st/2nd June. These arrivals breed and give rise to a new generation in late July and August. Return migration takes place in late August and September. Stragglers have usually lingered to November or even December in recent years.

EARLIEST/LATEST DATES, 1990–1999 The earliest was on 6th January 1999 at Titchfield Haven. The last was on 6th December 1994 at Needs Ore, but just before the decade, one was seen on 31st December 1987 at Christchurch. In the 1987/88 winter, records went through all months.

PARTICULAR OCCURRENCES Everything fades into insignificance alongside the 1996 invasion which is well documented (Taverner, Ed, 1996), Painted Ladies being joined by abnormal numbers of Red Admirals and Silver-Y moths. The Isle of Wight intercepted a large part of the initial invasion, thousands stopping there to breed in late May and early June. However, masses continued to fly north over Hampshire and the first reports of large numbers from the county were of such movements. At Martin Down, 120 flew north past one vantage point in two hours; several hundred flew north in six hours at Ashley Walk on June 8th; there were several reports from places such as Lepe of a steady stream crossing The Solent from the Isle of Wight.

Numbers were even greater in late July and the first half of August as offspring of the original immigrants hatched and were reinforced by fresh waves of immigrants from the continent. It seemed impossible at the time but the population of early June was almost dwarfed by this generation. A mass of counts was received from all over Hampshire that would have been unbelievable in previous years. The count of over 700 on St Catherine's Hill was mentioned above, but one small clump of *Buddleia* bushes at the base of the hill held over 100 Painted Ladies on 5th August, along with an even greater count of Red Admirals. Over 500 were taking nectar from flowers on 28th July at Ibsley Gravel Pits and over 250 were nearby at Sopley on the following day. To put this into perspective, the 100 plus on the one clump of *Buddleia* at St Catherine's Hill was in excess of the entire number of Painted Ladies reported from Hampshire in the following year.

In early August, when the hatch was in full swing, lines of Painted Ladies were seen from a fishing boat in the English Channel heading north for Wight and Hampshire, accompanied by masses of hoverflies. In and around Winchester, some *Buddleias* were packed with Painted Ladies, again with comparable counts of Red Admirals, and similar stories came from elsewhere. One such bush was by a main road in Winchester and as each lorry passed by, the resulting rush of wind caused a shower of Ladies and Admirals to rise into the air before descending like a mass of falling leaves. In a Lower Froyle garden, Sue and Barry Clark keep annual records of butterfly numbers seen and they recorded a total of 175 Painted Ladies compared with a previous best of 19. Transect indices supported the pattern painted by all the records received by showing a marked peak in the first half of June that was exceeded by a larger peak in the first half of August.

By September the bulk had left, large southerly movements being seen on the Isle of Wight in the last half of August (Taverner, Ed, 1996). A number of small individuals were seen through the year, such differences being expected in large populations, but one was not much larger than a Blue.

HISTORICAL CHANGES Apart from occasional years of plenty, the Painted Lady has tended to be less common in Hampshire than the Red Admiral. Records indicate that it had a stronger general presence in the county in the past than is normally the case today, although it was always prone to years of scarcity. It is clear that the 1996 influx was considerably greater than any in entomological history; early in that year, Andy and Linda Barker were in Rhodes where it was apparent that Painted Lady numbers were abnormally high. Prior to 1996, significant influxes occurred in early June and late July 1980, in April 1985 and in 1988. Sadly, these three influxes coincided with poor summers and breeding success was relatively low. Earlier major immigrations occurred in 1903, 1906, 1920, 1945, 1947, 1948, 1966 and 1969. The immigration of 1879 was probably the best recorded during the late 19th century, but it too coincided with a poor summer. Furthermore, the number of good British summers wherein the Painted Lady has been scarce, or almost absent, is surprisingly high, the most recent examples before the 1990s being 1984 and 1989.

Small Tortoiseshell
Aglais urticae

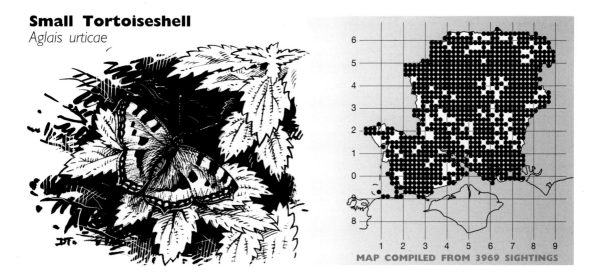

MAP COMPILED FROM 3969 SIGHTINGS

DISTRIBUTION 1990–1999 This is certainly one of the most widespread and common species in Hampshire. Being a wanderer, a migrant and a species where the adult is likely to be found in almost any habitat with suitable nectar sources, it must have occurred in every tetrad in the last decade. Indeed, in all probability it does so every year apart from the occasional year of scarcity, such as 1999.

HABITAT AND FOODPLANTS The main larval foodplant is Common Nettle, though Small Nettle is used occasionally, females tending to avoid the older growths and very new growth. Rough and waste ground is therefore often attractive, but the species will lay in gardens, on path and roadside verges, in woodland clearings and anywhere where nettles grow in sunny and sheltered conditions. The adults will take nectar from a wide variety of plants, especially some cultivated species such as *Buddleia*, so Small Tortoiseshells are likely to be found almost anywhere.

MAJOR SITES As it is so catholic in its tastes and is found in so many places, it is not easy to pick out major sites. Gardens with plenty of nectar sources can be major sites in a good year. It is occasionally numerous where there is an abundance of favoured late-summer nectar sources, such as Devil's-bit Scabious, Small Scabious and Hemp-agrimony, often well away from breeding areas.

POPULATION TREND AND SIZE, 1990–1999 *Trend* – 1990 was a poor year due to a disastrous second brood that was hit by poor weather. In 1991 the Small Tortoiseshell was voted Hampshire's 'Butterfly of the Year', which shows how the species can recover and it soared to even greater heights in 1992. 1993 saw a major slump due once again to poor weather, 1994 seeing only a modest recovery. The transects below show the depth of the 1993 slump and the low numbers in the following year. To take a few examples from 1993, Graham Ferguson did not have a single Small Tortoiseshell at Petersfield in 0.2 ha laid out especially for them; John Taverner at Winchester did not see a single specimen visit *Sedums* in his garden; several observers reported *Buddleia* bushes devoid of the species; in their Lower Froyle garden, Sue and Barry Clark had an annual total of 50 sightings compared with 654 in 1991 and 491 in 1992.

A recovery then occurred so that the species was back to excellent health by 1997, the weather being considerably better, and the 1997 Annual Index at Noar Hill was almost the highest for *any* transect since our records began. 1998 also started very well with a number of early awakeners in the very mild weather, but numbers collapsed in the poor weather of June/July, although they did not fall to the low levels of 1993 as the transect data show. Few went into hibernation as a result of this collapse so that 1999 was the poorest year of the decade, observers reporting a dearth of records from all over the county with only a minor recovery in the summer brood. It is obvious from the above that this species has had fluctuating fortunes over the decade, but the lows have rapidly reverted to years with healthy populations. It is to be hoped that the nadir of 1998/99 follows this pattern.

	1990	1991	1992	1993	1994	1995	1996	1997	1998	1999
Alresford Farm	171	196	**637**	30	23	277	306	277	77	22
Farlington Marshes	53	151	169	49	52	69	43	93	28	8
Hengistbury Head	7	185	38	11	10	20	34	83	22	1
Magdalen Hill Down	65	177	496	44	40	90	133	185	109	32
The Mountain	67	196	305	4	24	64	60	180	15	*
Noar Hill	94	232	373	13	23	132	165	626	49	28
Winnall Moors	126	342	364	71	52	193	393	322	*	31

Size – A count of over 100 at the best sites would be worth recording but would not cause eyebrows to be raised. High counts during the decade are 200+ at Noar Hill on 16th August 1997, 206 on scabious and thistles at Overton in 1992, 150 on Common Fleabane at Radnal Wood in 1991, 150 in a Wildhern garden on 8th August 1997 and "hundreds" at Martin Down on 28th August 1997 and on Lucerne at Meonstoke in 1991.

FLIGHT PERIOD The species is likely to be seen in any month of the year; a small number of hibernators will awake in the early months whenever there are warm and sunny days and isolated individuals will go on flying into December if the weather is suitably mild. The first might be in January, February or March, depending on the weather, with the first brood starting typically in the first half of June. The summer brood usually starts in the second half of August and numbers are likely to be at their peak in late August or September, perhaps swelled by continental immigrants and again depending upon the weather. Late November Small Tortoiseshells are few and far between and December records have only come from 1996 and 1997 in the last decade.

EARLIEST/LATEST DATES, 1990–1999 The earliest record was on 5th January 1999 at Chandlers Ford and the latest was on 13th December 1997 at Alderhill Inclosure.

PARTICULAR OCCURRENCES Considerable variations in size have been noted, with a number of very small specimens seen, such as one no larger than a Gatekeeper at Yew Hill on 15th October 1996. There were also a number of deformities after the poor weather of 1992 led to a disastrous second brood.

On 15th September 1996 one was seen at Magdalen Hill cemetery with one pair of normal wings and the other pair like ab. *lutea*, whilst a symmetrical ab. *lutea* with a ground colour of pale peach was seen at Winchester on 15th August 1973. A specimen of ab. *conjuncta* with all the black forewing markings fused to a single smudge was at Portchester on 30th August 1996.

HISTORICAL CHANGES It is probable that this is one of the species to have been least affected in Hampshire during the 20th century. Its main foodplant has undoubtedly increased in the county due to phosphates contained in artificial fertilisers (Brewis, Bowman and Rose, 1996), though any benefits here have probably been offset by a number of adverse developments in the urban and rural environments. Certainly, the latter part of the Victoria County History statement that this species occurs "chiefly in gardens, lanes, and by roadsides" no longer applies.

Large Tortoiseshell
Nymphalis polychloros

The Large Tortoiseshell's appearances in Britain were always enigmatic and its demise during the 20th century has been particularly puzzling. Most authorities hold that all recent sightings are either of immigrants or bred specimens released into the wild. Thomas goes further and gives reasons for his belief that recent records have been either misidentifications or released stock (Thomas and Lewington, 1991). However, many recent records come from the south coast, suggesting that the insect *is* capable of crossing the English Channel. The only Hampshire records in the 1990s were one seen by Geoff Flower taking nectar from Traveller's-joy at Hookheath on 9th August 1991, and one caught at Titchfield Haven on 10th July 1999. The Titchfield Haven individual was seen by a number of people and a photograph appeared in the annual Butterfly and Moth Report (Taverner, Ed, 1999).

Until the early 20th century, Large Tortoiseshells occurred throughout much of Britain and were locally and intermittently common in the south. However, it had become scarce by the 1920s, rallied briefly in the late 1940s before falling into obscurity. Bretherton suggests that its demise was due to the attacks on its gregarious larvae by parasites (Heath and Emmet, 1989).

The Victoria County History for Hampshire states that the species occurs throughout the county, being very common in the New Forest in some seasons in villages and woodland, "especially about the keepers' and woodmen's cottages". The species could be common in the Inclosures in the late 19th century, Frohawk relating that "It was in 1893 that *N. polychloros* was in abundance, sitting on the tree trunks in the sun and with wings closed in the rides, at a distance resembling fallen fir cones" (Castle Russell, 1942). Castle Russell (ibid) states: "This insect I never fail to meet with during my excursions to the Forest in the old days".

Nevertheless, it was a species which visiting collectors diligently sought, tending to take larvae and breed through the adults. During a North London N.H.S excursion to the Forest in 1893, "Mr Tremayne ... discovered another nest of *Vanessa polychloros* high up on a high elm tree. After breakfast, accordingly, the members 'went for' that elm. A long piece of string was procured, and a stone tied to the end of it, which was then thrown over the bough. The bough was then shaken with force, and the *V. polychloros* larvae descended rapidly into umbrellas spread out carefully to receive them" (Entomologist 26:229). The butterfly regularly used certain trees, such as a sallow growing in the grounds of the Beaulieu Road Hotel, which was regularly plundered (Donisthorpe, 1918).

Pitman (1963) describes the species as "Uncommon as adults but frequent as larvae" in the Forest during the period 1928–1931, perhaps supporting the theory that the build up of parasites on the larvae brought about the butterfly's decline. There are no substantiated New Forest records since 1949.

Outside the Forest, it was locally common but unpredictable during the late 19th century. Pearce (1890) reports that the insect was disappearing from the Portsmouth area: "I have not observed *polychloros* since August 1883". It was seen most regularly in southern Hampshire and there are no records from the north-west later than 1857. It had become an exceptional find by the 1930s until the short-lived revival of the late 1940s produced a scattering of records from central and eastern Hampshire, particularly from the south-east. Heslop (1964) held that the species "still continues to lead a somewhat exiguous existence in the area between Salisbury and Southampton". Since then, there are two records from the Havant area in the mid-1970s, one at Chilcomb in 1980 and some curious sightings in the northern East Hampshire Hangers during the late 1970s and early 1980s.

The East Hampshire Hanger records begin with a probable specimen in Hartley Wood, Oakhanger, in 1977. On 23rd April 1978, one was seen there near Wild Cherry trees by four observers including Matthew and Sally Oates and on 8th August 1978 one was seen nearby by the same observers. Despite searches by Matthew, none was seen until 8th August 1981 when he watched a fresh specimen for two hours in Wick Wood, Oakhanger, followed by a possible specimen a few days later at King John's Hill, East Worldham. The final sighting, by Matthew and Sally, was a female at Cobden's Copse, Blacknest, on 29th April 1984. Searches for larval webs during the entire period drew blank. It may be coincidental that sightings ceased when an enthusiast who was known to breed a wide range of butterflies moved from the Alton area, though that person was certainly not active in the hangers.

Peacock
Inachis io

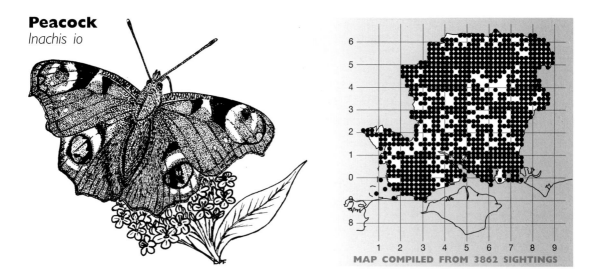

MAP COMPILED FROM 3862 SIGHTINGS

DISTRIBUTION 1990–1999 During the decade, this common nomad must have appeared frequently in every Hampshire tetrad, gaps in the map being due to insufficient observer coverage. Of course, some habitat types such as woodland clearings and rides are especially favoured, as outlined in the following section.

HABITAT AND FOODPLANTS The larval foodplant is almost exclusively Common Nettle where ova are deposited in sizeable batches. Large clumps of Common Nettles are usually chosen, a sunny site being preferred. Open areas in woodland are favourite sites, although the species will adapt to most habitats where suitable growths of Common Nettles are found. In summer and autumn, adults are much attracted to gardens where nectar sources such as *Buddleia* are abundant. In the countryside, Common Ragwort, Hemp-agrimony, Lesser Burdock, Marjoram, thistles and Wild Teasel are amongst the species' favourite nectar sources. Spring adults frequently visit the flowers of Dandelions and Primrose.

MAJOR SITES With such a wanderer, it is not possible to name major sites, either for breeding or taking nectar. There are so many sites where large gatherings have been recorded that it is meaningless to list them here.

POPULATION TREND AND SIZE, 1990–1999 *Trend* – Some years have been outstanding; 1992 stands out as the best, as the transect counts below demonstrate, with 1996 and 1997 also showing strong numbers. The decade has not seen a really poor year, although 1993 and 1994 were mediocre at best, whilst numbers in the summer of 1998 were extremely low after a good record of ovipositing by the awakened hibernators. 1999 also saw disappointing numbers until late July, when there was a marked, sudden and widespread appearance of Peacocks in reasonable numbers.

	1990	1991	1992	1993	1994	1995	1996	1997	1998	1999
Alresford Farm	30	98	248	50	35	59	104	126	48	38
Farlington Marshes	25	87	125	52	35	71	133	116	51	35
Hookheath Meadows	*	*	*	*	30	73	273	237	76	*
Noar Hill	37	97	**376**	59	41	53	140	92	32	48
Pamber Forest	87	82	259	124	71	194	262	256	*	*

Size – The largest gatherings are in summer and autumn at sources of nectar. In the best years, patches of *Buddleia* often hold around 30 adults and counts of around 50 have been recorded in such favourable settings. For a whole site, as opposed to a concentration on particular bushes, a count of 100+ would not be extraordinary; for example, over 100 were counted at St Catherine's Hill in August 1996.

FLIGHT PERIOD In a very mild winter, the first records are in January and six years in the decade have had a few records in that month. Otherwise the first will be in February, whilst March generally sees hibernators begin to make a more widespread appearance. This population disappears in June and the first emergence of the summer brood may be late in the same month, but mid-July normally sees this emergence. Numbers gather strength through July with peak numbers in late July or the first half of August. A few may wake prematurely from hibernation in October and November, much dependent on the weather, whilst some years in the decade have produced December records.

EARLIEST/LATEST DATES, 1990–1999 The earliest was on 1st January 1999 at Acres Down. The latest was on 31st December 1997 at Froxfield.

PARTICULAR OCCURRENCES In each year from 1992 to 1995, Ron Eastman rescued many hundreds of pupae from spraying by farmers in the Whitchurch area. He collected 1,200 in 1994 and released 844. The other 300 were found to be parasitised by *Zenilla vulgaris*.

In 1995, Ron Eastman found several second broods of larvae. A batch of second brood larvae was also recorded in the Bordon area in 1976 (Holmes, 1976).

HISTORICAL CHANGES It is probable that this species' status has not changed greatly in Hampshire over the decades. Certainly, there is no shortage of suitable Common Nettles, though large areas of the county's countryside are now hostile to butterflies due to the severity of agricultural practices and the lack of shelter and nectar. There is little in the entomological literature to suggest any major changes, though it is probably safe to assume that it must have occurred in greater numbers in the past.

Comma
Polygonia c-album

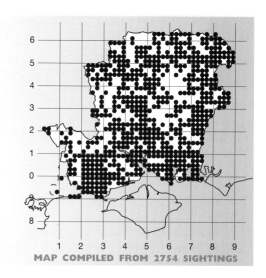

MAP COMPILED FROM 2754 SIGHTINGS

DISTRIBUTION 1990–1999 The distribution map shows the species to be widespread in Hampshire, with no relationship to the underlying geology. Apart from autumn groups at nectar sources, it is seldom found in any numbers, the typical sightings being of lone individuals or counts in single figures, so it can be more easily overlooked than those species that occur *en masse*. Consequently, the map may well underestimate the extent of the Comma's range in Hampshire. Males hold territories, but these are well-spaced and individuals do not confine themselves to one area. However, it is less mobile than most other British Nymphalids; typically, a male in a garden will be seen day after day, especially in spring.

HABITAT AND FOODPLANTS Sufficient and suitable cover is the keynote of Comma habitat. It is found in woodland, hedgerows, urban areas with well developed gardens and a range of sites where tree or bush cover and larval foodplants are available. It shuns open country, though it does wander freely.

Common Nettle is the most widespread larval foodplant, especially straggly patches that are partially shaded along rides and wood edges. Matthew Oates has frequently found larvae on both English Elm and Wych Elm, and occasionally on sallows. Hop was certainly a major foodplant, but growers in the Alton area much disliked the wild plant because of possible cross-pollination with cultivated plants, and the wild Hops were often destroyed (see later text). Thomas (Thomas and Lewington, 1991) gives Black, Red and White Currant as other larval foodplants, and there is evidence in Hampshire of Comma larvae feeding on currant leaves.

Adults will take nectar from a variety of sources. Bramble (both flower and fruit), Blackthorn, Hemp-agrimony, Michaelmas Daisy and rotting fruit in autumn are all much favoured and this is where the largest gatherings of Commas are found.

MAJOR SITES It is not really possible to talk of major sites with such a species. The largest autumn gatherings are likely to occur wherever a food source is found. All that can be said is that there are a number of sites in the county where the species can be described as common, although the transect figures below show that sites such as Hookheath Meadows and Pamber Forest have counts that are pleasingly high. Matthew Oates believes it to be commonest in areas where there is an abundance of elms.

POPULATION TREND AND SIZE, 1990–1999 *Trend* – 1990 and 1991 were good years, followed by a mediocre 1992. 1993 was poor, with numbers picking up through 1994 to an excellent season in 1995. 1996 was mediocre but this was followed by 1997 which was thought to be the record year for the decade. 'Moderate' is the best that can be said of 1998 and 1999. On the whole, the species has thrived in Hampshire in the 1990s, though varying from year to year with the weather.

	1990	1991	1992	1993	1994	1995	1996	1997	1998	1999
Alresford Farm	6	18	15	8	6	24	13	18	9	5
Hookheath Meadows	*	*	*	8	17	129	79	**228**	61	178
Noar Hill	36	36	19	2	4	47	28	24	17	39
Pamber Forest	101	81	49	10	23	72	66	127	*	*

Size – For the most part, a double-figured count at one site would be considered good, apart from the autumn gatherings at nectar sources. For such gatherings, we have descriptions such as 'abundant' and 'common', but the two largest counts were 52 feeding on Blackberries on 22nd September 1991 at Abbott's Wood, Alice Holt Forest, and 40 on Blackberries at Pamber Forest on 17th September 1991.

FLIGHT PERIOD This varies from year to year with the weather and the following timings are generalisations. In the 1990s, the first have emerged in February or early March, with a January appearance in 1996 and 1998, but the awakening really gathers strength in mid-March with numbers typically peaking in mid-April and rapidly tailing off with the brood ending in late May or early June. Mid or late June typically sees the arrival of the summer brood and it is then that the *hutchinsoni* forms appear from the larvae that developed fastest in spring. This brood is extended into the autumn, and all years in the 1990s have had the last Commas in late October or November.

EARLIEST/LATEST DATES, 1990–1999 The earliest record was on 9th January 1998 at Bitterne and the latest on 30th November 1991 at Chilworth.

INTERESTING OCCURRENCES At Whitely Pastures on 6th July 1984, an ab. *suffusa* was seen by Mike Gibbons sunning itself on a gravel ride and another *suffusa* was at Curbridge reservoir on 14th July 1995. An ab. *dilutus*, was seen at Wickham on 20th/21st September 1991, a photograph appearing in the Hampshire and Isle of Wight Butterfly Report for that year. In 1995, females were watched ovipositing on the undersides of Common Nettle leaves, which is thought to be unusual. In 1997, a Comma was seen repeatedly visiting a ripe Stinkhorn, along with many flies. Adults are also attracted to sap runs.

HISTORICAL CHANGES The Comma has had a chequered career, not only in Hampshire but in southern England. It was rare in Hampshire until well into Victorian times when it quite suddenly made an appearance in some strength. It then almost disappeared, only to make a spectacular reappearance in the mid-1920s. Pratt (1986/87) explored reasons for these changes, highlighting climatic change and a switch in foodplants as possible reasons, but in truth we do not really know why the species has experienced such amazing changes in its fortunes.

Fassnidge (1924) says that it appeared in Winchester in 1871 and he also lists the species as formerly occurring at Worldham, possibly breeding in the Alton Hop fields. Pratt (1986/87) suggests that the species was wholly dependent on Hops in Victorian times and blames the demise until the 1920s recovery on the wholesale spraying of Hops with insecticides. The decline in Hop farming and the decline of wild Hops due to deliberate destruction (see previous text) might be a reason why the species switched to other larval foodplants.

There are no Hampshire records for the period 1886–1919, but the species then returned in force, and with amazing speed, seemingly colonising from both the south-west and north-east. By 1926, especially in the autumn, it was common at Fordingbridge (Demuth, 1927) and it was also common in the Aldershot area at the same time (Richards, 1957). It was described as abundant throughout the county in 1929, which must be one of the most remarkable increases of any butterfly species in Hampshire. Around 1935, Fraser (1961) saw over 100 at Woodfidley in March, an incredible number for such an early date, which suggests that the Comma was more numerous just before World War II than is the case today. Whatever the causes of this quite spectacular reappearance, the Comma is firmly established in Hampshire today.

Small Pearl-bordered Fritillary
Boloria selene

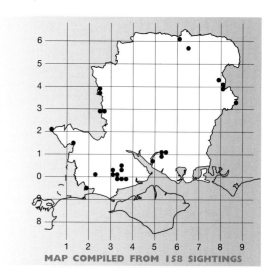

MAP COMPILED FROM 158 SIGHTINGS

DISTRIBUTION 1990–1999 The map shows that the Small Pearl-bordered Fritillary is extremely local and restricted in its distribution. This very much reflects the present situation all over south-eastern Britain. It has declined drastically in Hampshire in recent years and is one of the most endangered species in the county.

HABITAT AND FOODPLANTS In Hampshire, this species, like the Pearl-bordered Fritillary, is strongly associated with open woodland or woodland edge habitat, and in particular with clearings and young plantations created where broad-leaved or mixed woodland has been felled. However, the Small Pearl-bordered Fritillary tends to use early successional woodland that is slightly older in re-growth, damper and often with more grass than that which is ideal for the Pearl-bordered Fritillary. There are no instances of it breeding in clearings from mature coniferous woodland. The Small Pearl-bordered Fritillary also occurs in Bracken and damp grassland habitat and has occasionally formed colonies on chalk grassland. In all situations, the key factor is the existence of the larval foodplant growing within very precise micro-habitat conditions.

The most frequently used larval foodplant in Hampshire is the Common Dog-violet, with females preferring to oviposit on, or most often near, violets that receive at least 50% of direct sunlight during the day. Shade levels greater than this seem to be poorly tolerated (Thomas *et al.* in press). In contrast to the Pearl-bordered Fritillary, which likes small-leaved violets with some surrounding bare ground and leaf litter, the Small Pearl-bordered Fritillary prefers large-leaved violets growing amongst other vegetation. These micro-habitat conditions usually occur when woodland re-growth is between two and five years old and will exist for a maximum of ten years after clearance, even if woodland re-growth is slow or hindered by herbicides or mowing. Usually, conditions decline more rapidly than this (Barnett and Warren, 1995). The species can survive for a while on broad, sunny woodland ride verges but its existence under these conditions is usually precarious. Despite the two species' slightly differing larval requirements, these overlap and both can be found on the same site, an example being Bentley Wood, and will even breed in the same violet patches. In the New Forest, small colonies occur where violets abound under low Bracken canopies in the open heath, and also along the edges of streams in wet heaths, such as those around Crockford Stream. On the edges of the Forest and also locally on the north-east Hampshire Tertiary deposits, colonies have occurred in fen and marshland pockets breeding on Marsh Violet.

Larvae overwinter in leaf litter and feed again next spring before pupating. Adults feed regularly on a variety of spring and early summer nectar sources, particularly buttercups and Ragged-Robin, usually fairly close to the breeding area.

MAJOR SITES Five main population centres existed in 1990, based around Pamber Forest, Alice Holt Forest, Bentley Wood, Botley Wood and the New Forest. By the end of the decade, the Botley Wood population seems to have disappeared and the continued existence of the Alice Holt population was questionable, whilst in the New Forest the 1990s did not produce any double-figured counts. However, Pamber Forest and Bentley Wood can still produce fair numbers in favourable years.

POPULATION TREND AND SIZE, 1990–1999 During the 1980s, there was an estimated loss of colonies over southern Britain at 41% per decade (Warren, 1993) and the Hampshire populations have certainly not been exempt from such declines. As well as a fall in the number of colonies, there also seems to have been a decline in the number of individuals recorded on most of the surviving sites. The Abbots Wood, Alice Holt Forest, colony shows a typical pattern (see transect below) with a steady decline in numbers from a peak in 1991, followed by a sudden decline to the situation of 1996 when none was seen despite an intense search of the whole locality. Most losses appear strongly related to loss of habitat combined with habitat fragmentation. Colonies are often so isolated that even with the recent changes in woodland management with the aim of producing suitable Small Pearl-bordered Fritillary and Pearl-bordered Fritillary breeding areas, the probability of these new areas being colonised naturally is not high. Under these conditions, poor weather during the flight period can greatly exacerbate the problem.

	1990	1991	1992	1993	1994	1995	1996	1997	1998	1999
Abbotts Wood	58	114	95	43	28	24	0	*	*	*
Pamber Forest	40	5	23	6	23	6	8	21	2	9

FLIGHT PERIOD Adults usually emerge in late May, peak in the first half of June and may fly until early July. The flight season in the New Forest has traditionally been later peaking in the second half of June. Occasionally there is a second brood in August, but this is usually seen only within the larger colonies. A second brood was noticed at Alice Holt Forest in 1990, at Alice Holt and Pamber Forests in 1991 and a single individual at Alice Holt in 1995.

EARLIEST/LATEST DATES, 1990–1999 The earliest sighting was at West Tytherley on 7th May 1990, with the latest first brood sightings at Bentley Wood on 16th July 1996. These represent the extremes of the first brood flight period, but it is possible that very early Small Pearl-bordered Fritillaries are under recorded, assumed to be the earlier Pearl-bordered Fritillary. Earliest and latest second brood records were on 5th August 1995 and 31st August 1991, both at Alice Holt.

INTERESTING OCCURRENCES No aberrations have been recorded in the decade. The occasional singletons found some distance from any known colony have been reported, which gives hope for the recolonisation of new habitat, although these may only indicate released specimens or unofficial introductions.

HISTORICAL CHANGES In Hampshire, the species is following the same pattern as the Pearl-bordered Fritillary and may well become extinct in the county. As recently as the mid-1970s, it was widespread and well established off the central chalk belt. Goater (1974) considered it sufficiently well established not to warrant the naming of specific localities, as was his practice for the scarcer species, though he emphasised that it had been in decline since the late 1940s.

Within the New Forest, the Small Pearl-bordered Fritillary was considered a locally common and widespread butterfly until the early 1970s. It then declined rapidly in the Inclosures and became restricted to a handful of small colonies in the open Forest (Oates, 1996). It may now be in the process of beginning to recover some lost ground in the New Forest woods, Busketts Lawn being a new site for our database. However, traditionally the butterfly was associated more with open heathland in the Forest. The Victoria County History states that it "prefers the heaths where it is often abundant" and Lister (1917) describes it as being "fairly abundant in the moister heathery tracts". It seems likely that this species declined in the New Forest due as much to the increase in grazing pressure in the open Forest as to changes in silvicultural practice within the Inclosures.

There is clear evidence that heathland was a major habitat for this butterfly elsewhere in Hampshire, particularly in the south between Southampton and Portsmouth and along the northern and north-eastern boundaries. Apart from Silchester Common, adjoining Pamber Forest, these colonies have been lost due to the abandonment of grazing and the consequent

Bracken and tree invasion, and to afforestation, fragmentation and isolation. The last north-eastern colonies were along the edge of Woolmer Forest, but these died out in the early 1980s.

Until quite recently, the Small Pearl-bordered Fritillary was almost a standard butterfly in clearings, young plantations and unplanted moist grasslands in woods throughout the county, though it avoided the driest woods such as Harewood Forest. It thrived in young coniferous plantations in clay woods. Large populations existed in the larger woodland systems, such as Alice Holt Forest and Botley Wood as recently as the mid to late 1980s. It abounded to the extent that many aberrations occurred in Hartley Wood, Oakhanger, during the 1970s and early 1980s. Sadly though, the species died out rapidly at the site after the woods changed hands and the practice of mowing between rows of young conifers ceased. Shortly afterwards, it collapsed in Alice Holt Forest and at Weston Common, its other east Hampshire strongholds. In Alice Holt, the species retreated to experimental research areas, but died out in these when the use of herbicide, which was used to control Tufted Hair-grass between rows of young trees, was abandoned. This suggests that the herbicide benefited the butterfly. It appears now to be extinct in east Hampshire.

The Oakhanger population spawned several short-lived colonies, including one that lasted for three years at Noar Hill. There are other records of recent, if ephemeral colonies, on chalk grassland in Hampshire at Porton Down and Stockbridge Down.

Pearl-bordered Fritillary
Boloria euphrosyne

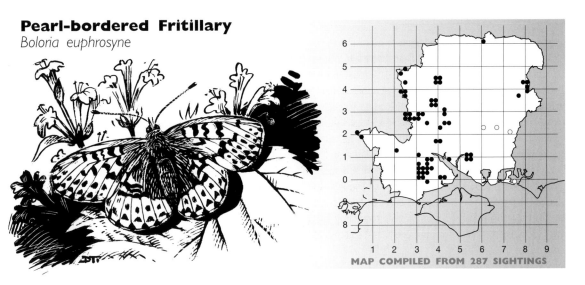

MAP COMPILED FROM 287 SIGHTINGS

DISTRIBUTION 1990–1999 Considerable recent effort has been directed into surveying the status of this butterfly nationally. Despite great effort in Hampshire to conserve and create habitat, the Pearl-bordered Fritillary is currently restricted to a handful of sites in the south and west of the county and there are probably no more than 15 separate colonies in existence. The map shows a more widespread distribution, but major populations at Alice Holt Forest, Ampfield Wood, Botley Wood, Crab Wood and Harewood Forest have all been lost during the 1990s. More significantly, only two new colonisations have been recorded during the decade, though it does appear that the species is undergoing a recovery in parts of the New Forest. Nonetheless, it can be considered to be an endangered species in the county.

HABITAT AND FOODPLANTS In Hampshire, the butterfly is strongly associated with clearings and young plantations on ancient broad-leaved woodland sites and in particular with the early successional stages of coppice woodland and young plantations, though it can occur along newly cleared woodland rides and electricity wayleaves. The foodplant in Hampshire is believed to be exclusively Common Dog-violet, although additional species of violet are known to be utilised in other parts of Britain. Small-leaved plants growing in sheltered sunny situations are especially favoured. Recent research led by Butterfly Conservation has found that the butterfly requires good densities of violets growing amongst litter, particularly from trees or Bracken, and little grass cover. Browsing by deer can extend habitat longevity.

A number of colonies in Hampshire occur in one or two-year-old coppice blocks in traditionally managed Hazel-coppice woods. These provide a range of early successional, if transitional, habitats with a warm and dry microclimate, together with abundant nectar and foodplant resources. The practice of annually cutting adjoining blocks allows this normally sedentary butterfly to move around freely in response to changing habitat suitability.

The species also occurs in the early stages of plantations, created where broad-leaved woodland has been felled. However, unlike a traditionally managed coppice woodland, where small areas of suitable habitat are being continuously created, a commercial coniferous plantation provides a single large area that is only suitable for a very short period. Although these areas can support very large populations during the early stages, colonies soon become restricted to the plantation edges where they may persist for a short period depending on the width of the surrounding rides and the condition of the surrounding woodland. Colonies are normally lost completely within the space of a few years unless other suitable areas are created nearby. The butterfly dies out shortly after the planting of conifers has been completed within a woodland complex when there are no new clearings to colonise.

In large woodland systems, the species also utilises large glades and the edges of wider rides and has the ability to survive at extremely low densities for some years in such situations. Many of these colonies appear to be associated with Bracken and exist under areas of medium to high density cover. This is typical habitat in New Forest Inclosures, for example.

MAJOR SITES The largest remaining colonies are now at Bentley Wood, in a few private estates in the Romsey and Stockbridge areas, and at Porton Down. The species also remains fairly widespread in the east of the New Forest, generally at low density although Pignal and Pondhead Inclosures support stronger colonies.

POPULATION TREND AND SIZE, 1990–1999 There has been a steady contraction of range towards the south and west of the county during the past decade and an even greater decline in abundance; all remaining colonies are now small. Populations fluctuate from year to year according to weather and local conditions, but it is now unusual to record more than ten individuals at a site on any single visit unless the site is one of the larger ones and conditions are very favourable; for example, 33 were seen at Pignal Inclosure on one visit during 1998 and in 1999 the population was equally strong, if not stronger. 1994 and 1996 were particularly bad years, mainly due to prolonged spells of poor weather during the flight season. A considerable amount of apparently suitable habitat has been created in many woods during this period, but the sites have not been colonised, probably due to their isolation from existing populations. The species has now been lost from virtually all sites where transects are carried out, the following figures being typical.

	1990	1991	1992	1993	1994	1995	1996	1997	1998	1999
Alice Holt (Lodge)	1	15	18	0	0	0	0	0	0	0
Pignal Inclosure	*	*	*	*	*	*	*	*	26	43
Roydon (Bakers)	11	4	2	1	0	0	0	0	0	0

FLIGHT PERIOD The normal flight period is from the second week of May through to mid-June, with a peak in late May. In early springs, adults will appear in late April, whilst in late seasons they may not appear until the end of May. Many textbooks (e.g. Fassnidge, 1923) mention the occurrence of an occasional second brood during particularly favourable seasons, but there are no records of second brood specimens in Hampshire more recently than a singleton in Alice Holt Forest in August 1976.

EARLIEST/LATEST DATES, 1990–1999 Our earliest sighting was from Bentley Wood on 19th April 1997, which is believed to be the earliest sighting since 1893. The latest was on 22nd June 1996, also from Bentley Wood. It is interesting that there are references in the historical literature to sightings as late as mid-July. For example, three were reported seen at Bishop's Dyke on 9th July 1950 (Saundby, 1951) and there are numerous 19th century records. It is possible that in recent years, late-flying individuals have been overlooked due to confusion with the very similar Small Pearl-bordered Fritillary. It is also possible, as we have no descriptions of the individuals seen, that they were Small Pearl-bordered Fritillaries that were misidentified.

INTERESTING OCCURRENCES A single, worn butterfly was seen at Sandy Point on 31st May 1992. There is no suitable habitat at this locality and the nearest known colonies were in West Sussex, or across The Solent on the Isle of Wight. It is unusual to find individuals away from known breeding colonies but this sighting seems to indicate that, just occasionally, the species can be far more mobile than is generally believed. There have also been one or two single specimens noted in atypical habitat in the east of the county during recent years and these may also represent wanderers from the West Sussex colonies.

   The only aberration reported in the last decade was a single ab. *pittionii*, seen by Mike Gibbons at Whiteley Pastures during 1992.

HISTORICAL CHANGES The Pearl-bordered Fritillary has experienced one of the most dramatic declines of any Hampshire butterfly. In contrast to its present extreme scarcity, this was formerly one of the commonest and most widely distributed woodland species in Hampshire, being particularly associated with actively managed coppice and woodland managed for navy oak timber. It would be inconceivable to an entomologist living at the turn of the 19th century that this butterfly would become one of the county's rarest species. From the beginnings of butterfly recording until the early 1950s, all writers almost invariably described its status as abundant and this term appears so frequently that one feels writers were simply struggling for alternative descriptions. Fassnidge (1923) dismisses it as "common everywhere in woods" and Goater (1974) states that it was always the commonest of the two spring fritillaries. For several decades after the decline of coppicing, this butterfly survived in woodland by breeding in young coniferous plantations.

The species was locally abundant in New Forest woods well into the 1960s, particularly favouring Inclosures on neutral clays. Sizeable colonies developed where broad-leaved or mixed woodland had been felled and in many parts of the Forest the butterfly had a diffuse presence along broad rides and in open glades, often breeding along Bracken edges. It abounded in many of the young coniferous plantations created during and after the two World Wars, but started to decline when the rate of plantation slowed down as the broad-leaved woodland resource began to dwindle. The population collapsed spectacularly after the 1970 Minister's Mandate, which prevented the Forestry Commission from further large scale fellings of broad-leaved woodland. In effect, its habitat supply was cut off. At the same time, heavy grazing pressure marginalised suitable conditions for the species in the open Forest.

In woodland away from the New Forest, inexorable decline set in during the late 1960s as the rate of coniferisation decelerated and the associated supply of clearings from broad-leaved woodland slowed down. There then began a spate of local extinctions as individual woods became unsuitable. By the mid-1970s, the species had become far more local, although it could still be found in most well-wooded parts of Hampshire, sometimes in considerable numbers. On 15th May 1976, for example, 80 were seen in young coniferous plantations at Harewood Forest (Dickson, 1977). In that spring, it also abounded in parts of Alice Holt Forest, notably in Lodge Inclosure where there were five large and distinct colonies. Elsewhere in east Hampshire at that time, sizeable colonies were in Oakhanger, Weston Common and Woolmer Forest, though these collapsed during the poor summer of 1977. All sites in the north and east of Hampshire, with the exception of Alice Holt Forest, had lost the species by the mid-1980s. In 1987, the Forestry Commission contracted Matthew Oates to carry out a survey and advise on the conservation of the species in Alice Holt Forest, but his recommendations were not taken up and the last specimens were seen there in 1992. The Botley Wood complex, the last stronghold in south-east Hampshire, also lost the species around that time.

In recent years, the butterfly has fared best in the west of the county, though even here there have been significant losses. For example, it was last seen in Crab Wood in 1994 and has not been recorded from Harewood Forest since 1995. Steadily, it has retreated to the actively managed Hazel-coppices of the Stockbridge area, though even here numbers fluctuate wildly and the species cannot be considered to be secure. In good summer sequences, when populations are high in nearby woods, short-lived colonies are formed on Stockbridge Down, breeding on Hairy Violet amongst tussocks of Upright Brome.

Several attempts have been made to re-establish colonies in suitable habitat, most notably at Crab Wood during the early 1990s and at Pamber Forest in 1987 and 1990. None resulted in colonies that lasted longer than three years, which suggests that not enough is known about the ecology of this species. More worrying still is the fact that no colonies have formed in fellings from tall conifers in the county, which indicates that much of Hampshire's woodland resource has little or no potential for the butterfly.

High Brown Fritillary
Argynnis adippe

DISTRIBUTION 1990–1999 This fritillary underwent a massive decline in Hampshire and much of Britain during the second half of the 20th century. The only records from the 1990s are from the Hampshire section of Bentley Wood where individuals were seen annually between 1993–1998. The habitat is only marginally suitable and the records may not be from a natural population, although the species was breeding in the clearing concerned in 1986 and 1987 and was known from the wood during the early 1980s.

The only other *possible* sighting during the decade is of what appeared to be a female seen at 15 m range by Matthew Oates in the New Forest at Matley Passage on 30th June 1992, close to an area of suitable Bracken. Further searches by Matthew Oates in the open Forest during 1994 and 1995 failed to locate the species.

HABITAT AND FOODPLANTS The Victoria County History for Hampshire records that "The High Brown Fritillary is not uncommon in the county, occurring in most of the woods and on the heaths. It is far more common in the New Forest than *A. aglaia* (Dark Green Fritillary) ... it generally prefers the open heaths where thistles are abundant". This, and other descriptions, suggest that the butterfly occurred in actively managed broad-leaved woods, breeding in young plantations created where trees had been felled and clearings in worked coppice, and also in Bracken on heaths and commons. There was probably a strong association with Bracken, females laying around flushes of violets growing under the Bracken, especially around Common Dog-violets.

FLIGHT PERIOD Heslop (1964) states that the New Forest flight season usually commenced around Midsummer Day. The earliest records *in litt.* are 11th June 1943 (Buckhardt, 1943) and 12th June 1933 (de Worms, 1934), although it is reputed to have been out in late May in 1893. The recent Bentley Wood records were in early and mid-July. Only in very late years such as 1879 did the butterfly occur in any numbers in August.

HISTORICAL CHANGES *The New Forest* – The species' history in the New Forest is well documented, at least into the late 20th century. Up to World War II it was locally common in the Inclosures, breeding in recently felled areas, young plantations, and in broad rides and large glades filled with Bracken. Lister (1917) describes the butterfly as "moderately common in open parts of the Forest about Denny Lodge and more so in the plantations north of the Ober Water". In the open Forest, the practice of cutting Bracken for animal bedding undoubtedly produced much good habitat, although few collectors searched the heaths for fritillaries. Between the two World Wars the species began to become localised, although there were some strong colonies during the hot summers sequence of the early 1930s and mid-1940s. Marcon (1980) describes the capture of an aberrant black High Brown Fritillary in Roe Wood in 1934 and it is clear that during this period the species abounded in several localities, notably Frame Wood, Islands Thorns Inclosure and the two Oakley Inclosures.

By the early 1950s an irreversible decline had begun, linked to changes in silviculture. All post-war colonies in the Inclosures were probably in young coniferous plantations which only supported the butterfly for a few years. Turner (1951) writes: "It is now something of an event to see more than a few *Argynnis adippe* ... anywhere in the Forest". The species became increasingly local. Rear Admiral A.D. Torlesse (pers. comm. to Matthew Oates) recalls the High Brown Fritillary as being "not at all uncommon in Wootton (Coppice) in the late '60s and early '70s, in young conifer plantations". Its loss from the Inclosures became inevitable after the Minister's Mandate of 1970, which effectively cut off the continuity of supply of clearings from broad-leaved woodland upon which the butterfly was dependent in Forest woods. One of the strongest colonies was lost when the Hollands Wood camp site was allowed to engulf the breeding area. The last indisputable record of the High Brown Fritillary in the New Forest is of one netted during a Salisbury Natural History Society field meeting, led by Dr Bob Gibbons, at Burley Inclosure in 1982.

The butterfly's apparent disappearance from Bracken stands in the open Forest is more of a mystery. The last open Forest records appear to be of individuals near Burley and at Thorney Hill in 1983 (A.P. Fowles, pers comm. to Matthew Oates). The basics of the butterfly's ecology and conservation requirements were clarified during the late 1980s and early 1990s (Warren, 1995; Warren and Oates, 1995). This suggests that stock grazing in the open Forest has been too selective to provide the breakdown of dead Bracken litter which is essential for the production of violet flushes used by the butterfly. In effect, the animals do not penetrate the Bracken stands sufficiently to break down dead litter and so encourage violets. The cessation of Bracken harvesting may also have been a major factor. However, surveys conducted by Matthew Oates during the mid-1990s revealed pockets of suitable Bracken habitat remaining on the edges of several Inclosures and that there is a considerable potential for recreating suitable habitat by thinning out self-sown trees along Inclosure edges (Oates, 1996). This suggests that the butterfly could yet be rediscovered within the New Forest.

Outside the New Forest – Elsewhere, the species was locally common in sizeable tracts of woodland until the early 1950s. Fassnidge (1924) describes it as being "locally common in all larger woods". However, the Burghclere Commons complex appears to have been the only Bracken-invaded heath used, the species persisting there until the 1960s. There are surprisingly few records of this butterfly from central and southern Hampshire, although it occurred at Crab Wood into the early 1970s (Brian Fletcher saw four on 7th July 1973) and Goater (1974) records a colony at Cranbury Park, Chandlers Ford, which died out in 1947.

There were several localities in north Hampshire. The species died out in Alice Holt Forest and Chawton Park in the 1950s, survived in Pamber Forest until at least 1968, occurred in coppiced woods west of Basingstoke into the 1950s, bred in young conifers in Faccombe Wood and Easton Park Wood in the 1950s (Goater, 1974), lasted on Earlstone Common, Burghclere, into the 1960s and had a major stronghold in worked oak coppice in Harewood Forest. The last-named was effectively dependent on the tannery at Andover but benefited from the forest being used as an ammunition dump during World War II. The collapse at Harewood was spectacular, for the butterfly was plentiful in 1956 but was last seen in 1961.

The High Brown Fritillary lasted into the early 1980s at Butlers Copse, near Ashford Hill, where Dr Brian Baker discovered a colony in young conifers in the mid-1960s. It moved from clearing to clearing until oak felling ceased in the mid-1970s. With the assistance of the 1976 drought, which hindered succession and killed many newly-planted trees, the last colony survived until 1982.

Dark Green Fritillary
Argynnis aglaja

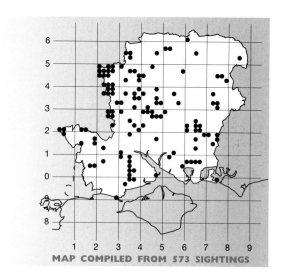

MAP COMPILED FROM 573 SIGHTINGS

DISTRIBUTION 1990–1999 There are currently around 30 Dark Green Fritillary colonies in Hampshire, plus a number of temporary and satellite colonies. In addition, wandering individuals have been seen in most parts of the county, a large number of these in areas where there is no suitable breeding habitat. The butterfly is largely restricted to the chalk.

HABITAT AND FOODPLANTS In Hampshire, the species occurs in two main habitat types. The first and most numerous of these is lightly-grazed, unimproved chalk grassland, often where there is some scrub. Many downs maintain permanent or long-term populations, but at others, such as Noar Hill, the species colonises for a few years before suddenly dying out, only to reappear a few years later. The second habitat involves short-lived colonies which form in woodland clearings, including Crab Wood, Harewood Forest, Bentley Wood, Botley Wood and in one or two of the New Forest Inclosures, although the majority of Hampshire woodlands are now too shady to support viable populations. This fluctuating status suggests that the butterfly is relatively mobile in the county, which augurs well for its future.

The main foodplant is the Hairy Violet, although other violet species are also used, particularly away from the chalk. Large-leaved specimens are chosen, often growing in sheltered or lightly shaded conditions. At Porton Down, a massive population is based on an abundance of small Hairy Violet plants growing in short turf, often amongst incipient Bramble cover.

MAJOR SITES The two largest populations are both in the extreme west of the county, at Porton Down and Martin Down. The colony at Porton Down, much of which is in Wiltshire, is probably the largest remaining colony in England (outside the Salisbury Plain Training Area) and several thousands of adults can easily be seen at peak flight time. Other strong colonies exist at Stockbridge Down and Pitt Down, and in the Meon valley at sites such as The Mountain and Old Winchester Hill.

POPULATION TREND AND SIZE, 1990–1999 *Trend* – Numbers fluctuate considerably from year to year, apparently linked to weather conditions in the flight period, with many more adults noted during hot summers. 1993 was a good year, as were 1994, 1995, 1996 and 1999, whilst 1997 and 1998 were described as excellent, despite some poor weather in June and July. Indeed, no year during the decade has been poor.

	1990	1991	1992	1993	1994	1995	1996	1997	1998	1999
Martin Down (North)	108	68	228	112	210	255	228	194	91	83
Martin Down (South)	90	71	110	64	82	162	127	346	135	258
The Mountain	57	128	29	54	61	211	112	575	613	348
Noar Hill	2	1	0	0	0	0	2	3	27	15
Stockbridge Down	27	17	7	3	6	16	40	30	31	32

Size – It has already been said that numbers at Porton Down will reach several thousand on the best days, although we cannot say what proportion of these are in Hampshire. At strong sites such as Martin Down and Stockbridge Down, it may be possible to see 200 in a day and at Pitt Down, counts of 100+ have been made. The best woodland sites cannot match downlands for numbers; seeing five on a visit to Botley Wood or Bentley Wood would be considered very good.

FLIGHT PERIOD The normal flight period is from the third week of June through to the middle of August, with a peak in the second half of July. This flight season is remarkably consistent from year to year and only under very exceptional circumstances will the species emerge any earlier.

EARLIEST/LATEST DATES, 1990–1999 The earliest sighting we have was from Dean Hill on 29th May 1997, an exceptionally early date that is by far the earliest on record during recent years. The latest was on 1st September 1991 at the Mountain.

INTERESTING OCCURRENCES Hot summers tend to increase this butterfly's mobility and numerous individuals have been seen well away from suitable breeding sites during such weather, appearing in urban areas, on heathland and at coastal habitats. No aberrations have been reported in recent years.

HISTORICAL CHANGES The Dark Green Fritillary was formerly a far more widespread and abundant species, occurring commonly on many downs and more locally on heaths and in woods.

On downland, it probably benefited from the decline in intensive sheep grazing and certainly increased well after myxomatosis decimated Rabbit populations during the early 1950s, until succession to woodland became too advanced. This increase was obviously more than countered by the widespread loss of downland to agricultural intensification. Most downland populations crashed after the severe drought of 1976 and the species only occurred at about a dozen sites in Hampshire during the late 1970s. It then underwent a tremendous expansion from 1983 to 1985 and could be found at 30 sites during that period. There was a further population crash in the late 1980s and early 1990s, probably associated with high Rabbit numbers, followed by yet another strong recovery through the last years of the 1990s.

In the New Forest, the Dark Green Fritillary was primarily a creature of the open heaths, particularly around Bracken stands, though it readily occurred in young plantations, broad rides and large glades. It declined steadily after World War I and Castle Russell (1944) laments that "The species has almost entirely disappeared from the Forest in recent years". In recent decades, a few colonies have persisted in young plantations and in parts of the open Forest, notably around Beaulieu Heath.

Away from the Forest, heathland colonies steadily dwindled during the 20th century, due initially to the abandonment of stock grazing and the cessation of Bracken harvesting, and more recently to woodland succession, natural or otherwise. Few heathland colonies existed after about 1950, with the last at Woolmer where the butterfly died out in the late 1970s.

It was never a butterfly of coppiced woodland and its occurrence in woodland outside the New Forest has mainly been in the form of short-lived colonies in young plantations, usually established from populations on nearby downs. Most woodland colonies have been formed during hot summer sequences, and have disappeared during ensuing poor summers. For example, it was well established in Alice Holt Forest and Botley Wood during the great summers of 1975 and 1976, but then immediately died out. Not one was seen in Alice Holt Forest during 1977, in places where it was relatively numerous in the previous year.

Silver-washed Fritillary
Argynnis paphia

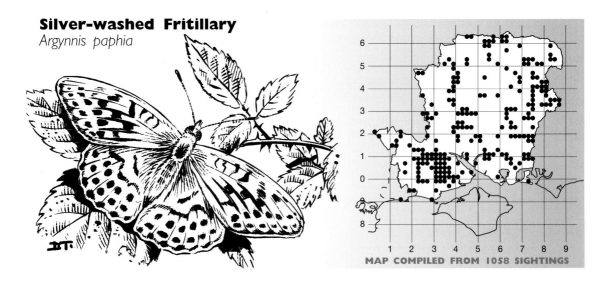

MAP COMPILED FROM 1058 SIGHTINGS

DISTRIBUTION 1990–1999 The Silver-washed Fritillary can be found in most broad-leaved woodlands in all but the extreme north-east and north-west corners of Hampshire. It is a far more mobile butterfly than the other woodland fritillaries and occasional specimens may be noted well away from known breeding colonies in areas such as gardens and coastal habitats. The distribution map can therefore give a false impression of the species' true status, because strong breeding populations now occur only in a few Hampshire woodlands. This spectacular insect, for which Hampshire is the classic county, has been in steady decline here for decades. Moreover, given its inability to survive in coniferous woods and the extent of coniferisation in Hampshire's woods, its future in the county is by no means secure.

HABITAT AND FOODPLANTS The Silver-washed Fritillary is strongly associated with open broad-leaved woodland on land that has been wooded for centuries and is probably the only British butterfly that can be regarded as a true ancient woodland indicator species. It breeds on violets, especially Common Dog-violets, amongst leaf litter and sparse ground vegetation beneath tall trees. Such conditions occur mainly under oaks and mature Beech. Ova are typically laid well away from the foodplant, often on the trunks of mature deciduous trees and in the following spring the tiny larvae somehow find their way down to the woodland floor and to their foodplants. High densities of violets are necessary for good larval survival.

Many types of woodland do not produce the necessary density of violets, notably coniferous and Beech plantations, carr, Sweet Chestnut and Sycamore. Ash woodland tends to support only weak populations, probably because the canopy closes too late in the year to suppress competitive ground vegetation. Even oak woodland on neutral clay can hold only weak colonies if the ground is dominated by Bluebells, Dog's Mercury or dense Bramble. Pole-stage oak plantations provide particularly good breeding conditions, as does worked Hazel-coppice provided there is a high frequency of oak standards.

The adults are creatures of sunny rides and glades, though they fly readily over the canopy. They require prolific supplies of nectar and therefore congregate where rides or glades are lined with Bramble or thistles.

MAJOR SITES The two best sites in the county are probably Harewood and Pamber Forests, but strong populations also occur in the southern parts of Alice Holt Forest, in Bentley Wood, Botley Wood and Crab Wood. Modest populations exist in a number of other well-established woodlands.

In the New Forest, the largest populations occur in the Inclosures to the immediate south and east of Lyndhurst, notably Pondhead and Churchplace Inclosures, though good concentrations of adults can be found locally in other parts. There are also some sizeable colonies in woods just outside the perambulation, such as Roydon Woods.

POPULATION TREND AND SIZE, 1990–1999 *Trend* – Numbers obviously fluctuate from year to year according to weather and habitat conditions, especially the latter. 1995 was the best year of the decade for this species, whilst 1998 was particularly poor, but at many sites the species has remained relatively stable over the decade. However, heavy exploitive thinning work in many Forestry Commission oak stands has radically reduced populations during the 1990s, particularly in Alice Holt Forest. Fortunately, population increases have been dramatic at other sites where coppice management has been reinstated and, especially, where programmes of ride-widening have been introduced. A good example here is Wick Wood, Oakhanger, which supported only a weak population until the main ride was widened in the early 1990s, whereupon the butterfly increased spectacularly. Similar coppice work has been carried out at Crab Wood, cutting patches on a rotational basis so that a mosaic of various aged clearings has been created.

	1990	1991	1992	1993	1994	1995	1996	1997	1998	1999
Bentley Station Meadow	*	*	*	14	11	59	67	60	16	34
Hookheath Meadows	*	*	*	*	7	49	158	166	76	56
Pamber Forest	100	157	207	141	171	311	503	445	192	223
Roydon (Bakers)	76	74	153	27	30	41	71	104	30	29
Roydon (Newlands)	41	47	80	32	25	35	54	38	17	14
Wick Wood	*	*	*	*	*	477	**584**	337	82	86

Size – It is possible to see 100+ in a single visit at the best sites during peak flight season.

FLIGHT PERIOD In normal seasons, the first males begin to appear during the last few days of June with the females emerging in early July. The peak is usually during the second and third weeks of July with the last usually seen in late August.

EARLIEST/LATEST DATES, 1990–1999 The earliest record we have was from Harewood Forest on 7th June 1997, which is exceptional and appears to be the earliest since 1893. The latest was on 7th September 1991 at Radnall Wood.

INTERESTING OCCURRENCES Hampshire produces a good number of *valezina* records. Victorians regarded this form of the female as an extreme rarity outside of the New Forest, although it is now known that it was always widespread in Hampshire. There is some evidence to suggest that the form has become more widespread in central southern England during the course of this century and such an increase may be continuing. The highest *valezina* counts in the period were 11 at Wick Wood in 1996 by Penny and Ted Raynor and 10 in Crab Wood on 12th July 1995 by John Taverner, the last-named observer seeing specimens on every visit to Crab Wood in 1995 and in every year of the decade save for 1999.

Although Hampshire, and especially the New Forest, were traditionally renowned for *paphia* aberrations, very few have been reported in recent years. These have included ab. *nigricans,* a male at Alice Holt on 8th July 1990 (Matthew Oates) and ab. *ocellata*, a male in 1994 (Bob Giddings) and another male (A.M. Jones) exhibited at the 1994 British Entomological Society Annual Exhibition.

A sexual mosaic captured in the New Forest in 1912 was mainly male but with silver-grey patches on the forewings. A perfectly formed ab. *gynandromorph* (left side female, right side male) was taken by I.G. Farwell in the New Forest in 1939. Of particular interest was an almost black *valezina*, ab. *nigricans,* taken by Frohawk.

HISTORICAL CHANGES Although this species has declined far less in the county than most woodland butterflies during this century, it has been steadily eliminated as a breeding species from many of its former Hampshire localities by a combination of modern silviculture, especially coniferisation, and the neglect of coppice woodlands. In particular, there has been a massive decline in the New Forest, although there is now some recovery in a few areas.

Accounts of the species' abundance in the New Forest from the 1890s to just after World War I seem almost fantastic by today's standards and a few such accounts were given in an early section of this book. It is clear from the number of aberrations that were collected in those days that populations must truly have been enormous, since aberrations are associated with high population levels. The 1890s were the golden years of *paphia* in the Forest and were particularly renowned for white-spotted aberrations. Castle Russell (1942) describes the butterfly occurring "as thick as a heavy snowstorm" and larval abundance such that the clothes of two collectors "were covered with the larvae". A.H. Jones (1882) also graphically describes an abundance of larvae. Today, of course, larvae are extremely hard to find anywhere in the county.

1917–1919 was another era of great abundance in the New Forest. A.E. Burras (1917) relates that "*Dryas paphia* was to be seen in thousands: every flowering bramble-clump was alive with them. As many as a dozen *valezina* could be seen on a single clump". J.J. Lister (1917) provides the nearest thing to a quantified description, recalling "about 300 examples of *paphia* crowded on the sunny side of one ride, and all intent on feeding".

Other periods of abundance occurred in the Forest during the early years of the 1930s and 1940s, though more locally. The summers of 1941 and 1942 were the last great years for *paphia* aberrations in the Forest; over 60 extreme aberrations were taken, mainly ab. *confluens* and ab. *ocellata*. In 1941 the majority were taken in Dames Slough, Oakley and Roe Wood Inclosures, whilst in 1942 they occurred in the Park Hill/Pignal area. Marcon (1980) provides a detailed account.

However, the extensive clear-fellings of the two World Wars greatly reduced the extent of suitable habitat and by 1950 no vast populations remained. The Forestry Commission's programme of coniferisation rendered increasingly large areas of the Forest unsuitable for a butterfly associated with oak woodland and the legacy of this damage may last for centuries. The policy of eliminating ride-side Bramble also had a massive adverse impact on this butterfly and by 1960 the Forest's Silver-washed Fritillary populations were a shadow of their former glory. Harper (1962) only located one sizeable colony in an entire summer's exploration. The mass incursion of stock into the Inclosures from the late 1960s, coupled with rising deer numbers, further reduced vital nectar sources whilst the shading of overhung rides has been yet another major adverse factor. Even so, large areas of the Forest remain of significant potential for this species.

In bygone days, the species was common in much of Hampshire's woodland. Fassnidge (1923) lists it as being "More or less common in woods everywhere". It abounded in oak forests and was often common in worked coppice with standards and in some Beech woods. It also occurred freely along wooded lanes and hedges. Sadly, during this century the butterfly has been steadily eliminated as a breeding species from most of its former Hampshire haunts through the widespread coniferisation of ancient woodland sites and the neglect of surviving coppice woodland. The latter, though, still has the potential to harbour the species in numbers. The signs are that this butterfly is benefiting from recent initiatives intended to revitalise the coppice market and from measures taken at a number of broad-leaved woodland sites which are managed for nature conservation.

Marsh Fritillary
Euphydryas aurinia

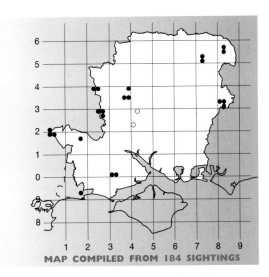

MAP COMPILED FROM 184 SIGHTINGS

DISTRIBUTION 1990–1999 Three sites are currently known, all in the extreme west of the county, these being the National Nature Reserve at Martin Down, the Hampshire portion of Bentley Wood and a wet meadow which cannot be named at present. A fourth site, Stockbridge Down, produces records in some years that may be clandestine releases. The three western sites all appear to be genuine colonies and not introductions. The species has recently collapsed in Hampshire and is now an endangered species in the county.

HABITAT AND FOODPLANTS The three western colonies each utilise markedly differing habitats, these being an ancient chalk grassland, a wet meadow, and clearings in a damp wood. Although the sites are quite large, actual breeding patches are mostly tiny, often confined to a particular sheltered corner or stretch where conditions are right, although temporary colonies can occasionally spread into less favourable overspill sites following a succession of suitable summers.

Martin Down is the chalk grassland site, where oviposition occurs typically on small to medium-sized plants of Devil's-bit Scabious, with leaves around 6–10 cm in length, even though larger plants are available. The plants occur at a density of 5–10 per square metre and grow on the west-facing bank of an ancient dyke. The best habitat develops during the second year after the cessation of grazing. In the first year, the scabious plants are small and suppressed, whilst by the third year they are large but crowded by rank grasses. The current management regime fully caters for this species.

A large clearing in Bentley Wood, on the Wiltshire border, supports our only surviving woodland colony. Here, foodplant densities at the breeding areas are as high as 10–15 plants per square metre but only large and lush plants growing in wet and very sheltered situations are utilised. The area is managed specifically to cater for the needs of the Marsh Fritillary and other fritillaries, being mowed periodically to control scrub incursion. Grazing has been recently introduced.

A patch of wet meadow surrounded by urban development in the Avon valley currently supports the largest of the Hampshire colonies. Several experienced observers consider this site to be natural, since lost colonies once existed not so very far away in Dorset, but new evidence suggests that it is the result of a release. This colony may not survive for long in the absence of special habitat management.

Stockbridge Down is not rich in suitable foodplants, although it contains a reasonable amount of Small Scabious which on chalk downland is the Marsh Fritillary's alternative foodplant. For this reason, clandestine release is suspected at the site; in some years reasonable counts have been made, whilst in other years the species has been absent.

MAJOR SITES Care must be taken when visiting the Hampshire sites as the habitats are highly vulnerable. Visitors, especially those photographers who do not take the greatest care, can cause considerable damage by trampling. There are a number of open access sites supporting larger populations in other parts of southern Britain that are more able to cater for visiting butterfly enthusiasts.

POPULATION TREND AND SIZE, 1990–1999 – *Trend* In the 1990s, *aurinia* has been recorded with varying degrees of regularity from 15 sites. By halfway through the decade, only four colonies remained and the annual Hampshire Butterfly Report warned that the species could disappear from the county within five years. If the Avon valley site is truly wild, only three natural colonies now remain. Considerable conservation effort has failed to halt the decline, the rate of which has been distorted by a number of both sanctioned and clandestine introductions, none of which supported colonies for longer than 12 years.

Size – It is quite normal for populations to build up quickly, only to crash suddenly a year or two later. This strongly suggests a non-synchronous parasite/host relationship, probably exaggerated or caused by climate conditions which favour *aurinia* one year and the parasite *Cotesia bignelli* the next (Porter, 1983). In the past, minor satellite colonies were often depleted or temporarily lost, only to be restocked when nearby stronger colonies recovered and dispersed. Now that the remaining colonies are so small and isolated, it is extremely important to stabilise populations by managing the water-table, grazing regime and scrub in accordance with available guidelines.

Numbers at the two nature reserves have remained low but fairly stable during the past decades. Periodically, populations have been affected adversely by inclement seasons, typically crashing to single-figured levels when wet or cold weather has predominated in spring, resulting in high larval mortality.

Population dynamics of introduced colonies are more extreme, typically producing very large populations in the first few years (when parasite populations are minimal) followed by a sudden collapse and extinction. The Avon valley colony built up to over 120 adults in 1997 and a peak of 74 was counted there in 1998 on 24th May.

It is interesting to recall here the rise and fall of two former introduced colonies that show this explosion and collapse pattern.

Up to six at the Winchester colony in 1997 were probably a further release.

	1985	1986	1987	1988	1989	1990	1991	1992	1993	1994
Near Brockenhurst	0	2	47	77	42	16	3	2	0	0
Near Winchester	0	0	33	14	2	16	2	10	6	0

FLIGHT PERIOD Emergence times vary from site to site and are strongly affected by weather. In west Hampshire the first males generally appear in the second week of May, followed by the first females a week later. Peak numbers typically occur in late May and the flight period is over by mid-June. At former sites in the north-east, the first rarely appeared before the first week of June, peaked in mid-June and lasted until late June, although precise records reflecting this are not available.

EARLIEST/LATEST DATES, 1990–1999 The earliest was on 1st May 1997 from the Avon Valley colony. The latest was on 20th June 1991 from an extinct, introduced colony near Liphook.

INTERESTING OCCURRENCES In 1985 near Fleet, where a population of several hundred Marsh Fritillaries then existed, Adrian Hoskins saw several dozen adults that had inadvertently committed suicide by settling on the very sticky caps of fungi. The previous year, the butterfly had been even more abundant there, and dozens were found dead in funnel-trap spiders' webs during a Butterfly Conservation field meeting on 16th June.

HISTORICAL CHANGES The distribution of this species has been contracting westwards in Britain for several decades, following the spread of urban and agricultural development. The main reason for this decline is thought to be the insect's tendency to occur in clusters of habitat patches, not all of which are occupied at one time. It therefore needs freedom to wander around sizeable areas of countryside, breeding wherever potential habitat patches become suitable within what are termed 'metapopulation structures' (Warren, 1994). Such a strategy is scarcely viable in the fragmented landscape of modern Hampshire. Once too much actual and potential habitat is lost or fragmented, the metapopulation structure of colonies is shattered and the species becomes over-dependent on individual sites, few of which remain suitable for long. The demise of the Marsh Fritillary in Hampshire is therefore due to increasing fragmentation and isolation of habitat patches.

A large number of Hampshire localities are mentioned, somewhat obscurely, in entomological literature. It is clear that the butterfly occurred widely over much of Hampshire, with concentrations of colonies on the western and central chalk, in the Avon, Test and lower Itchen valleys, along heathland edges in the north-east, in the Woolmer Forest district and in the Bishops Waltham area. Strangely, it has never been strong in the New Forest, though some colonies were known during the early 1920s (Fassnidge, 1923). It was unknown from the Hampshire chalk until just after World War II. Few sites appear to have held colonies for long, supporting the view expressed above that the species moved about colonising patches when they became suitable and dying out when they deteriorated.

During the 1975–1985 period, the butterfly was reported from 41 Hampshire tetrads. Most colonies were in damp, acidic meadows in the north-east and on chalk grassland sites in the west, whilst small and short-lived colonies appeared in a few woodland glades. Many of these colonies appeared during a major Marsh Fritillary expansion during the good summer sequences of 1982–1984, perhaps from strong colonies in east Wiltshire. Oates and Warren (1990) give a detailed account of the many attempted introductions involving this species in the county and argue that most of the colonies occurring in Hampshire during the latter part of the 20th century have been artificially influenced.

The county stronghold was a complex of meadows near Fleet which regularly produced populations of between 300–800 adults in good years; in 1984, for example, the butterfly swarmed in two areas of grazed meadowland. The species had been discovered in this area by Castle Russell in 1892 (Castle Russell, 1895) and was studied in depth by A.W. Richards between the mid-1940s and mid-1960s. Accounts in the literature show that the butterfly's fortunes in the district ebbed and flowed within a cluster of sites that fluctuated in and out of suitability, this being a classic metapopulation situation. Richards (1949) states that "*E. aurinia* is increasing all over the whole district and appeared in many unexpected places (in 1948)". In his 1957 account of butterflies in the Aldershot district, he lists it as "Widespread and locally common". However, from the late 1970s the habitat patches became more fragmented and isolated by major urban developments following the construction of the M3. Tenant farmers found it too difficult to run cattle in pockets of poor quality grassland on the urban fringe and so grazing ceased. The remaining habitat dried out and scrubbed over and by the 1990s the Marsh Fritillary was recorded only in ones and twos. By 1996 it was apparently lost. The protection of some sites as nature reserves, and associated reinstatement of grazing, came fractionally too late, though it is possible that the butterfly might still survive in very low numbers.

Glanville Fritillary
Melitaea cinxia

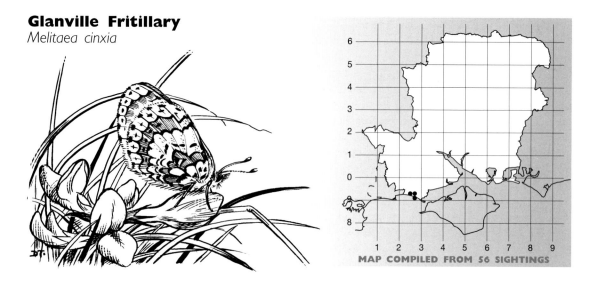

MAP COMPILED FROM 56 SIGHTINGS

DISTRIBUTION 1990–1999 In 1991, three individuals were seen at Hordle Cliff, near Milford on Sea. Since then, numbers have increased dramatically with sightings further west along the coast to Beckton Bunny near Barton-on-Sea. This stretch of collapsed sea-cliff is the only active site in Hampshire. It is thought to be a natural colonisation from the Isle of Wight.

HABITAT AND FOODPLANTS As in its Isle of Wight stronghold, the main colony is confined to the unstable sandy undercliff where Ribwort Plantain, the main larval foodplant, grows on the slippage areas. The colony is mainly south-facing and relatively well sheltered from prevailing winds. This, combined with the extra warmth generated by the exposed sandy soil, is ideal for the Glanville's ecological requirements.

In the young larvae live in groups under silken webs, which can be very obvious in early spring, where they feed and spend the winter. Larval webs can contain over a hundred individuals, which soon consume the surrounding foodplant, forcing the voracious larvae to move on to Buck's-horn Plantain as a second choice.

In May, the area is carpeted with Thrift and trefoils, nectar sources which the adults eagerly visit when they are not basking or trying to mate in the spring sunshine. The colony has its nucleus at Hordle Cliff and it is here that the highest density of butterflies is to be found.

MAJOR SITES The only known Hampshire site is the stretch of coast around Hordle Cliff.

POPULATION SIZE AND TREND, 1990–1999 Apart from weather conditions, landslips and larval parasites are the two main influences on population size, both of these being themselves influenced by weather. In such a small colony, a landslip can threaten the species' very survival in the short term, for entire breeding areas can be smothered or eroded, but landslips are very necessary in the long term as they allow the foodplant to regenerate with little competition from other vegetation. Lower numbers of adults were recorded in 1994 after the severe landslips of the previous winter and if a small colony can survive this then its long term prospects should be bright.

1997 was a truly remarkable year for the Hordle colony. A total of 152 were recorded on 29th May, some observers estimating 200+ at this time, the previous highest count being c.30 on 8th June 1993. Unfortunately, 1998 and 1999 saw much lower counts due to poor weather, in common with most sites on Wight.

FLIGHT PERIOD The beginning of the flight period is dependent on a settled spell of warm weather and so it is subject to variation. The usual flight period is from mid-May into June, with late May usually showing the peak in numbers.

EARLIEST/LATEST DATES, 1990–1999 The earliest record in our database is 10th May 1993 and the latest is 22nd June 1998, both at the Hordle colony of course.

INTERESTING OCCURRENCES The Isle of Wight population expands its range from time to time in seasons of high numbers and warm settled weather. From the densely populated southern undercliffs, wanderers have occurred some distance north on the Island, such as one in 1994 at Norton Spit, a small shingle and sand dune near Yarmouth and only a short flight to Hurst Castle Spit. The Hampshire colony has probably grown from such wanderers rather than from releases, although a release cannot be ruled out.

One interesting variety was recorded and photographed in 1993, this being a pale biscuit-coloured individual with even paler forewings, the butterfly retaining the normal spotting.

HISTORICAL CHANGES There is evidence to suggest the species was present in Hampshire during the 19th century from records in the Wherwell area of the Test valley (Moon, 1857) and also in the Winchester area according to records from Winchester College. G.A. Lewcock also took the species at Old Park, near Farnham, in the mid-1800s (Lewcock, 1888).

Various introductions have been attempted. In 1930, S.G. Castle Russell introduced the species to Laffan's Plain, Farnborough, where it survived for three years. The species was also introduced at Milford on occasions between 1930–1935.

The introduction on the railway at Sway in 1945 by R.W. Watson and F.S. Reeves is remarkable since it flourished for 22 years and supported many thousands of adults at its peak, providing stock for introductions elsewhere in Britain. Entomologists of the day reported removing hundreds of adults and larvae for further introduction attempts, but the colony died out when the railway was closed in 1967. Watson and Reeves also introduced the species to the New Forest at Stillwells Lane, but the colony did not survive for long. They used larvae from Compton Chine for their Hampshire releases. Another introduction on the railway near Sway was in 1947 by C.B. Antram, but the colony did not apparently survive for long. Antram also tried to introduce the species into his Sway paddock and at another "suitable site" further afield (see Oates and Warren, 1990).

Dr C. Suffern reported an introduction near Gosport. The exact location is uncertain, with Browndown, Gilkicker Point and Titchfield Haven as possibilities; it met with no long-term success. The last known introduction was also unsuccessful, this being at St Catherine's Hill in 1982.

The Hordle colony has an interesting history. Although the area was worked by collectors since before 1900 in search of the beautiful ab. *alsoides* variety of the Small Blue, there were no Glanville records. It may, of course, have been a closely guarded secret. Then, in 1928, William Fassnidge saw several on Hurst Spit. Between 1938–1949, H.J. Turner recorded Glanville Fritillaries from the New Forest, at Studland in nearby Dorset, at New Milton, Highcliffe and Christchurch, a strong indication that the species was resident along the west Hampshire/east Dorset coastline during the 1940s (Turner, 1949). In 1971, Mrs J. Goater almost certainly saw this species flying at the Milford end of Hurst Spit in late May, possibly further evidence of Wight emigration (Goater, 1974).

Glanville Fritillaries had an exceptional year on the Isle of Wight in 1989 and it is thought that the present Hordle Cliff colony originated from dispersing butterflies crossing The Solent. It is therefore an intriguing riddle as to what the exact status has been over the years, the weight of evidence suggesting that the mainland colony is natural, fluctuating and disappearing over time, then reappearing. It seems at present that the colony is strong and well-established, but in the long term it may be dependent on the Island to perpetuate the species' continuing existence in Hampshire. The New Forest District Council has no plans for sea defences in the Hordle Cliff section, but rather intends to allow that part of the coast to follow its natural course of erosion. In view of this, the long term future of the Hordle colony seems reasonably positive.

Speckled Wood
Pararge aegeria

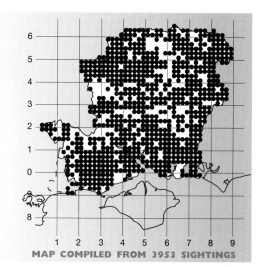

MAP COMPILED FROM 3953 SIGHTINGS

DISTRIBUTION 1990–1999 Since its rapid expansion in the 1930s, this species has succeeded in becoming widely established. Looking at its distribution map, it is hard to believe that there are no 19th or early 20th Century records of its existence in north-west Hampshire, particularly as this area now supports such a concentration. Apart from large open tracts of downland or intensive agriculture and areas of New Forest heathland, this butterfly can be seen almost anywhere, albeit in small numbers.

HABITAT AND FOODPLANTS With the exception of wet Alder carr, the Speckled Wood can be found in all types of woodland, preferably damp woodland with small glades and narrow open rides. It is scarce in relatively more arid habitats, for example on sandy heathland and south-facing slopes of chalk scarps. However, it can be quite numerous amongst scrub and developing woodland on the south-facing slope of Portsdown Hill, which is perhaps Hampshire's warmest down. Primarily it is a species which prefers dappled shade and readily breeds along the fringes of dense woodlands. It is also found along tree-lined hedges, sunken lanes, scrub-invaded downland, coastal marshland, scrub belts, shaded road verges and disused railway lines. The Speckled Wood often ventures into mature urban parks and gardens, in the latter especially if oaks are present.

Spring and autumn females appear to prefer sparse tussocks of soft grasses along the edges of woods, whereas the midsummer females select grasses in the more dense and protective shade of trees and bushes. A variety of grass species is used, except for those which are too coarse. In woods and meadows on clay soils, Wood Meadow-grass and Rough Meadow-grass are preferred. False Brome is a favourite on chalk downland sites, whilst Yorkshire-fog and young Cock's-foot are also used in a variety of habitats.

The spring and early summer adults seldom visit flowers, although occasionally they can be seen on the flowers of Wood Spurge, Hawthorn and Wayfaring-tree. The adults of mid and late summer are regularly attracted to honey-dew on trees, the sticky buds of Ash trees, ripe Blackberries, windfall apples and other over-ripe fruit, and are more likely to visit flowers than their predecessors.

MAJOR SITES With approximately 16% of Hampshire covered by woodland, it is not surprising that this is where most major sites occur. For the past decade, one of the Speckled Wood's major strongholds has been Pamber Forest. Other significant sites are Ashford Hangers, Cheriton Wood, Crab Wood, Crowdhill Copse, Micheldever Forest and West Wood (Southampton). Coastal sites include Cams Bay, Farlington Marshes north of the motorway, Sandy Point and Wicor. Sightings and transect figures from these last localities show that this species is not confined to woodlands.

POPULATION TREND AND SIZE, 1990–1999 *Trend* – The success of the species over the previous decade was not sustained throughout the 1990s, possibly due to the adverse impact of drought summers. The highest-ever Annual Index of 749 for Pamber Forest in 1989 could not be matched and the two following years could only be described as average. Optimistically, numbers then started to pick up and 1994 saw a year in which Winnall Moors and Farlington Marshes achieved their highest Annual Index figures for eight years. However, populations declined in 1995 at most sites, except at Sandy Point and Dean Hill. 1996 records in general indicated low numbers across the whole county, although transect figures indicated an improvement on the previous year. Annual Indices for 1998 were again low, but not always representative of numbers seen at some other locations.

	1990	1991	1992	1993	1994	1995	1996	1997	1998	1999
Alresford Farm	55	39	74	76	79	30	20	37	28	25
Crowdhill Copse	*	*	*	256	281	199	216	326	207	267
IVCP (woods)	*	*	105	81	113	85	107	*	67	73
Noar Hill	151	165	141	163	135	145	81	105	54	76
Pamber Forest	315	289	421	315	368	175	287	249	227	223
Roydon (Bakers)	135	129	177	99	102	98	137	180	96	129

Our highest-ever Annual Index was **749** at Pamber Forest in 1989

Size – Although rarely seen in prolific numbers, Speckled Wood counts at any one site commonly go well into double figures. Eighty were seen on transect at Pamber Forest in September 1993, over 70 were counted in Crab Wood on 22nd August 1994 and 45 were seen on another transect walk at Crowdhill Copse in August 1994. Counts in the 20s and 30s have come from widespread sites such as Brown Candover, Cheriton Wood, Dibden Bay, Itchen Stoke Down and Martin Down.

FLIGHT PERIOD The species has the unique ability amongst British butterflies to hibernate either as pupae or larvae. Adults can therefore be seen at almost any time from early spring to mid-autumn. Larvae develop at widely differing rates with some going through four moults whilst others go through only three. Consequently, distinct broods do not occur since there is a series of continuous emergences throughout the spring and summer months.

The first butterflies usually appear in late March/early April, having presumably overwintered as pupae. In late springs however, they may not surface until early to mid-May. This initial emergence can peak at any time from early May to mid-June, depending on weather conditions. The second emergence usually starts towards the end of June or early July. Numbers for this emergence are invariably greater than those of spring and early summer. Further waves emerge through August and September. Generally, their numbers peak during late August to mid-September and in most years the Speckled Wood flies until mid-October. An Indian Summer, of course, can take the butterfly into early November.

EARLIEST/LATEST DATES, 1990-1999 The earliest was seen at New Milton on 9th March 1992 and the latest was at West Wood, Southampton, on 14th November 1995.

INTERESTING OCCURRENCES The first sighting of 1994 was on 1st April at Hythe where an adult was found trying to escape from a garden shed. On 22nd August of the same year, many were seen taking nectar from Burdock in Crab Wood. On 28th August 1995, 45 were on Bramble fruits at Micheldever and in 1999 the species took a liking to rotting bananas in Mike Gibbons' garden.

HISTORICAL CHANGES Prior to the late 1930s, the Speckled Wood had a restricted distribution in Hampshire. It was common in much of the New Forest and in other large woods in southern Hampshire, but distinctly scarce in the north of the county. The Victoria County History statement of "Common throughout the county in woods and lanes" is probably erroneous, emanating from the fact that the author, Herbert Goss, was very much a man of the New Forest. Pearce (1890) describes it as being "local and rarely common" in the Portsmouth district. Fassnidge (1923) paints a picture of a very localised butterfly, especially away from the New Forest region. He even mentions an attempted introduction at Owslebury in 1921.

Stowell (1924) states that it is "sometimes common" on Selborne Common, adding "the only place in our district where it is – though I see about one specimen per annum in Alice Holt". However, it was well established on Ashford

Hangers, a few miles to the south, during the period 1920–1924 (J.A.C. Greenwood, quoted in Goater, 1974). A.W. Richards (1943) describes in some detail how the butterfly colonised the Aldershot district in the late 1930s and early 1940s: "When I first came to N. Hampshire in 1924 this species occurred in Alice Holt and Woolmer forests, but sparingly, I never found it anywhere else locally until 1932, when a few specimens were about on the Hog's Back. During the last six years it has occupied nearly all the smaller woods in the district and is apparently still expanding its range. At [Church] Crookham it has become quite common in gardens during the last two years, whilst at Winchfield it is now plentiful along the hedgerows, and has appeared this year in fields and hedgerows in Hawley, apparently slowly progressing eastwards".

Three separate notes telling a similar story appear in The Entomologist for 1944: S. Jackson describes the butterfly's colonisation of the Bishop's Waltham area; E. Rivenhall-Goffe, one of Hampshire's most senior entomologists, records the first specimen in his King's Somborne garden in 20 years, and Capt. Alban Bacon records his first specimen in 63 years residence in the Burghclere area.

Goater (1974) writes that "prior to 1940, it was very locally common to abundant in the larger woods ... In the early 1940s, it spread rapidly from these nuclei into almost every wood and copse in the county, and even along hedgerows, and it remains one of the commonest butterflies in Hampshire". The species underwent a similar expansion in Wiltshire during the same era (Fuller, 1995).

Wall Brown
Lasiommata megera

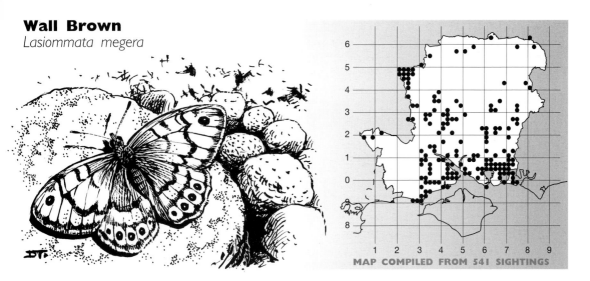

MAP COMPILED FROM 541 SIGHTINGS

DISTRIBUTION 1990–1999 The distribution map for the Wall Brown in Hampshire shows a heavy concentration along the coastal belt, a liberal scattering over the chalk and in the New Forest, with a few isolated pockets in the north of the county. However, since the mid-1990s the species has become *almost wholly* a butterfly of the coast, confined to a belt that stretches only a few miles inland. In 1996, the only inland reports came from Flowerdown, Ropley and Shipton Bellinger; in 1997, the only records away from the coastal strip were on two August dates at Shipton Bellinger; in 1998, Shipton Bellinger was again the only inland site. Yet as recently as 1994, 29 seen were at Shipton Bellinger on 5th August and it was also seen "in good numbers" around South Tidworth and Kimpton. In 1992, it had been abundant at Shipton Bellinger, common at Kingsworthy and the Annual Index at Beacon Hill–Warnford was 29. However, 1999 saw a slight increase in the number of inland records that may be the start of a reappearance away from the coast, *possibly* heralding the recovery stage of a cycle such as those described below in 'Historical changes'. On the other hand, even at coastal sites numbers are now small, and were it not for evidence of past periods of scarcity, followed by recovery, we might feel that we could lose the species from Hampshire. Until the mid-1980s, the Wall Brown was one of the most widespread of Hampshire's butterflies.

HABITAT AND FOODPLANTS The Wall Brown is strongly associated with hot, arid grassland habitats where there is an abundance of bare and broken ground. Adults are often seen basking along paths and in other bare, disturbed ground situations. At Needs Ore, one of the remaining coastal sites, adults are found especially along one bare path, sheltered on one side by a thick hedgerow, that runs between two fields of thick cultivated grassland where the species is seldom seen.

The ecology of this species was studied by Matthew Oates in the late 1970s and early 1980s, though his studies were not completed due to the sudden collapse of the species in Hampshire. He found that spring brood ova are typically deposited on the edges of large, isolated tussocks of a range of grass species, often close to low bushes or at the base of fence posts, and invariably where there is a mix of fine and coarse grasses. Summer brood ova are laid in even more precise situations – on the roots of herbs and grasses protruding through banks or tracts and especially into the roofs of Rabbit holes. Favoured overhangs and excavations can be utilised by more than one female, revealing little Aladdin's caves of pearly ova. Matthew also found larvae through the winter at Noar Hill, finding that larvae change from being initially dependent on fine grasses, notably fescues and bents, to taking a diet of coarser grasses and sedges when fully grown. This suggests that swards containing fine, medium and coarse grasses are essential. Larvae were often found basking or feeding on dry, mild winter days. He found that in early spring the larvae return to the overhangs and holes to pupate, though the contents of many pupae were eaten by unknown predators.

MAJOR SITES Sadly, there are no sites left that warrant the adjective 'major'. During the decade, some of the best sites have been Beacon Hill–Warnford, Farlington Marshes, Hook-with-Warsash, Needs Ore, Pennington Marshes, Portsdown Hill, Shipton Bellinger and the South Tidworth area.

POPULATION TREND AND SIZE, 1990–1999 *Trend* – It is clear from the preceding text that the trend has been steadily downward. 1991 showed a dramatic fall almost everywhere and although 1992 saw some recovery, 1993 witnessed a further decline that was not arrested until 1998, apart from isolated and temporary recoveries at odd sites such as Beacon Hill–Warnford in 1994. Coastal numbers in 1998 were encouraging and the minor recovery inland during 1999 has already been noted.

	1990	1991	1992	1993	1994	1995	1996	1997	1998	1999
Badminston Common	*	*	*	7	2	0	0	0	2	1
Beacon Hill–Warnford	5	4	29	5	7	1	0	0	0	0
Brownwich and Chilling	10	5	8	*	0	0	0	0	3	1
Portsdown Hill (West)	*	*	*	25	18	5	4	0	1	4
Yew Hill	2	2	12	0	1	0	0	0	0	0

Size – Today, any count at one site on a single day that reached double figures would be considered good.

FLIGHT PERIOD The first emergences are in late April or the first fortnight in May, depending on the weather. The second brood usually starts to emerge in mid or late July, peaks in August and typically finishes in the first half of September. In some years, even in this poor decade, there has been a small third brood which may last into October. This third brood featured strongly in hot summers and mild winters prior to the mid-1980s.

EARLIEST/LATEST DATES, 1990–1999 The earliest record was on 17th April 1990 at Portsdown Hill with the latest on 20th October 1990 in the New Forest at Hawkshill.

HISTORICAL CHANGES There is some evidence to suggest this species has experienced very marked, temporary declines and subsequent recoveries in the past at regional level. In an interesting paper on population fluctuations in the Wall Brown, Walsh (1945) states "It is well known that this butterfly will suddenly disappear from a district where it has been common, and will then, often after many years, as suddenly reappear". Thomas (Thomas and Lewington, 1991) cites such collapses in the early 1860s and the mid-1980s, suggesting that poor summers were the cause, although the recent decline in Hampshire began during the hot summer of 1984 and after a very strong second brood in 1983. However, the bulk of Hampshire's decline occurred during the poor summer sequence of 1985–1988.

The literature from Hampshire suggests much fluctuation at county and district levels over the years. Certainly, the butterfly had a very patchy distribution in the county during the early 1920s (see accounts by Fassnidge and Stowell) and Goater (1974) records a general decline after the hot summers of the early 1940s. However, during the hot summers of 1975 and 1976, the Wall Brown was one of the most frequently encountered butterflies in Hampshire, particularly along road verges. It then collapsed during the ensuing poor summers, only to recover again during the good summers of 1982 and 1983. What is worrying is the fact that no recovery occurred during the hot summers of 1989, 1990 and 1994–1996.

Marbled White
Melanargia galathea

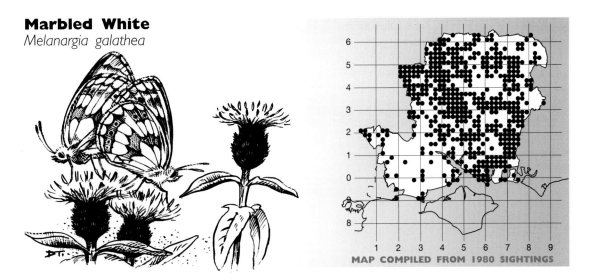

MAP COMPILED FROM 1980 SIGHTINGS

DISTRIBUTION 1990–1999 With the exception of the New Forest and north-east Hampshire, the Marbled White is widespread across most of the county. Primarily, it is a species of chalk downland; in fact, the outline of the South Downs can virtually be traced on the distribution map. However, it is not restricted to the chalk and can be seen, albeit in fewer numbers, in dry and damp grassland that is either neutral or acidic. In 1992 it was seen at Sandy Point for the first time, establishing the only known colony on Hayling Island, and throughout the 1990s, many small colonies became well established in the Southampton and Chandlers Ford area. Occasional vagrants are reported well away from suitable areas of breeding habitat. In the New Forest area, there is a scattering of small colonies in pockets of enclosed meadowland near settlements, especially around Lyndhurst. From these areas, it appears to be attempting to recolonise some of the Inclosures following the removal of stock and strengthening of fences. For example, one was seen near Denny Lodge in 1999. After the Essex Skipper, the Marbled White has colonised more new sites in Hampshire than any species in the 1990s.

HABITAT AND FOODPLANTS This species may be seen in most open, grassy areas, especially open downland, but also improved meadows, woodland rides, wide road verges, disused railway lines and occasionally gardens. It will breed in many situations where grass is left to grow, provided the sward consists of a mix of fine and coarse grasses and there is an abundance of nectar. It abounds on chalk grasslands which are either ungrazed, or grazed during the autumn and winter, or grazed only lightly by cattle in summer. It has a poor tolerance of summer sheep grazing.

The larvae appear to eat a wide range of grasses and probably the smaller sedges. In Hampshire, they have mostly been found eating Cock's-foot and False Oat-grass during the early summer. However, young larvae seem to require finer grasses, notably Red Fescue, and breeding grounds consist of taller, coarse grasses protruding from a mattress of finer grass. It is in such situations that the females deposit ova, whilst perched momentarily on tall stems. It is possible that some of the Bent grasses fulfil the role of Red Fescue on acid sites.

Across the downs, adult Marbled Whites can commonly be seen taking nectar on Greater and Common Knapweed, scabious species, Marsh Thistle, Creeping Thistle and Betony.

MAJOR SITES The best sites are on the chalk, high counts coming from such places as Magdalen Hill Down, The Mountain, Noar Hill, Pitt Down, Portsdown Hill, Stockbridge Down, Whiteshute Ridge and Yew Hill. At Butter Wood, Hook, which is off the chalk, they were seen vying for "air space and thistles" in 1992, whilst at Pitt Down in 1999, Ashley Whitlock reported that virtually every thistle was occupied by Marbled Whites battling for space with Six-spot Burnets. Braemore Wood has also had good numbers.

POPULATION TREND AND SIZE, 1990–1999 *Trend* – The 1990s appeared to be a consistently good period for this species. Most of the transect sites produced high numbers throughout the decade, particularly in 1992 and

1998. Conversely, the latter year produced a low Annual Index at Martin Down, even though more than 100 were seen there on 14th July. Similarly, the 1999 Annual Index at The Mountain fell dramatically following the previous year's highest-ever Index of 1,000. Even in years when numbers dipped, as they did in 1995, they were not significantly low. Numbers have fluctuated at individual sites according to changing local conditions; a Rabbit increase at St Catherine's Hill in 1990 kept the sward short and consequently caused Marbled White numbers to fall, and in 1989 the sea deluged the Hurst Spit site, again causing numbers of the species to fall.

	1990	1991	1992	1993	1994	1995	1996	1997	1998	1999
Magdalen Hill Down	391	401	522	297	494	380	317	425	470	454
Martin Down (North)	77	112	376	106	203	121	316	116	81	119
Noar Hill	195	480	684	241	247	391	543	471	596	552
Stockbridge Down	415	549	601	513	463	177	325	230	332	502
The Mountain	622	714	680	618	794	445	624	945	1000	342
Yew Hill	267	736	735	477	908	220	567	668	898	718

Size – On 12th July 1994, John Taverner stopped counting systematically at 400 on Stockbridge Down and went on to assess the day's population to be well in excess of 1,000. The same observer counted over 500 at both Abbotstone Down and Pitt Down on 4th July 1998 and a day's population of 1,000+ at our leading sites in a good season is very possible. There have been few attempts to estimate an entire day's population at any site and surveys of this type would be very useful.

FLIGHT PERIOD At most sites the Marbled White has a flight season of six to nine weeks, with a relatively short peak and a lengthy tail. The first tend to emerge around mid-June, after which the numbers normally peak in mid-July and slowly peter out towards the end of August.

EARLIEST/LATEST DATES, 1990–1999 The earliest record was on the extremely early date of 31st May 1990 at Ashford Hangers. The latest sighting came from Hookheath Meadows on 5th September 1996.

INTERESTING OCCURRENCES Matthew Oates saw an abnormal specimen at Noar Hill on 14th July 1991. This aberration was a female with underwings of a deep tan colour.

Marbled Whites of differing sizes were observed by David Green on 22nd July 1995 at Kingsclere, two of which were the size of male Gatekeepers.

In 1993 and 1994, adults were noted to be infected with abnormally high numbers of red parasitic mites. On 13th July 1994, 90% of the Noar Hill population was found to be infected by these mites but they seemed to have little or no detrimental effect as Marbled Whites were still present in numbers a month later.

HISTORICAL CHANGES There is a long history of this species appearing and disappearing from New Forest woods, the appearances generating much excitement in entomological literature as far back as 1857. It has probably wandered into the Inclosures from downland sites to the north and west, from coastal marshlands to the south and from unimproved meadows within the Forest over a long period of time. Hollaway (1952) describes finding Marbled Whites in numbers near Lyndhurst, in "meadows of cowslips patched here and there with wild iris".

The Marbled White has always been a standard species on the downs, summer grazing pressure permitting, and its downland status has only changed in the 20th century in proportion to the loss of downland to agriculture. Its status in non-calcareous grassland habitats appears to have ebbed and flowed considerably, with spells of relative scarcity and periods of strength. There does appear to have been a significant expansion off the chalk since the early 1980s, especially in acid grasslands in the north-east of the county and along the coastal fringe.

Grayling
Hipparchia semele

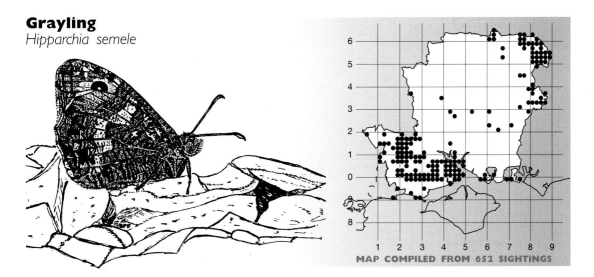

MAP COMPILED FROM 652 SIGHTINGS

DISTRIBUTION 1990–1999 The map shows today's distribution as two main areas of population on the northern and southern heathlands, a weak scattering of coastal colonies and an almost complete absence from the central chalk. Within this pattern, the New Forest is the main stronghold. Until the late 1950s the species was also found quite widely on chalk downland where the turf was short and brown, but today it remains only on MoD land at Porton Down.

HABITAT AND FOODPLANTS The Grayling is a butterfly of arid places, breeding in grass tussocks amongst bare ground. The adults can be seen basking with closed wings in bare pockets and along paths where the vegetation is worn or heavily grazed. On New Forest heaths, the species can be abundant where heathers are regenerating after burns, whereas in adjoining dense heather Graylings may be missing or present in sparse numbers. It is therefore very much a species of managed heathland and is absent, or in the process of dying out, from neglected heaths. On the north-eastern heaths, which are ungrazed by stock, it is heavily dependent on disturbance, particularly by MoD machinery; indeed, on many sites here the butterfly is strongly associated with mown firebreaks. The exception is Eelmoor Marsh SSSI, which is sensitively and imaginatively managed using a grazing regime that employs a combination of Highland cattle and a small herd of Przewalski's Wild Horse from the Marwell Preservation Trust. It is no coincidence that this site currently supports the strongest population of Graylings in north-east Hampshire

In the New Forest, the species is strongly associated with Bristle Bent but females tend to select isolated clumps for ovipositing, especially where two or three tussocks grow close together amongst bare ground. Solid carpets of Bristle Bent are mostly ignored, which is just as well because such areas are heavily grazed. Pathside tussocks of Purple Moor-grass and Wavy Hair-grass are also used. It has such a strong status within the Forest that small colonies can be found along sunny rides with suitable vegetation in Inclosures, whilst individuals can be seen just about anywhere.

On northern heaths, Bristle Bent is near the eastern limit of its range and is scarce. In the Bordon area, Matthew Oates found the species using Fine-leaved Sheep's-fescue, Tall Fescue and Wavy Hair-grass.

On the coast, there is a thriving colony on old dunes at Sandy Point, Hayling island. Colonies exist on pebble storm beaches, most notably at Park Shore and Needs Ore Point and at sites such as Hamble Common and Browndown. In 1993 the species was found on Hordle Cliff, which may have been a new site or one that was overlooked before the arrival of Glanville Fritillaries attracted observers.

When it was found in the past on chalk downs, the butterfly was strongly associated with ungrazed or lightly grazed Sheep's-fescue tussocks that grew amongst exposed chalk in hot situations, though other grasses that occurred in similar situations were also used.

In hot weather, adults will readily take nectar from flowers, especially Bramble and heathers. *Buddleia* is also visited, whilst at Sandy Point they have been seen on Sea-holly and at Blackbushe airport the species was seen taking nectar from Marjoram along old runways.

MAJOR SITES Almost any dry New Forest heath can hold a large population if the above habitat occurs. The programme of burning heathland at regular intervals obviously causes the species to move locally, as do unplanned heath fires. Away from the New Forest, the coast between Southampton and the Sussex boundary holds some important colonies, these including Hamble Common, Browndown and Sandy Point. In northern Hampshire, most extant colonies are on active army training heaths. Away from MoD heathland, colonies occur along path edges and other situations where human activity creates some bare ground, such as along pipeline routes. Eelmoor Marsh, Silchester Common and Bramshill are examples of northern sites that have produced good numbers in recent years.

POPULATION TREND AND SIZE, 1990–1999 *Trend* – In the New Forest there have been changes from year to year in response to weather conditions. Few of our transects cover Grayling habitat and so they do not give a good guide to recent trends. As the only changes within the last decade have been on isolated sites, it follows that the causes must be due to a variety of factors that can influence local habitat.

	1990	1991	1992	1993	1994	1995	1996	1997	1998	1999
Badminston Common	*	*	*	114	79	233	82	83	105	141
Ludshott Common	*	*	*	*	2	0	1	11	6	12
Roydon (Woodhouse)	10	12	19	4	*	2	0	1	8	23
Sandy Point, Hayling	63	119	89	29	74	121	101	182	125	137
Silchester Common	*	*	*	*	31	24	20	12	7	28

1990, 1991, 1992, 1995, 1998 and 1999 were excellent years. 1993, 1994 and 1996 had conflicting records with some areas performing well and others badly. On the whole there is no obvious change in status over the decade.

Size – Individual counts can be quite impressive. In 1997, on the heathland around Black Gutter Bottom, the species was counted in its hundreds. A total of 138 were counted on Hampton Ridge in one day in 1989 and counts of 100+ are not surprising from the New Forest. On the northern heaths, 130 at Eelmoor Marsh on 7th August 1996 is the highest count for the period in question, this locality being an important Grayling site. Colonies on the eastern heaths are much smaller.

FLIGHT PERIOD Mid-July to mid-September is the typical flight time with the peak normally in late July and early August. This period can obviously move a little either way depending on the year's weather.

EARLIEST/LATEST DATES, 1990–1999 The earliest record we have was from Roydon Woods on 3rd June 1992. The latest was on 25th September 1998 at Beaulieu Heath, although a later sighting in the previous decade was on 8th October 1986 at Laffans Plain, Farnborough.

PARTICULAR OCCURRENCES Adrian Hoskins found Graylings drinking sap from Pedunculate Oak and Ash and basking several feet up on Oak trees at Pamber Forest in 1989.

Occasionally, Graylings have been seen in unusual habitat, such as one in a built-up area at Highfield, Southampton, on 26th August 1994.

HISTORICAL CHANGES During the 20th century, this species has declined more than any other butterfly on Hampshire's chalk. Fassnidge (1923) lists it as being "Common on downs and heaths" and the Victoria County History describes it as "Common about Winchester ... and elsewhere in the chalk district". Indeed, it appears to have been a standard species on downs, particularly in the west of the county. The downland decline started in the 1930s, was accentuated by ploughing of downland in World War II and was completed by the onset of myxomatosis in the 1950s. Until myxomatosis appeared, there were still strongholds at Martin Down, Shipton Bellinger, the downs west of Winchester, the Meon valley and on Portsdown Hill where it lingered in a quarry until the 1980s. A downland population still exists on MoD land at Porton Down. The only other recent chalk locality is Toyd Quarry, near Martin.

In the New Forest there has been no major change to the Grayling's status throughout the 20th century; it is the butterfly that has most successfully survived the ravages that have taken place in the Forest during that period. However, it has disappeared from many heaths outside the Forest and has been drastically reduced on others, due primarily to afforestation, fragmentation by development, and neglect (especially in the form of the abandonment of grazing on common land). Its status has always fluctuated on the northern and eastern heaths, mainly in response to the intensity of use by the MoD. Thus Richards (1957), writing of the Aldershot area, described the Grayling as being "abundant on heaths before 1945, now more local". The butterfly's status is highly vulnerable now in the north and east of the county. Concern can also be expressed over the future of coastal colonies, which are restricted to small and isolated sites in contrast to its former more widespread distribution, although some of the coastal sites are well managed nature reserves.

Gatekeeper
Pyronia tithonus

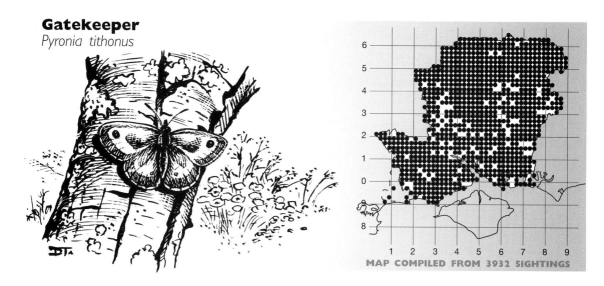

MAP COMPILED FROM 3932 SIGHTINGS

DISTRIBUTION 1990–1999 This butterfly of high summer is widespread across the length and breadth of the county, occurring wherever suitable habitat exists. It can best be described as being widespread and locally common, absent or scarce only in central urban areas, closed canopy and wet woodland, intensively-managed agricultural land and similar unsuitable country.

HABITAT AND FOODPLANTS Hedge Brown, another name for this species, indicates its close association with hedgerows. In Hampshire, it is commonest on rough, scrub-invaded downs, dry coastal grassland, relic meadowland, light woodland with open rides and scrub-invaded heathland. These habitats provide the warm sheltered conditions that this species requires.

Ova are laid amongst loose grasses, bare ground and litter in dry, warm and shady places under shrub canopies. Sometimes they are laid on the fine and medium-bladed grasses that are the larval foodplants, but more usually they are laid on dead grass stems or tree and shrub debris. Occasionally they are simply scattered amongst grassland from the air. After hatching, the larvae may be found feeding on Common Couch, various bents, fescues and meadow grasses. At first they feed around bare ground pockets under the scrub edge, but they wander into open rough grassland as they develop.

Apart from warmth and an abundance of larval foodplants, the adults require suitable sources of nectar, and as the species has a short proboscis, flowers with deeply buried nectar are of no use. Favoured nectar sources are Bramble, Common Fleabane, Common Ragwort and Marjoram. Indeed, Bramble and Marjoram are preferred to *Buddleia* in such places where the choice exists.

MAJOR SITES Whilst most nature reserves, downs, open woods and hedgerows will support sizeable populations, a few sites regularly return reports of impressive numbers, including Eelmoor Marsh, Farlington Marshes, Pamber Forest, Stockbridge Down and Yew Hill. It is often abundant around Bramble and Gorse in the New Forest.

POPULATION TREND AND SIZE, 1990–1999 *Trend* – The warm conditions of the 1990s have favoured this species, with every year apart from 1993 and 1994 being rated as excellent. Even 1993 and 1994 were rated as quite good, the following transect data showing how favourable the decade was for this species.

	1990	1991	1992	1993	1994	1995	1996	1997	1998	1999
Alresford Farm	304	286	302	188	225	441	332	104	115	152
Beacon Hill–Warnford	266	537	729	611	549	932	686	*	387	324
Farlington Marshes	1591	1529	2634	1589	1970	2412	**3454**	2262	1099	1984

	1990	1991	1992	1993	1994	1995	1996	1997	1998	1999
Hengistbury Head	519	432	461	241	304	414	449	213	590	507
Magdalen Hill Down	253	167	651	588	609	576	388	160	238	298
Pamber Forest	544	1128	1421	474	542	993	2303	863	543	588
Roydon (Bakers)	490	464	575	145	167	127	268	285	125	107
Stockbridge Down	586	672	636	266	327	288	392	100	118	472
Yew Hill	600	743	990	483	308	602	373	354	412	538

Size – Counts of over 100 for a site on one day are commonplace, over 40 sites having such records in 1996 for instance. Over 400 were seen in Carpenters Wood, near Sherborne St John, during 1997 and the above transect indices give an idea of the relative strengths of various populations.

FLIGHT PERIOD During the 1990s, the first Gatekeepers have emerged in June, dates varying from the 2nd to 30th, but numbers are unlikely to be seen until early July with peaks in late July or early August. From mid-August, numbers decline rapidly with the last, at least for the 1990s, usually being seen in the second or third weeks of September.

EARLIEST/LATEST DATES, 1990–1999 The earliest was at Otterbourne on 2nd June 1992, a year when there were early records on nearby Wight, and with one exception, the last sighting was at Noar Hill on 21st September 1991. The exception was a pale-coloured but freshly emerged female, seen at Sherfield on 9th October 1995 on a very hot day. It seems likely that this was from a partial second brood.

OUTSTANDING OCCURRENCES A number of aberrations have occurred. In ab. *subalbida*, the normal fulvous colour is replaced by creamy white and this form was seen in the New Forest on 16th August 1991 and again in 1994. Four specimens approaching ab. *subalbida* were recorded in 1993 at Bartley by Joyce and Edwin Gifford. Two pale aberrations were recorded in 1993, one with pale patches on the upper forewing at Harewood Forest on 28th July and one at Westwood on 6th August with the whole submarginal area of the hindwings creamy white. The form ab. *excessa* has extra spots on the forewings, and three males and a female were seen in a Winchester garden during July and August 1994 with one, two or three extra spots. Dwarf adults occur in hot summers and were seen in 1990, 1995 and 1997.

Unusual behaviour has also been recorded. At Fleet Pond in 1990, a Gatekeeper was caught in a moth trap. In the bumper year of 1992, a male was found mating with a Small White whilst another male was found mating with a Ringlet. Pairings between different butterfly species are rare and do not produce viable offspring.

HISTORICAL CHANGES It is clear that this butterfly was formerly far more abundant than it is today. The Victoria County History lists it as being "everywhere abundant" and Fassnidge (1923) gives it as being "very common everywhere". Richards (1957) is the first to indicate a decline, describing it as being "Widespread, becoming less abundant" in the Aldershot district. This is a theme followed by Goater (1974), who writes that "it has certainly decreased so much that it is now seldom more than common". The main reason for this decline is undoubtedly agricultural intensification; colonies are indeed scarce in modern agricultural land.

Meadow Brown
Maniola jurtina

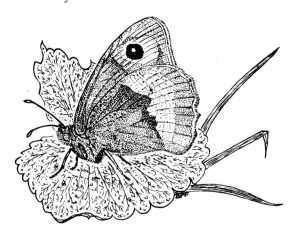

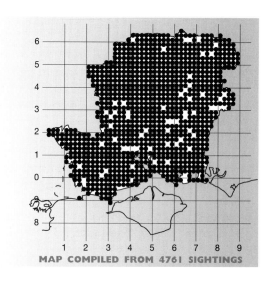

MAP COMPILED FROM 4761 SIGHTINGS

DISTRIBUTION 1990–1999 This is one of the most widespread and common species in Hampshire, occurring wherever there is sheltered, unimproved grassland with wild flowers for nectar. It is found in all parts of the county and as it only needs a small amount of suitable habitat to support a colony, almost every tetrad has produced records. The species lives in colonies, but individuals wander so that records may come from gardens and other habitat types.

HABITAT AND FOODPLANTS The Meadow Brown is common wherever rough ground is found. In Hampshire it is strongest on the chalk downs, especially where there is warmth and shelter, and it is also numerous in woods with grassy rides and clearings and on coastal grazing land such as Farlington Marshes. Roadside verges can hold large numbers and in 1991 country lanes produced myriads that were disturbed as cars passed. Only town centres, reed beds, salt marshes, wet carr woodland, expanses of dwarf shrub heathland, acid bogs, dense coniferous plantations, modern cereal fields and agriculturally improved grassland offer little prospects for Meadow Browns. It is now possible to walk for miles over farmland in Hampshire without seeing a single Meadow Brown.

   As the larvae feed on a variety of wild grasses growing amongst a diversity of sward structures, the butterfly thrives in most semi-natural grassland habitats. It is possible that the finer fescues, bents and meadow grasses are most favoured and there is apparent preference for swards wherein several species of grass occur.

MAJOR SITES All our best downland sites hold strong populations so that areas such as Beacon Hill–Warnford, Magdalen Hill Down, Martin Down, Noar Hill, Old Winchester Hill, Oxenbourne Down, Pitt Down, Portsdown Hill, Stockbridge Down and Yew Hill are major sites. Woods such as Ampfield Wood and Pamber Forest hold large populations in their rough, open areas, whilst the coastal grassland at Farlington Marshes has already been named as an important site. Roadside verges of importance are not confined to country lanes, the small rough area between Magdalen Hill Down and the Percy Hobbs roundabout on the A31 holding over 300 on 4th July 1993.

POPULATION TREND AND SIZE, 1990–1999 *Trend* – There has not been a poor Meadow Brown year in this period, although some have been outstandingly good and individual places have had bad seasons. For instance, in 1995 the species thrived on chalk downland but did not do so well on the acid grasslands of northern Hampshire.

	1990	1991	1992	1993	1994	1995	1996	1997	1998	1999
Beacon Hill–Warnford	2628	5138	4702	2042	1226	1879	2768	3955	5152	1431
Farlington Marshes	513	1022	1228	542	938	1031	795	456	380	1185

	1990	1991	1992	1993	1994	1995	1996	1997	1998	1999
Magdalen Hill Down	295	616	698	476	618	820	414	368	852	491
Martin Down (North)	1199	2524	2593	1070	568	957	1530	1132	2906	1464
Noar Hill	422	1471	1698	637	559	698	1037	895	1263	977
Pamber Forest	450	574	982	404	449	721	775	526	475	626
Stockbridge Down	1242	1845	2058	1143	753	639	935	1174	2295	1221
Yew Hill	817	1438	1025	786	1013	567	657	553	1139	920

Looking through the above transects, the summers of 1991 and 1992 stand out. 1994 appears to be poor, but that is only in comparison with the best seasons because the species fared quite well in 1994.

Size – Some colonies contain thousands of butterflies; at Stockbridge Down on 31st July 1992, 2,000 were counted in a relatively small part of the down, whilst the record Annual Index of 5,152 at Beacon Hill–Warnford would have been but a modest percentage of the true population. In 1998 and 1999, well over 50 sites returned daily counts of 100+ and this was by no means a comprehensive coverage of the county. In recent years, counts of 500+ at strong sites would be quite normal.

FLIGHT PERIOD At most sites, and in normal years, the first large-scale emergences occur in mid-June. However, flight season length and the timing of the peak season period varies from habitat to habitat. For example, in woodland the butterfly peaks in early or mid-July and finishes in mid-August, whilst on the downs the season usually lasts into early October with peak numbers in mid-August.

EARLIEST/LATEST DATES, 1990–1999 The earliest record was of one at Whitsbury on 14th May 1995 and the first have usually been recorded in recent years before the end of May. The latest record was on 14th October 1990 at Porton Down, but before the 1990s there was a record of one on 26th October 1986, at Noar Hill. The species has been recorded up to mid-October in several recent years.

PARTICULAR OCCURRENCES There have been a number of aberrations in recent years. On 21st July 1996, a perfect specimen at Lovedean was so pale that it was almost white. There have also been reports of great variation in size, a feature that has been reported for a number of species in Hampshire.

HISTORICAL CHANGES Management of grassland sites is clearly of major importance in the long run, but over the past decade it is hot, dry summers that have produced the highest numbers. In the 1940s, there were several such summers when the species thrived, although we do not have the quantitative data to compare with today. In places such as Stockbridge Down, control of Rabbit numbers has been critical. At times these animals have devastated parts of the down and Meadow Brown numbers in those patches have plummeted, whilst in those parts that are Rabbit-free the species has flourished.

The massive decline through the 20th century of its preferred habitat of rough grassland must have resulted in the species vanishing from large areas of countryside. Although it remains one of our commonest butterflies, it must be one of the species that has declined most in the county during the 20th century, the change being from near-ubiquitous abundance to localised abundance. As it was not one of the '*collectors' butterflies*' of old, quantitative data from the past is very limited, but whereas it was recorded as 'abundant' in New Forest Inclosures around 1900, it is now put into the 'locally common' category.

This last fact means that changes in forestry practices, such as the decline of coppicing and the cutting of ride-side vegetation in the New Forest, have contributed to its decline, but the main factors must be the use of fertilisers which have produced vast expanses of inhospitable grassland, the disappearance of so much downland and the development of rough pieces of land around towns.

Ringlet
Aphantopus hyperantus

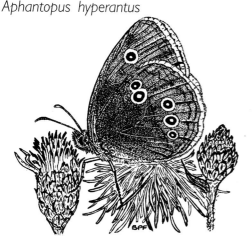

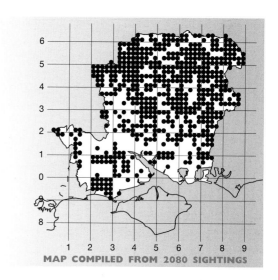

MAP COMPILED FROM 2080 SIGHTINGS

DISTRIBUTION 1990–1999 The Ringlet is widely distributed throughout the county. It appears to have strongholds in central and northern Hampshire, especially towards the north-west, although that may be due to very complete observer coverage in that area. It lives in discrete colonies of variable size, the largest being in sheltered rough grassland in or near scrub or woodland on moist soils.

HABITAT AND FOODPLANTS Traditionally, this species was associated with damp woodland and lush grassland habitats. It is a butterfly which needs shelter and is not a species of exposed or arid grasslands. It may occur in large concentrations along suitable woodland tracks and rides bordered by long, rank grasses, or in poorly grazed fens and meadows. Sizeable colonies also occur on scrub-invaded chalk downland on deep soils, which can be termed 'humic chalk grassland', and on rough roadside verges. It is local along the coast, seeming to avoid grasslands influenced by salt deposition, and it is not a species of open heathland. It is not, and never was, a butterfly of the open New Forest, though until relatively recently it abounded in most of the Forest's Inclosures. During the 1980s and early 1990s, there were few colonies in the Inclosures but the signs are now that the species is spreading due to the reduction in grazing pressure in many Inclosures and to more sensitive ride management.

The butterfly's favourite nectar sources are Bramble, Wild Privet, knapweeds, thistles and Field Scabious. It has also been recorded taking nectar on Wild Thyme, Red Campion, yellow Asteraceae and Marjoram, this being a wide variety that covers wet and dry habitats.

Larvae feed on the taller, lusher grasses, including Tufted Hair-grass, Cock's-foot, Common Couch, False Oat-grass and False Brome. Colonies occur mainly on rank swards. Females drop ova into the grasses, usually whilst perched momentarily on a grass flower spike, but sometimes during stuttering flights through the grassy head canopy.

MAJOR SITES Although recorded from many woodland, downland and river valley localities, the major site for this species at present is Pamber Forest. Good numbers are usually found at a number of other localities, such as Abbotstone Down, Ashford Hangers, Bentley Wood and Noar Hill.

POPULATION TREND AND SIZE, 1990–1999 *Trend* – This species rarely fares badly in its damp woodland haunts; numbers fluctuate more noticeably in open grassland habitats, where populations fare well in warm wet summers and poorly during hot dry seasons. Transect data reflect these differences and show how quickly the butterfly can recover from a bad season by the following year.

The transects reveal strong populations at Noar Hill and Pamber Forest throughout the decade, but they show conflicting trends. 1992 was an outstanding year for the species everywhere, but numbers dropped markedly in 1993 at Noar Hill and

Pamber Forest, although they rose at Stockbridge Down and The Mountain. 1996 saw numbers plummet all over Hampshire with the notable exception of a few places such as Crab Wood and Pamber Forest.

The 1997 season demonstrated the Ringlet's astonishing powers of recovery with numbers rising strongly at a number of localities. It is not clear why populations vary in their trends from place to place, but it could possibly be due to the weather's different influence on larval and pupal development at specific sites. Management also plays a major role in such variations between sites. 1998 and 1999 were also good seasons for the species.

	1990	1991	1992	1993	1994	1995	1996	1997	1998	1999
Botley Wood	*	*	*	*	*	258	332	214	356	556
Magdalen Hill Down	97	13	53	55	129	91	6	12	15	41
Noar Hill	140	420	622	398	398	446	176	406	388	516
Pamber Forest	450	713	932	513	616	744	782	774	850	1219
Stockbridge Down	37	68	58	139	265	129	23	45	104	82
The Mountain	61	150	261	324	363	209	14	108	303	297

Size – We have limited data on actual population sizes, but counts in excess of 200 on one day have come from a number of places. At peak season, it can outnumber both Marbled White and Meadow Brown at some sites.

FLIGHT PERIOD The main flight period is from late June to early August with the peak in mid-July. This is usually the first of the common brown butterflies to disappear in August.

EARLIEST/LATEST DATES, 1990-1999 The earliest for the period was on 28th May 1990 at Roydon Wood, with the latest on 29th August 1991 at Oxenbourne Down.

INTERESTING OCCURRENCES The Ringlet is normally considered to be a highly sedentary butterfly, and so one at Hengistbury Head on 8th July 1990, well away from the nearest known population, was very unusual.

Two records of unusual flying times are of interest. One was found flying at 2115 hrs on 3rd July 1993, whilst another landed in a moth trap, well after dark, on 1st August 1993.

A variety ab. *arete*, with light dots but no surrounding rings on its underwings, was found at Ashford Hangers on 20th June 1995 and another was seen in Crab Wood on 27th July 1999. It is worth noting that similar individuals were seen on Stockbridge Down on 24th June 1989, slightly outside the main time range for this book. The striking ab. *lanceolata*, where the rings are squashed into almond shapes, has been recorded in the Forest in this decade. Stockbridge Down has long been known as a locality for these two aberrations.

HISTORICAL CHANGES The distribution of the Ringlet has changed significantly since the early part of the 20th century when it was regarded primarily as a woodland butterfly. The Victoria County History describes it as being "common in woods throughout the county" and Fassnidge (1923) gives it as "Common everywhere in woods". The Ringlet's decline, and recent incipient recovery, in its former stronghold of the New Forest Inclosures, has already been noted. Suffice to say that the old collectors turned their attention to this species on cloudy July days, due to the relative frequency of aberrations in the New Forest of old and to the fact that it flies readily in conditions which are too dull for other species.

Evidence strongly suggests that it has increased in other habitats during the 20th century, mainly as a result of the decline in grazing on the downs and the abandonment of fragmented meadowland in river valleys. Indeed, it may well be benefiting from an increase in ungrazed pockets of grassland resultant from the urbanisation of the Hampshire landscape and associated decline in grazing in urban fringes of unmanaged rough grassland. Whether the 21st century will be so kind remains to be seen, one particular threat being the drying out of damp grassland habitats as a result of increased water extraction for a burgeoning human population.

The species was affected severely by the drought of 1976, with colonies on downland and in clay woodland taking several years to recover. It was less affected by severe droughts in 1984, 1989 and 1990.

Small Heath
Coenonympha pamphilus

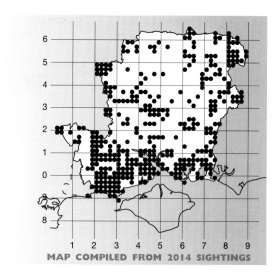

MAP COMPILED FROM 2014 SIGHTINGS

DISTRIBUTION 1990–1999 Although the Small Heath is distributed widely throughout the county, it occurs mainly as a weak and diffuse presence and there is only a scattering of sizeable colonies. Despite its vernacular name, the strongest Hampshire populations occur on the remaining unimproved chalk grassland sites, although large populations do occur on dry coastal grasslands, in parts of the open New Forest, on some of the heaths in north-east Hampshire and on unimproved grassland in the main river valleys. Until recently, it was frequently encountered in woodland rides and clearings. It is generally a sedentary species, although individuals are occasionally capable of dispersion in very warm summers.

It has experienced a considerable decline in the grasslands of the Southampton to Portsmouth belt during the 1990s, partly due to the housing and industrial developments that have isolated many sites.

HABITAT AND FOODPLANTS The species uses a variety of dry grassland sites, as the previous section suggests, but the main Hampshire habitats are chalk grassland and grassy heaths. It is not a typical species of roadside verges, or rough and improved grassland, and it is now a surprisingly scarce insect in Hampshire's woodland.

The larvae feed on a range of small, fine-leaved grasses, especially fescues. Matthew Oates has found the species to have a strong association with Sheep's-fescue on downland sites in Hampshire and a lesser association with Red Fescue. On heaths, Fine-leaved Sheep's-fescue is also used and it is possible that other grasses may be important at some sites, particularly the finer bent grasses. The species typically uses fescues growing in areas of short and medium height grasses. It is highly vulnerable to overgrazing, but conversely, it also performs badly in years of strong grass growth when the foodplants are shaded by coarser grasses. It is not a species of downs which are dominated by coarser grasses, and this explains its relative scarcity on the central and western downs which are dominated by Upright Brome.

MAJOR SITES Large populations occur at Broughton Down, Butser Hill, Magdalen Hill Down, Martin Down, Noar Hill, Porton Down, Stockbridge Down, The Mountain and a number of other downland sites. It is locally common along the coast at sites such as Sinah Common on Hayling Island and Keyhaven Marshes. Sizeable colonies also occur on grass heaths in the New Forest and north-east Hampshire, an example of the latter being Blackbushe airfield.

POPULATION TREND AND SIZE, 1990–1999 *Trend* – 1989 had been a bumper year for this species and so in comparison the decade started with something of a crash. In 1993, a dramatic decline in numbers was noted since 1989, but by 1995 observers were noting a dramatic increase (Taverner, Ed, 1993 and 1995). There seems to be no apparent synchronisation between localities due to factors such as management regimes and Rabbit grazing, which makes it difficult to discern any overall pattern; in most years there are localities that have gone against the trend. Since this appears to be a species that is much affected by the growth rate of grasses, such a pattern is not surprising. Despite annual fluctuations, the species seems to be maintaining its status.

	1990	1991	1992	1993	1994	1995	1996	1997	1998	1999
Hengistbury Head	122	102	136	70	182	127	78	148	228	136
Magdalen Hill Down	490	118	151	55	59	229	352	405	326	146
Martin Down (South)	384	330	311	304	729	763	569	624	339	279
Noar Hill	450	257	220	109	154	455	594	423	225	253
Stockbridge Down	282	250	159	123	66	92	84	702	335	143
The Mountain	744	693	703	356	271	283	293	359	261	207

Our highest-ever Annual Index is **1278** at Noar Hill in 1989

Size – At sites with the strongest populations, a day's count may be between 100 and 200 adults at the peak of the flight season; daily transect counts at Yew Hill and Magdalen Hill Down have produced figures of 86 and 80 respectively.

FLIGHT PERIOD The Small Heath is double-brooded in Hampshire. In a normal year, the first adults appear during mid-May, the first generation peaking in the middle of June and tailing off at the beginning of July. At most sites there is a gap of about two weeks before the first of the second generation appear. The second brood typically peaks towards the end of August and lingers into late September. Many books claim that a partial third brood occurs following hot summers, and the date for our latest record in the following section *may* be too late for the second brood. When late summer weather is poor, the second generation tends to hold over until the following spring.

EARLIEST/LATEST DATES, 1990–1999 Our earliest record is from Basingbourne Woods on 8th April 1997. This is quite unprecedented and appears to be by far the earliest appearance on record. It is highly unusual for the butterfly to appear before the last week of April and the next earliest sightings we have are from three sites on 29th April 1990. The latest was on 16th October 1990 at Hook-with-Warsash.

INTERESTING OCCURRENCES Apart from the very early specimen noted above, there have been no reports of unusual occurrences during the decade and no aberrations of any sort have been reported.

HISTORICAL CHANGES The butterfly has experienced a steady decline in Hampshire during the 20th century. The Victoria County History states that "The Small Heath is abundant throughout the county ... in fields, on heaths, chalk downs, and in woods". Fassnidge (1923) was able to state that the Small Heath was "very common everywhere". Since that time, there have been many local extinctions due to the destruction of heathland and chalk grassland. Much grazing land has also been rendered unsuitable due to the use of fertilisers and changes in grazing practices. By 1974, it was said to be "still common in suitable localities ... though less so than formerly" (Goater, 1974).

Until the late 1970s, the species was far more common in grassy clearings in woodlands, but it is now scarce in such localities. The reasons for this marked decline in woodland habitats are unknown, but it is interesting to note that the woodland decline coincided with the cessation of the formerly widespread practice of mowing woodland rides in midsummer. For Hampshire generally, there has been a gradual contraction of range to the habitats outlined in the opening section.

PART SEVEN

LOST SPECIES

Sadly, we have lost several resident species from Hampshire or even Britain, including the Large Tortoiseshell and High Brown Fritillary (both covered in the Systematic List) and Black-veined White, which used to be present in some strength. Square brackets in this section indicate that the species' status as a natural Hampshire resident is not proven.

[Chequered Skipper]
Carterocephalus palaemon

There are old reports of the species from the New Forest (Allen, 1952; Goater, 1974; Harvey and Harvey, 1857a) and there are similar reports from Netley and Southwick (Barrett, 1893; Harvey and Harvey, 1857b); the well known Portsmouth naturalist, Henry Moncrieff, apparently took the insect at Southwick in the mid-1800s (Sperring, 1952). However, Canon Hawker (1952) saw and identified specimens said to have been taken near Lyndhurst by Mr Johns, a dedicated collector. It is possible that the species was naturally resident in Hampshire, but the records may have been of releases so that such a status must be considered as suspect.

Wood White
Leptidea sinapis

The Wood White became extinct in Hampshire around 1940–1945. The Victoria County History (1900) describes it as plentiful in some woods in north Hampshire, especially near Basingstoke, but it was already on the decline. Castle Russell (1942) describes its sudden collapse from being common in the Pamber Forest area in the late 1880s and Fassnidge (1923/24) lists a few sites where it was local or rare. It was common in Alice Holt Forest between 1926–1931 but then vanished (Richards, 1957). It was reintroduced to Alice Holt at Lodge Inclosure around 1949 and at Straits Inclosure in 1976, persisting in the latter until 1981 and might have thrived had not its favoured ride been pulverised by forest machinery (Oates and Warren, 1990). It colonised woodland at Headley Down naturally in 1976 from Chiddingfold Forest, appearing in low numbers in 1977. Other woods such as Crab Wood also held the species in numbers.

The Victoria County History relates that "It was formerly very abundant in the enclosed woods of the New Forest, but suddenly disappeared as a common insect about 1883". Its disappearance from Stubby Copse, the best known locality, may have been at least partly due to collecting; Sheldon (1923) claims that one collector captured the whole brood in one season and that *sinapis* was never again seen in Stubby Copse (Sheldon, 1923). Whatever the reality, Nicholson (1912) laments: "I seem to have had the melancholy privilege of taking one of the last of the New Forest *Leucophasia sinapsis*, for I captured a male specimen in Stubby Copse on June 13th, 1888".

Recently, there have been two or three sightings in Queen Elizabeth Country Park in 1984, which may have been an introduction. Two were seen in Bentley Wood in 1997 and a first brood specimen was caught there on 27th May 1998. These were the first to be seen in Hampshire since 1984, but as the species is not known at any site in either Hampshire or Wiltshire, they may have been released from captivity.

The reasons for this species' disappearance from Hampshire are not at all clear; it survives close to the county border in Surrey.

Black-veined White
Aporia crataegi

Detailed accounts of the Black-veined White's disappearance from the New Forest (Goss, 1887; Victoria County History, 1900) and a scattering of records from elsewhere, suggest that this butterfly collapsed spectacularly in Hampshire during the mid-Victorian era and was last seen in 1880 or 1883. Goss (Victoria County History, 1900) describes how the butterfly plunged from local abundance to extinction in the space of a few years. The Victoria County History reads: "In 1866, 1868,

1869 and 1870 it occurred in thousands about Butt's Lawn, Holme Hill and Puck Pitts; between Boldrewood and Burley (in Oakleigh Enclosure); and in Warwickslade and Rhinefield; also more sparingly on the eastern side of the Forest, about Little Holme and Denny. I caught a few specimens as late as 1878, and it is believed that the last stragglers were taken by my old friend, the late J. Jenner Weir, about 1883, between Vinney Ridge and Holmsley".

Goss adds: "By midsummer, 1870, the species had increased and multiplied in these localities to such an extent as to render the discovery of the pupae on sloe bushes, and the capture of five or six dozen imagos in the course of a few hours a matter of ease ... After the wet summer of 1871, *Aporia crataegi* gradually became scarcer in the New Forest. In 1872, it was again chiefly restricted to its head quarters in the neighbourhood of Burley, Boldrewood, and Vinney Ridge, and its numbers were apparently reduced from hundreds to a few dozens. In 1875, the species had become still rarer; ...".

P.B.M. Allen (1948) adds that the butterfly was particularly attracted to Oxeye Daisy and thistles in the New Forest and, more significantly, argues that these last New Forest butterflies were the last wild British specimens, claiming that all subsequent records from Kent resulted from introductions. He was probably influenced in this belief by Tutt (1905) who claimed that "every specimen taken in Britain since 1880 has been at least one generation removed from Hungary, Austria, Germany or Switzerland".

Away from the New Forest, there are very few records and these are mostly from the coastal belt. For example, the species is said to have been formerly common behind Lumley's Mill at Emsworth (Rivenhall Goffe, 1932) and Pearce (1890) states that the butterfly was common in Elm Grove, Southsea, around 1870.

Pratt (1983) provides a full review of the species' disappearance in Britain whilst Oates and Warren (1990) review the many attempts to re-establish the Black-veined White, including a large and unsuccessful attempt at Noar Hill in 1969.

[Mazarine Blue]
Polyommatus semiargus

There are two 19th century records of single adults (Goater, 1974). According to J.C. Dale, the species occurred in the Ringwood area prior to 1836 and there are eight or more specimens in the collection of William Bentley (1789–1859) labelled "Brockenhurst" dating from before 1839 (Allen, 1980 and Bretherton, 1951). This species has been placed in square brackets because we consider the evidence as insufficient to prove residence in Hampshire.

Large Blue
Maculinea arion

Prior to 1830, it was said to be plentiful around Winchester where specimens were taken and the species appears in the collection of Mr Curtis (Bretherton, 1951; Goater, 1974; Newman, 1871; Spooner, 1963; Tutt, 1905). If this were so, they are the only records of the Large Blue on chalk downland in Britain. Tutt also lists Parley Heath as a site, which is now in Dorset.

Large Tortoiseshell
Nymphalis polychloros

As this species was so plentiful and only disappeared in the last few years, it is dealt with in the main text (p.121).

High Brown Fritillary
Argynnis adippe

As this species has probably disappeared from Hampshire in the last few years, it is dealt with in the main text (p.132).

PART EIGHT

INTRODUCED SPECIES, CASUAL RELEASES, ESCAPES AND VAGRANTS

There are a number of butterfly farms and breeders and it is seldom clear whether the isolated rarity is genuine, an escape, a release, a misidentification or a deliberate fraud. We list the following, some possibly genuine wild species, some known releases and others of more dubious origin, because a book on the butterflies of the county ought to mention such records so that future workers will know the situation. Oates and Warren (1990) provide a detailed account of the many attempts to introduce species to Hampshire. In this section, if a species' name is not enclosed in square brackets, it is accepted that genuine wild butterflies have definitely appeared in Hampshire.

[Lulworth Skipper]
Thymelicus acteon
Incredibly, this species was established along the Holmsley branch line in the New Forest in the early 1920s. Fassnidge (1924), quoting A.H. Jones, states: "One locality known to several entomologists; whether originally put down or not I cannot say". Rear Admiral A.D. Torlesse knew the site and records this as a genuine introduction which persisted for several years (pers. comm. to Matthew Oates). The foodplant, Tor-grass, still occurs along the route of the old railway (N. Sanderson, pers. comm. to Matthew Oates); see also Brewis, Bowman and Rose, 1996.

[Scarce Swallowtail]
Iphiclides podalirius
A pair said to have been caught in the New Forest in the early 1820s were mentioned by Morris and a male labelled 'Lyndhurst' in the Henry Jennings collection could be one of these. For such a species, it is highly unlikely that a pair would be found together in Hampshire and such records must be highly suspect, our equivalent to 'The Hastings Rarities' in ornithology.

Swallowtail
Papilio machaon gorganus
This is the continental race. Records go back to the start of butterfly recording and this is one of the few butterflies noted by Gilbert White in his journals. He records individuals at Selborne on 2nd August 1780, 14th July 1782 and 18th August 1782, which suggests that the species may have been temporarily resident in the area at that time. This butterfly appears on rare occasions, Goater listing 15 with the latest in 1949. He also lists several records of larvae on carrot, parsnip and clover (Goater, 1974). The most notable year was 1945 (the 'Bath White Year') when a minimum of seven adults was recorded and larvae were found in at least five localities. Larvae were also found in a Lymington garden in 1984 (Goater, 1992).

In recent years, one in 1988 was listed in the Hampshire Butterfly Report amongst the "silly" records, but individuals of the continental race may well reach here on occasions. One appeared in 1990, another was at Queen Elizabeth Country Park on 11th September 1991, whilst a further individual was seen on nearby Wight in 1995.

Pale Clouded Yellow and Berger's Clouded Yellow
Colias hyale and *Colias alfacariensis*
Difficulties with identification mean that we do not really know the status of these two species in Hampshire. During the 1990s, there has not been a single record of either butterfly that has been established beyond all doubt. A male that was considered to be either a Pale or Berger's Clouded Yellow was seen by Brian Fletcher at Abbotstone Down on 15th October 1994. On 19th July 1995, a lemon-coloured male patrolled a flower-rich area at Magdalen Hill Down where Patrick Fleet was able to see that there was not enough black bordering on the wings for *croceus*; it was identified as either a Pale or Berger's Clouded Yellow. There were three 'possibles' in 1996 and it is also possible that either a Pale or Berger's Clouded Yellow was seen at Fort Gilkicker in October 1998.

Bath White
Pontia daplidice

In the 'Bath White Year' of 1945, considerable numbers of this rare migrant must have arrived in Hampshire, the invasion covering the entire Channel coast of England. Most Hampshire records came from the Bournemouth area. A steady flight to NNW against a light wind was recorded from 24th July–31st July, but when the wind veered to SW on 1st August, the flight direction changed to SW. Twenty-two were captured amongst thousands of *whites* in a 20-acre field; 10 or 15 were taken in a clover field on 1st/2nd August; 'many' were taken in late July and in the first week of August, all these captures being around Bournemouth. There is evidence that these immigrants produced a brood that emerged in late August/early September (all Goater, 1974).

Goater also notes that many were seen at Hayling Island in August 1859, three being taken, but apart from 1859 and 1945 there are only around a dozen records from the county, the last being at Bournemouth on 16th August 1958 (French, 1959), one at Fair Oak on 16th July 1984 (Goater, 1992) and one at Itchen Valley Country Park on 11th August 1991 (Barker and Williams, ED, 1991).

[Black Hairstreak]
Satyrium pruni
The Petersfield record, mentioned in *The Entomologist* during 1877, was in fact a misidentified White-letter Hairstreak (Goater, 1974). There has been a long history of introduction attempts in Hampshire, the first probably taking place in the New Forest during 1922 using stock from Monks Wood. There is also an undated 20th century record from Southampton (Heslop, 1958). Further introductions took place in the New Forest in 1969 and at the Bentley Station Meadow reserve in the early 1980s (Oates and Warren, 1990). There is evidence that further attempts may have been carried out around this time, but all appear to have been unsuccessful.

Introductions are still continuing. In April 1999, a contributor to an Internet Lepidoptera discussion group ("Nigel") claimed to have introduced the species to a wood adjacent to his house in south Hampshire using stock from an unspecified source. Such unofficial releases are highly irresponsible and do nothing for conservation.

[Large Copper]
Lycaena dispar batavus
In 1930, John Spedan Lewis wrote to the Lepidoptera Protection Committee of the (Royal) Entomological Society asking for approval to establish this butterfly on his private estate at Leckford. Approval was granted and a release apparently took place. No documentation was released and the attempt was presumably unsuccessful (Oates and Warren, 1990; Webb and Pullin, 1996).

[Green-underside Blue]
Glaucopsyche alexis
One reported in a Bournemouth garden in August 1988 may have been a misidentification (Taverner, Ed, 1995). There is one other British record of this non-migratory species (Heath and Emmett, 1976).

Long-tailed Blue
Lampides boeticus
Goater lists 17 between 1859 and 1953, six of these being in 1945 when Bath Whites invaded England (Goater, 1974). Subsequently, one was recorded at Highcliffe on 21st October 1985 and was not taken at actinic light as reported in Goater (1974), whilst in 1995, one was at Bartley on 30th August and one at the Lower Test Nature Reserve on 5th October (Taverner, Ed, 1995).

[Geranium Bronze]
Cacyreus marshalli
There was an unconfirmed report of this South African species in 1997 from the Gosport area. Now a widespread resident in the western Mediterranean, the first recorded in Britain was in Sussex during September of the same year.

Short-tailed Blue
Everes argiades
Goater lists three between 1885 and 1945 (Goater, 1974). Two of these were from Bournemouth, as are so many of the rare Hampshire species.

[*Chlosostrymon tela*]
An example of this South American lycaenid was found in a house at Bishop's Waltham on 7th March 1997. It is presumed to be an accidental import (Swift and Walker, 1998).

American Painted Lady
Vanessa virginiensis
One was seen at Christchurch on 30th August 1876, one of four to be seen in southern England in that year (Goater, 1974).

[Yellow-legged Tortoiseshell]
Nymphalis xanthomelas
This was introduced at North Baddesley in 1975 (Oates and Warren, 1990).

Camberwell Beauty
Nymphalis antiopa
The past saw some notable Camberwell Beauty years. Barrett (1893) notes that in 1793 the species was "as common as garden whites", that 1846 was known as "the Antiopa Year" and that in 1872, 17 were captured in Hampshire. Goater lists around 14 in the 19th century and 17 in the 20th century, the last of these in 1948 (Goater, 1974). This favourite with breeders and butterfly farms always makes records suspect, and no doubt many seen in Britain are not genuine migrants. Apparent releases

include one at Farnborough in 1986, one at Basingstoke in 1988 and six together at Straits Inclosure, Alice Holt Forest, on 20th July 1993.

In recent times there have been more frequent records, some of which are genuine immigrants and others obvious releases. In the Christchurch Harbour area, individuals were seen in 1975, 1976 and 1982.

The August 1995 records were part of a large invasion of Britain and there is no doubt that the following were real immigrants: one at Lyndhurst on 6th; one at Gosport on 11th; one at Southampton on 12th, 13th and 18th; one near Whitchurch on 18th; one at Bournemouth on 19th; one at Ringwood on 21st and 22nd; one landed briefly in a Drayton garden on 30th. There were also acceptable reports during August of one at Hengistbury Head and two by the Avon causeway. On 5th September, one was feeding on fallen fruit in the same Drayton garden that saw the 30th August specimen and another was reported by the Avon causeway in September.

One was seen at Fleet on 18th June 1996. In 1997, one was basking on a post at Hillier's Braishfield Arboretum on 16th April and one was at Old Alresford on 9th August. 1998 saw one in a Fareham garden on 4th July. There is no way of knowing whether or not these were genuine migrants, but there was no large invasion as there had been in 1995.

[Chinese Peacock]
Papilio bianor
Large numbers were released at Bagshot, Witley and elsewhere in June 1917. The butterfly bred successfully in at least two localities, at Liss, where females were seen ovipositing on *Choisya ternata*, and at Emsworth where it survived the winter and emerged in fair numbers in the following summer (Roig, 1918; Oates and Warren, 1990). An escape was reported in the county in 1990 (Hoskins, ED, 1990).

[European Map]
Araschnia levana
The species was released unsuccessfully in the New Forest in 1922 (Oates and Warren, 1990). A single specimen was seen by Hughie Todd in Alice Holt Forest in late May, 1988 (Hoskins, Ed, 1988).

[Cardinal]
Argynnis pandora
One was claimed in the New Forest in the 1950s (Howarth, 1973).

[Weaver's Fritillary]
Boloria dia
A specimen was alleged to have been captured near Christchurch on 27th July 1887. The specimen still exists in the Hope Department at Oxford (Heath and Emmett, 1976).

Queen of Spain Fritillary
Issoria lathonia
Six (four taken) were at Highcliffe in August 1899. Two were taken at Petersfield in July 1923. One was seen at Denny Bog on 20th June 1928. One was taken at Bournemouth on 11th September 1949 (all Goater, 1974). In recent years, one was reported at Hengistbury Head on 1st August 1988 and another at Martin Down on 2nd August 1997 (Hoskins, Ed, 1988 and Taverner, Ed, 1997).

[Niobe Fritillary]
Argynnis niobe
A specimen was supposedly captured at Lyndhurst in July 1868 flying with Dark Green Fritillaries. It was purchased from a

Mr Gerrard by the Rev Windsor Hamborough. To complicate matters, it seems as if the experts of those days could not agree on its identification (*The Entomologist*, Vol.4, 1869 and Vol.5, 1870).

[Heath Fritillary]
Melitaea athalia

Two specimens are in the collection of the British Entomological and Natural History Society labelled: "E.coll. Murray Gladstone, Swanmore, Hants circ 1830–1890".

There have also been a number of introduction attempts. Some 250 adults were put down by S.G. Castle-Russell at Bourley in 1925, but no colony appears to have resulted (Fassnidge, 1930). Castle-Russell also attempted an introduction at Longwood, near Owslebury, in 1931 (Hawker, 1978). There were unsuccessful attempts to introduce the species at Pamber Forest by G.B. Oliver around 1950 and by N.T. Easton around 1960, and also probably to other unknown north Hampshire sites in the 1950s. In 1957 the species still occurred in some north Hampshire woods and almost certainly represent these introductions (Richards, 1957). Several attempts to establish colonies in the New Forest were made in the 1950s, mainly by C.B. Antram. Two adults were seen in Woolmer Forest in 1966 (Goater, 1974) and more recently, the species became established in Pamber Forest for three seasons from 1979 and a few more were found in Roydon Woods in 1986 (Oates and Warren, 1990).

[The Large Silverstripe]
Childrena childreni

A specimen of this large Asian fritillary was taken in the New Forest around 1890 (Robertson, 1928). It is more normally found at altitudes between 1,600 and 3,200 m in the Himalayas.

Monarch
Danaus plexippus

Goater lists two in the 19th century and nine in the 20th century with the last of those in 1955 (Goater, 1974).

In 1981 there was a quite large invasion into Britain.

One on a Stockbridge window-sill in September 1991 was probably genuine as the date is right for migrants.

In 1995 there was an invasion of Monarchs that was probably greater than the 1981 influx. Around 170 were seen nationally and those who plotted the movement nationwide showed that the butterflies did originate in the United States. The main arrival in Britain was on 8th October and those seen in Hampshire were as follows: 6th August, one in a Winchester garden. This may have been an escape as the date was much earlier than the rest. One at Mortimer West End on 7th October. On 8th October there were single Monarchs at Southbourne, Needs Ore Point, Brownwich, Hedge End and Pennington. One was at Christchurch on 11th October; on 12th October two were at Keyhaven and one at Hurst and then on 13th October one flew south at Hurst. The last was on 17th October, at Needs Ore Point.

In 1996, one at Lymington on 23rd July may not have been a migrant due to the date, although its coastal position makes that possibility quite likely. In the same year, one was seen near Mudeford on 2nd October. There was a further invasion of England in 1999 and although five were seen on the Isle of Wight, there were no Hampshire records.

VERNACULAR AND SCIENTIFIC NAMES OF FLORA AND FAUNA

FLORA

Agrimony *Agrimonia eupatoria*
Alder Buckthorn *Frangula alnus*
Ash *Fraxinus excelsior*
Aspen *Populus tremula*
Aubrietia *Aubrieta* spp.
Autumn Hawkbit *Leontodon autumnalis*
Beech *Fagus sylvatica*
Bents *Agrostis* spp.
Bell Heather *Erica cinerea*
Betony *Stachys officinalis*
Bilberry *Vaccinium myrtillus*
Black Current *Ribes nigrum*
Black Medick *Medicago lupulina*
Black Mustard *Brassica nigra*
Blackthorn *Prunus spinosa*
Bluebell *Hyacinthoides non-scripta*
Bog-myrtle *Myrica gale*
Bracken *Pteridium aquilinum*
Bramble *Rubus fruticosus* agg.
Bristle Bent *Agrostis curtisii*
Broad-leaved Dock *Rumex obtusifolius*
Broom *Cytisus scoparius* ssp. *scoparius*
Buck's-horn Plantain *Plantago coronopus*
Buckthorns Rhamnaceae
Buckthorn *Rhamnus cathartica*
Buttercups *Ranunculus* spp.
Cat's-ear *Hypochaeris radicata*
Charlock *Sinapsis arvensis*
Clovers *Trifolium* spp.
Clustered Bellflower *Campanula glomerata*
Cock's-foot *Dactylis glomerata*
Common Bird's-foot-trefoil *Lotus corniculatus*
Common Cottongrass *Eriophorum angustifolium*
Common Couch *Elytrigia repens*
Common Dog-violet *Viola riviniana*
Common Fleabane *Pulicaria dysenterica*
Common Ivy *Hedera helix*
Common Knapweed *Centaurea nigra*
Common Mallow *Malva sylvestris*
Common Nettle *Urtica dioica*
Common Ragwort *Senecio jacobaea*
Common Rock-rose *Helianthemum nummularium*
Common Sorrel *Rumex acetosa*
Common Stork's-bill *Erodium cicutarium*
Cowslip *Primula veris*

Cranberry *Vaccinium oxycoccus*
Creeping Bent *Agrostis stolonifera*
Creeping Cinquefoil *Potentilla reptans*
Creeping Thistle *Cirsium arvense*
Creeping Soft-grass *Holcus mollis*
Cross-leaved Heath *Erica tetralix*
Crucifers Brassicaceae
Cuckooflower *Cardamine pratensis*
Cut-leaved Crane's-bill *Geranium dissectum*
Daffodils *Narcissus* spp.
Dame's-violet *Hesperis matronalis*
Dandelions *Taraxacum* spp.
Devil's-bit Scabious *Succisa pratensis*
Dog's Mercury *Mercurialis perennis*
Dogwood *Cornus sanguinea*
Dove's-foot Crane's-bill *Geranium molle*
Dyer's Greenweed *Genista tinctoria*
English Elm *Ulmus procera*
False Brome *Brachypodium sylvaticum*
False Oat-grass *Arrhenatherum elatius*
Fescue spp. *Festuca* spp.
Fine-leaved Sheep's-fescue *Festuca filiformis*
Flax *Linum usitatissimum*
Fool's Watercress *Apium nodiflorum*
Fragrant Orchid *Gymnadenia conopsea*
Garlic Mustard *Alliaria petiolata*
Gooseberry *Ribes uva-crispa*
Goosefoots *Chenopodium* spp.
Gorse *Ulex europaeus*
Great Sallow *Salix caprea* ssp. *caprea*
Greater Bird's-foot-trefoil *Lotus pedunculatus*
Greater Knapweed *Centaurea scabiosa*
Hairy Bird's-foot-trefoil *Lotus subbiflorus*
Hairy Rock-cress *Arabis hirsuta*
Hairy Violet *Viola hirta*
Hawkweed Ox-tongue *Picris hieracioides*
Hazel *Corylus avellana*
Heather *Calluna vulgaris*
Heathers Ericaceae
Hedge-bedstraw *Galium mollugo*
Hedge Mustard *Sisymbrium officinale*
Hemp-agrimony *Eupatorium cannabinum*
Hoary Cress *Cardaria draba*
Hogweed *Heracleum sphondylium* ssp. *sphondylium*
Holly *Ilex aquifolium*
Honesty *Lunaria annua*
Honeysuckle *Lonicera periclymenum*

Hop *Humulus lupulus*
Horse-radish *Armoracia rusticana*
Horseshoe Vetch *Hippocrepis comosa*
Ice Plants *Sedum* spp.
Kale Brassicaceae
Kidney Vetch *Anthyllis vulneraria*
Large Thyme *Thymus pulegioides*
Lesser Burdock *Arctium lappa*
Lesser Marshwort *Apium inundatum*
Leyland Cypress *Chamaecyparis* x *leylandii*
Lucerne *Melilotus sativa* ssp. *sativa*
Marjoram *Origanum vulgare*
Marsh Cudweed *Gnaphalium uliginosum*
Marsh Thistle *Cirsium palustre*
Meadow grasses *Poa* spp.
Nasturtium *Tropaeolum* spp.
Oaks *Quercus* spp.
Orchids Orchidaceae
Oxeye Daisy *Leucanthemum vulgare*
Pedunculate Oak *Quercus robur*
Primrose *Primula vulgaris*
Prickly Sow-thistle *Sonchus asper*
Purple Moor-grass *Molinia caerulea*
Ragged-Robin *Lychnis flos-cuculi*
Rape *Brassica napus*
Red Clover *Trifolium pratense*
Red Current *Ribes rubrum*
Red Fescue *Festuca rubra*
Ribwort Plantain *Plantago lanceolata*
Rough Hawkbit *Leontodon hispidus*
Rowan *Sorbus aucuparia*
Rusty Sallow *Salix cinerea* ssp. *oleifolia*
Salad Burnet *Sanguisorba minor* ssp. *minor*
Sallows *Salix* spp.
Scabious Dipsacaceae
Scots Pine *Pinus sylvestris*
Sea Campion *Silene uniflora*
Sea Couch *Elytrigia atherica*
Sea-holly *Eryngium maritimum*
Sea Mouse-ear *Cerastium diffusum*
Sessile Oak *Quercus petraea*
Sheep's-fescue *Festuca ovina*
Sheep's Sorrel *Rumex acetosella* ssp. *acetosella*
Silver Birch *Betula pendula*
Slender Thistle *Carduus tenuiflorus*
Small Nettle *Urtica urens*
Small Scabious *Scabiosa columbaria*
Smith's Pepperwort *Lepidium heterophyllum*
Smooth-leaved Elm *Ulmus carpinifolia*
Springbeauty *Claytonia perfoliata*
Strawberry-tree *Arbutus unedo*
Sweet Chestnut *Castanea sativa*
Sycamore *Acer pseudoplatanus*

Tall Fescue *Festuca arundinacea*
Thale Cress *Arabidopsis thaliana*
Thistle spp. *Cirsium* spp. and *Carduus* spp.
Thrift *Armeria maritima*
Timothy *Phleum pratense*
Tor-grass *Brachypodium pinnatum*
Tormentil *Potentilla erecta*
Traveller's-joy *Clematis vitalba*
Trefoils *Lotus* spp.
Tufted Hair-grass *Deschampsia cespitosa*
Tufted Vetch *Vicia cracca*
Turkey Oak *Quercus cerris*
Upright Brome *Bromopsis erecta*
Viper's-bugloss *Echium vulgare*
Watercress *Rorripa* spp.
Wavy Bitter-cress *Cardamine flexuosa*
Wavy Hair-grass *Deschampsia flexuosa*
Wayfaring-tree *Viburnum lantana*
White Clover *Trifolium repens*
White Currant *Ribes rubrum* (var. *album*)
Wild Basil *Clinopodium vulgare*
Wild Cabbage *Brassica oleracea*
Wild Cherry *Prunus avium*
Wild Gladiolus *Gladiolus illyricus*
Wild Mignonette *Reseda lutea*
Wild Privet *Ligustrum vulgare*
Wild Strawberry *Fragaria vesca*
Wild Teasel *Dipsacus fullonum*
Wood-sedge *Carex sylvatica*
Wych Elm *Ulmus glabra*
Yorkshire-fog *Holcus lanatus*

Fungi
Stinkhorn *Phallus impudicus*

FAUNA

Mammals
Fallow Deer *Dama dama*
Przewalski's Wild Horse *Equus terus przewalskii*
Rabbit *Oryctolagus cuniculus*

Birds
Great Bustard *Otis tarda*
Magpie *Pica pica*
Pheasant *Phasianus colchicus*
Red-footed Falcon *Falco vespertinus*

Insects
Hoverflies *Syrphidae* spp
Silver Y *Autographa gamma*
Six-spot Burnet *Zygaena filipendulae stephensi*

APPENDIX TWO

LIST OF OBSERVERS

R. Abbot
Mr & Mrs Acock
Sean Adams
Alan Albery
Greg Alexander
Chris Allen
John Anderson
C. Archbold
Graham Armstrong
Ivan Arnold
Doris Ashby
Alasdair Aston
R. Aston
Daphne Austin
Miss N. Bacciu
Joyce Baigent
Ted Baigent
Eric Bailey
June Bailey
Ken Bailey
Steve Bailey
Ted Bailey
Anthony Baines
Brian Baker
D. Baker
Ivor Baker
Janet Baker
Mike Baker
S. Baker
David Ball
Geoff Bantock
Dr Andy Barker
Linda Barker
George Barrett
Esme Bartlett
Graham Bathe
Kim Batten
Peter Beale
Patricia Bell
Reg Bell
Mark Bennett
Tim Bernhard
Lionel Bidwell
David Billett
Norman Binstead
Graham Birkett
Rex Black
Brian Blacker
G. Blake

Stephen Blaskett
T. Blee
Juliet Bloss
A.C. Blunden
Alison Bolton
Chris Bolton
Peter Bonnington
Steve Bonnington
Robin Boston
Lyn Boswell
Dr Paul Boswell
Chris Boulton
Mike Boxall
Rosemary Boyes
Mr & Mrs C. Bradley
Ian Bradwell
Tom Brerton
C. Brett
Melvyn Brickwood
Dr Roger Bristow
Linda Broad
Anne-Marie Broadway
Holly Broadway
Rupert Broadway
Sharron Broadway
Pat Brockway
Andrew Brookes
Les Broomfield
I.H. Brown
Nicholas Brown
Paul Browning
Peter Bruce-Jones
Mrs Margaret Bruton
Michael Bryant
Phil Budd
Mrs S. Bulman
Peter Burford
Rev C.B. Burland
David Burton
T.A. Burton
Patrick Carden
Ches Carpenter
Richard Carpenter
Margaret Carr
Tim Carr
Karen Cartwright
Mike Cartwright
J. Caws
John Chainey

Bob Chapman
R.A. Chapman
Mrs S. Charleton
Clive Chatters
John Cheyney
Marina Christopher
Abigail Chuter
Adrian Clark
Barry Clark
Jane Clark
John Clark
Mrs S.F. Clark
Sue Clark
Dr Julian Clarke
Dr Susan Clarke
Peter Clarkson
A.Claxton
Richard Clifford
Chris Cockburn
Anastacia Collins
Dr Andrew Collins
Barry Collins
C.B. Collins
Mrs S.A. Collins
John Coltart
Elizabeth Cook
Ralph Cook
Richard Coomber
Yvonne Cooper
Ian Cornish
Robert Coyne
Nicky Court
Peter Cramp
Ruth Croger
Ian Cunningham
Gerry Cushen
Martin Davey
Paul Davies
Tony Davis
Andrew Daw
Alan Dawson
Caroline Dawson
David Dell
Jean Dell
Graham Dennis
J. Densley
David Dicks
Dr Richard Dickson
David Dimmock

J.N. Dixon
Tony Dobson
P.J. Dominy
W. Donnea
Malcolm Dougal
John Dove
John Dover
Winston Downer
Brian Downey
Sue Downey
Barry Duffin
Gerard Dunniece
Pete Durnell
K. East
M.A. Easterbrook
Ron Eastman
B. Edgeworth
Bob Edmunds
Henry Edmunds
Rob Edmunds
John Edwards
Keith Edwards
Mary Edwards
Wing Cmdr Barry Elford
Mary Elliot
Sue Ellis
Mrs B. Elmore
D.G. Evans
Glynne Evans
Justin Evans
Julia Fairhall
Mrs R. Featherstone
Brian Fellows
Alan Ferguson
Graham Ferguson
Ian Ferguson
Mark Ferguson
Mick Finnemore
J. Fleet
Patrick Fleet
Brian Fletcher
Marion Fletcher
Jim Flight
Geoff Flower
Lynn Fomison
Paul Fomison
Paul Forecast
Dr Barry Fox
Richard Fox

B. Frampton
Colin Frost
David Fuller
Mike Fuller
Tim Gabriel
Mrs J. Gaffney
Hillary Gallagher
Mike Gallagher
Mr & Mrs Galton
Pat Gardner
Peter Gardner
Dr A.M. George
Melanie Gibbons
Mike Gibbons
Bob Giddings
Edwin Gifford
Joyce Gifford
Warren Gilchrist
Leigh Glover
J. Gloyn
Barry Goater
Rachel Godden
Robert Godden
Dr Keith Godfrey
David Goodall
Madge Goodall
D.P. Goodban
Bob Gorley
Mrs Fran Goswell
R.A. Gough
Sir Irvine Goulding
Nick Greatorex-Davies
Adam Green
Dr Alan Green
David Green
Richard Green
Arthur Greenwood
J.M. Greenwood
Mark Griffiths
M.J. Groom
Dr Robert Guest
Mary Gwilliam
Mike Gwilliam
Catherine Hack
Eric Hale
Chris Hall
Martin Hall
Patricia Hall
Bruce Halliday
Phil Halliwell
Elaine Hardy
Gordon Hardy
A. Hargrove
G. Hargrove
Kaye Harman
Alex Harmer

Alison Harper
Mrs M.A. Hart
David Hart
R.H. Hart
Jill Harvey
Martin Harvey
Stephen Harvey
Stephen Harwood
Geoff Hawkins
Anne Hayter
Don Hayter
Mrs Cicely Heathers
Brian Hedley
Bill Hellyar
A.G. Henderson
M.C. Henderson
Willie Henderson
Glyn Henwood
B.E.T. Herbert
Greg Herbert
Roger Herbert
J. Heritage
Geraldine Hicks
Neale Hider
P. Higginson
Tony Hiles
Hugh Hill
Barry Hilling
Robert Hoare
J. Hobbs
Donald Hobern
Alan Hold
Audrey Hold
Norman Holland
Ralph Hollins
Michael Holroyd
Christopher Holt
P.A. Hooper
Adrian Hoskins
Terry Hotten
D. Housley
Donald Hubern
K.D. Hughes
Dr Richard Hughes
John Hunt
Arthur Hurrell
Norman Hutchinson
Howard Inns
June Irvine
Brian Ivon-Jones
Hazel Jackson
Robert Jackson
P. Jacobs
Nigel James
Tony James
M. Jeffes

Dr Derek Jenkins
R.W. Jenkins
Terry Jennings
Amelia Jessell
Janet Jones
John Jones
Mark Joyce
Steve Keen
Jennifer Kelsey
Rev Michael Kelsey
Lois Kennedy
S. King
Tony King
Charlotte Kirtley
Fiona Kirtley
Steve Kirtley
Christine Knight
Alfred Knott
B. Lambert
Dr G.R. Lane
Roger Lane
Roy Lane
David Langley
Rosemary Langley
Dr John Langmaid
Martin Laux
D.C. Lawman
Tony Lear
F.H. Le Breton
John Leckie
Derrick Lees
Gordon Le Pard
Tony Leveson-Gower
Richard Levett
Mark Litjens
Ian Livermore
John Lobb
Alan Long
Derek Longe
Bob Lord
Phil Lord
Ian Loveday
R. Lowe
Amber Lowndes
R. McCartney
Anne McCue
John Maddocks
Jenny Mallett
Keith Marsden
Barbara Martin
Mr & Mrs K.J. Martin
Loraine Martin
Peter Martin
Colin Matthews
Miss H. Maybee
Guy Meredith

Paula Metherell
Mark Middleton
Sarah Miles
Fleurette Millar
D.L.H. Miller
Celia Millington
Mr & Mra B. Mills
Jeremy Mitchell
N.D. Mitchell
David Molyneaux
Denise Molyneaux
Dr John Moon
Charlie Morris
Malcolm Morton
D. Moteane
John Moulam
Carol Munday
Tony Mundell
N. Mutch
Denis Nash
Joy Nation
Iris Newbury
Ron Newbury
Mark Newell
Mrs S. Newell
Mrs S. Newman
John Norledge
Tim Norriss
Bill Norton
R.R. Noyce
Lucina Oates
Matthew Oates
Sally Oates
Maurice Opie
Mrs H. Osborne
Pete Owens
Andy Page
E.J. Pain
Jess Pain
Keith Palmer
M. Palmer
Sarah Palmer
Susan Palmer
Dave Paradise
Andy Parfitt
Ron Parfitt
Sue Parish
Naomi Patterson
David Payne
David Peach
Pauline Peach
Steve Peach
Nigel Pearce-Smith
Connie Pelham
Chris Pengelly
Dave Perkins

A.B. Petrie
John Phillips
John Phillips
Peggy Phillips
Chris Piatkiewicz
Tony Pickles
M. Pickworth
Bryan Pinchen
Stuart Pittman
Keith Plumridge
Jane Plumridge
Rod Pointer
B. Pollinger
Paul Potten
Peter Potts
Rev Ted Pratt
Mike Pratt
Annette Price
Barry Proctor
C. Proudley
Kevin Quay
Ian Rabjohns
J. Ralph
Ian Ralphs
Brian Ransom
Geoff Rapley
M. Raven
Penny Raynor
Ted Raynor
Alison Redman
David Reed
Richard Reeves
Dr Mary Rice
Ron Richardson
M. Riddett
M. Riddy
Sean Rider
Dr Adrian Riley
Fiona Roberts
Graham Roberts
Maureen Roberts
Dr Mark Roberts
Dr Theo Roberts
Tony Roberts
T. Robertson
D. Robinson
Geoff Robinson
Terry Rolf
Jo Rood
C. Rose
John Rowe
Mike Rowe
Steve Rudge
C. Rudgley
Philip Rushworth

Stuart Rushworth
Mrs C.K. Russell
Richard Ryan
Alan Sadgrove
Henry Sanderson
Mrs P. Saul
M.J. Schmieder
Janette Schubert
Mick Scott
Roy Scott
Pete Selby
Fran Sewell
Peter Sewell
David Sharrod
Mrs J.E. Shaw
Jane Sheehan
Paul Sheehan
Peter Sheehan
D. & C. Shepperson
M.Shore
Andy Silcocks
Eileen Simons
N.M. Sims
Nick Sival
Michael Skelton
Bernard Skinner
Dr Ian Small
Peter Small
A.C. Smallbone
Robert Smallman
Di Smith
Linda Smith
Mark Smith
Michael Smith
Mrs M. Smith
N. Smith
Pete Smith
Col & Mrs Peter Smith
R. Smith
S. Smith
Richard Smout
Andrew Southwell
Graham Sparshott
Avril Spears
Clare Spears
Jenny Spence
John Spence
Dr S. Spencer
Steve Stagg
Andrew Stanbury
P.A. Stancliffe
Peter Stannard
Ian Staples
Tony Steele
Keith Stevens

Chris Stock
Peter Strangeman
Margaret Stratford
Miss M. Summers
Andy Swash
Stewart Swift
Keith Talbot
John Taverner
Pat Taverner
Stephen Taverner
Terri Taverner
Chris Taylor
Graham Taylor
Marilyn Taylor
Jackie Taylor
Derek Telfer
Susan Telfer
David Thelwell
Ian Thirlwell
Marion Thomas
Maureen Thomas
Ray Thomason
Sally Tiller
Dr David Tinling
John Tinling
Hughie Todd
Mrs J.M. Todd
Pat Torrie
C. Townsend
Paul Townsend
Paul Toynton
Richard Tratt
D. Treacher
A.V. Trickey
R. Trim
Joan Truckle
K. Tulett
Elizabeth Tunnah
J. Tutt
Tony Tutton
Chris Tyler-Smith
Brenda Varley
Dr Margaret Vickery
Norman Villiers
Darren Walker
Paul Waring
J. Warren
Paul Warren
Mr & Mrs P.R. Watkins
Mr & Mrs P. Weakley
Mr & Mrs G.M. Weam
Mike Wearing
C. Webb
Tracy Webb
Patrick Webster

Brian Weeks
Andrew Welch
Pam Welch
Peter Welch
Noelle Welstead
Tony Welstead
Horace West
Val Weston
Sylvia Whalley
Robert Wheatley
Yvonne Wheeler
D.F. White
R. White
Susan Whitewick
Mr Alan Whitlock
Val Whitlock
Ashley Whitlock
Edwin Wilcox
Mike Wildish
Audrey Wilkinson
C.Willcox
Mrs J.R. Williams
Nicola Williams
John Willmott
Ken Willmott
E.W. Wills
Keith Wills
S.M. Wills
Jackie Wilson
David Wincott
Ivan Winslow
Leslie Winslow
R. Winspear
Tim Winter
John Wood
Michael Wood
Lt Col W.G. Wood
B. Woods
P. Woods
R.J. Woodward
Simon Woolley
Helen Worrell
John Worrell
Michael Wright
Mrs A.E. Wylie
L. Yates
George Yorke
Kevin Young
P. Young
Dr Simon Young

Our apologies for any
omissions.

REFERENCES

Allan, P.B.M. (1952). Current notes. *Entomologist's Rec. J. Var.* **64**: 151.

Allan, P.B.M. (1980). *Leaves from a moth-hunter's notebook.* E.W. Classey.

Anon, (n.d.). *Worldwide butterflies catalogue.* Worldwide butterflies, Dorset.

Asher, J., Fox, R., Harding, P., Jeffcoate, G., Jeffcoate, S. and Warren, M.S. (in press). *The millennium atlas of butterflies.* Oxford University Press.

Bacon, A.F.L. (1944). *P. aegeria* in North Hampshire. *Entomologist* **77**: 96.

Barker, A.J. and Barker, L.J. (1993). *Aspects of ovipositing and conservation of the Brown Argus butterfly.* Butterfly Conservation International Symposium "Ecology and Conservation of Butterflies". Keele University UK. Abstract volume: 18.

Barker, A.J. and Budd, P.A. (1997). *Butterflies of Southampton.* Butterfly Conservation (Hampshire & Isle of Wight Branch).

Barker, A.J. and Williams, L.J. (ed.) (1992). *Hampshire & the Isle of Wight butterfly report 1991.* Butterfly Conservation (Hampshire & Isle of Wight Branch).

Barker, A.J. and Williams, L.J. (ed.) (1993). *Hampshire & the Isle of Wight butterfly report 1992.* Butterfly Conservation (Hampshire & Isle of Wight Branch).

Barnett, L.K. and Warren, M.S. (1995a). *Species action plan: Pearl-bordered Fritillary, Boloria euphrosyne.* Butterfly Conservation, Wareham.

Barnett, L.K. and Warren, M.S. (1995b). *Species action plan: Small Pearl-bordered Fritillary, Boloria selene.* Butterfly Conservation, Wareham.

Barrett, C.G. (1893). *The Lepidoptera of the British islands: Volume one.* L. Reeve & Co.

Bibby, T. (1983). Oviposition by the Brimstone butterfly, *Gonepteryx rhamni* (L.), (Lepidoptera: Pieridae) in Monks Wood, Cambridgeshire in 1982. *Entomologist's Gazette* **34**: 229–234.

Blackwood, J.W. and Tubbs, C.R. (1970). A quantitative survey of chalk grassland in England. *Biological Conservation* **3**, No. 1.

Bourn, N.A.D. and Warren, M.S. (1998). *Species action plan: Duke of Burgundy, Hamearis lucina.* Butterfly Conservation, Wareham.

Bramwell, F.G.S. (1919). *Apatura iris* at sea near Brighton. *Entomologist* **52**: 257.

Brereton, T.M. (1997). *Ecology and conservation of the butterfly Pyrgus malvae, (Grizzled Skipper) in south-east England.* Unpublished PhD Thesis, University of East London.

Bretherton, C.B. (1951). Our lost butterflies and moths. *Entomologist's Gazette* **2**: 211–240.

Brewis, A., Bowman, P. and Rose, F. (1996). *The flora of Hampshire.* Harley Books.

Buckell, W.R. (1892). New Forest – Collecting notes. *Entomologist's Rec. J. Var.* **3**: 264.

Buckler. (1877). *Colias edusa* in Hants. *Entomologist's Monthly Magazine.* **9**: 40–41.

Burkhardt, V. R. (1943) New Forest Rhopalocera in 1943. *Entomologist's Rec. J. Var.* 55

BUTT (Butterflies under threat team). (1986). *The management of chalk grassland for butterflies.* Focus on nature conservation No. 17. Nature Conservancy Council.

Castle Russell S.G. (1895). The Rhopalocera of Fleet (north Hants) and district. *Entomologist* **28**: 194–195.

Castle Russell, S.G. (1942). The occasional scarcity and abundance of Lepidoptera, with special reference to the Rhopalocera. *Proc. Trans. S. London Ent. Nat. hist. Soc.* 1942-43: 40–47.

Castle Russell, S.G. (1944). New Forest and district notes. *Entomologist's Rec. J. Var.* **56**:

Castle Russell, S.G. (1952). The New Forest in the nineties and after. *Entomologist's Rec. J. Var.* **64**: 138–144.

Castle Russell, S.G. (1955). Phenomenal numbers of Rhopalocera larvae and imagines. *Entomologist's Rec. J. Var.* **67**: 111–113.

Chatfield, J. (1987). *F. W. Frohawk: his life and work.* Crowood Press.

Christchurch Harbour Ornithological Group. (1990–1999). *The birds of Christchurch harbour.* Privately published.

Clark, J.M. and Eyre, J.A. (1993). *Birds of Hampshire.* Hampshire Ornithological Society.

Colebourn, P. (1983). *Hampshire's countryside heritage: Ancient woodland.* Hampshire County Council.

Corbet, A.S. (1916). The butterflies of the south Salisbury downs. *Entomologist* **49**: 236.

Corbet, A.S. (1921). Butterflies on the south Salisbury downs. *Entomologist* **54**: 295–296.

Corbet, A.S. (1923). Lepidoptera of the south Salisbury downs. *Entomologist* **56**: 238.

Dale J.C. (ms). *Entomological journal and diary, 1806 to 1871.*

Demuth, R.P. (1927). *Polygonia c-album* on the Hants and Dorset border. *Entomologist* **16**: 16.

Dickson, R. (ed.) (1977). *The 1976 records of the Fareham group of entomologists, Lepidoptera: butterflies and moths.* Privately published.

Dickson, R. (ed.) (1978). *The 1977 records of the Fareham group of entomologists, Lepidoptera: butterflies and moths.* Privately published.

Dobson, A.H. (1977). The Queen of Spain Fritillary (*Argynnis lathonia* L.) at Bournemouth. *Entomologist's Rec. J. Var.* **99**: 78.

Donisthorpe, H. (1918). A fortnight in the New Forest in July. *Entomologist's Rec. J. Var.* **30**: 170–173.

Dyson, R.C. (1950). Butterflies in 1950. *Entomologist* **83**: 214.

Emmet, A.M. and Heath, J. (ed.) (1989). *The moths and butterflies of Great Britain and Ireland.* 7, part 2. Harley Books.

Fassnidge, W. (1923–24). *List of the macro-lepidoptera of Hampshire and the Isle of Wight.* The entomological society of Hampshire and the Isle of Wight.

Fassnidge, W. (1930) Additions and corrections to the lists of Lepidoptera of Hampshire and the Isle of Wight. *Trans. Ent. Soc. S. Engl.* **6**: 126–136.

Fuller, M. (1995). *The butterflies of Wiltshire.* Pisces publications.

Ford, E.B. (1945). *Butterflies.* Collins New Naturalist, London.

Fowler, J.H. (1893). Variation of Lepidoptera at Ringwood 1891–92. *Entomologist* **26**: 229.

Fraser, F.C. (1946). Ravages of the larvae of *Pieris brassicae* during the late immigration of Pieridae. *Journ. Soc. Brit. Ent.* **3**: 21.

Fraser, F.C. (1961). The changing character of the New Forest. *Entomologist's Rec. J. Var.* **73**: 129–131.

French, R.A. (1959). Migration records 1958. *Entomologist* **92**: 164–176.

Frohawk, F.W. (1934). *The complete book of British butterflies.* Ward, Lock & Company, Limited. London.

Frohawk, F.W. (1938). *Varieties of British butterflies.* Ward, Lock & Company, Limited. London.

Gaunt, D. (1937). Notes on butterflies 1932–1936. *Winchester College Natural History Society Report 1931–1936*: 33–34.

Goater, B. (1974). *The butterflies and moths of Hampshire and the Isle of Wight.* E.W. Classey.

Goater, B. (1992). *The butterflies and moths of Hampshire and the Isle of Wight: additions and corrections.* UK Nature Conservation No. 7. JNCC.

Goss, H. (1877). Is *Aporia crataegi* extinct in England? *Entomologist's Mon. Mag.* **23**: 217–220.

Goss, H., Fletcher, W.H.B. and Reid, S. in Doubleday, H.A. (ed.) (1900). *The Victoria history of the counties of England. Hampshire and the Isle of Wight.*

Haines, F.H. (1929). The New Forest as a nature reserve. *Entomologist's Rec. J. Var.* **41**: 161–162.

Hambrough, W. (1869). *Argynnis niobe* in the New Forest. *Entomologist* **18**: 351.

Hambrough, W. (1870). *Argynnis niobe* in the New Forest. *Entomologist* **19**: 16–17.

Harvey, R. and Harvey, A.S. (1857a). Captures at Lyndhurst. *Entomologist's Weekly Intelligencer.* **2**: 125.

Harvey, R. and Harvey, A.S. (1857b). *Steropes Paniscus. Entomologist's Weekly Intelligencer.* **2**: 125.

Hawker, P.C. (1952). *Carterocephalus palaemon* Pall. in Hampshire. *Entomologist's Rec. J. Var.* **64**: 215.

Hawker, P. (1978). Great collectors of the 1930s. *Entomologist's Rec. J. Var.* **90**: 321–324.

HCC. (1991). *Hampshire's countryside heritage. 2: Ancient woodland.* Hampshire County Council.

Heath, J. and Emmet, A.M. (ed.) (1989). *The moths and butterflies of Great Britain and Ireland.* 7 pt1. Harley Books.

Heslop, I.R.P. (1929). *Thymelicus lineola* in Dorset and the New Forest. *Entomologist* **62**: 137.

Heslop, I.R.P. (1958). *The butterflies of Blackmoor Copse Nature Reserve.* Unpublished survey.

Heslop, I.R.P. (1964). *Apatura iris* (Lep. Nymphalidae) in the New Forest. *Entomologist* **97**: 51.

Heslop, I.R.P., Hyde, G.E. and Stockley, R.E. (1964). *Notes and views of the Purple Emperor.* Southern Publishing, Brighton.

Hesseltine, G. (1888). *Apatura iris* in Hants. *Entomologist* **21**:209–210.

Holloway P.H. (1952). Butterfly hunting in Park Hills, Hampshire. *Entomologist's Rec. J. Var.* **64**: 317–318.

Hoskins, A.J. (ed.) (1989). *Hampshire butterfly report 1988.* British Butterfly Conservation Society (Hampshire Branch).

Hoskins, A.J. (ed.) (1990). *Hampshire and the Isle of Wight butterfly report 1989.* British Butterfly Conservation Society (Hampshire & Isle of Wight Branch).

Hoskins, A.J. (ed.) (1991). *Hampshire and the Isle of Wight butterfly report 1990.* Butterfly Conservation (Hampshire & Isle of Wight Branch).

Howarth, T.G. (1973). *South's British butterflies.* Warne.

Hudson, W.H. (1903). *Hampshire days.* Longman, Green & Co., London.

Huxley, J. and Carter, D.J. (1981). A blue form of the Small Skipper, *Thymelicus flavus* (Bruennich) (Lepidoptera: Hesperiidae), with comments on colour production. *Entomologist's Gazette* **32**: 79–82.

Jackson, S. (1944). Further notes on the spread on *Pararge aegeria* in Hampshire. *Entomologist* **77**: 158.

Johnston, J. (1998). *Biodiversity action plan for Hampshire. Volume one.* Hampshire Biodiversity Partnership.

Jones, H.P. (1920). 1919 in the New Forest. *Entomologist* **53**: 5–10.

Joy, J. (1995). *Heathland management for the silver-studded blue butterfly.* English Nature pamphlet.

Karshalt O. and Razowski J. (1996). *The Lepidoptera of Europe: A distributional checklist.* Apollo Books, Senstrup.

Kershaw, S.H. (1958). Some memories of S. G. Castle Russell. *Entomologist's Rec. J. Var.* **70**: 1–4, 237–241.

Lewcock. (1888). Notes on the collecting season of 1887. *The Young Naturalist.* 48–53.

Lister, J.J. (1918). Butterfly Hunting in the New Forest and elsewhere in 1917. *Entomologist* **50**: 51–56.

Lofthouse, T.A. (1902). Lepidoptera etc., in the New Forest in June 1902. *Entomologist's Rec. J. Var.* **14**: 272–274.

Luckens, C.J. (1977). Observations on British butterflies in 1976. *Entomologist's Rec. J. Var.* **89**: 172.

Marcon, J.A. (1980). Further reminiscences of a butterfly hunter. *Entomologist's Rec. J. Var.* **92**: 34–37.

Moon, J.F. (1857). Doings in Hampshire. *Entomologist's Weekly Intelligencer.* **2**: 117 and 172.

Morris F.O. (1853). *A history of British butterflies.* John C. Nimmo, London.

Newman, E. (1871). *An illustrated history of British butterflies.* William Tweedie, London.

Nicholson, C. (1912). New Forest notes 1911. *Entomologist* **45**: 158.

Oates, M.R. (1983a). The coming of the Clouded Yellow. *The Field*. November 12th 1983: 1058.

Oates, M.R. (1983b). Return of the Clouded Yellow. *Hampshire Magazine*. **23**: 12: 46–47.

Oates, M.R. (ed.) (1983c). Clouded days and Clouded Yellows. *British Butterfly Conservation Society (Hampshire Branch) Newsletter* No. 6.

Oates, M.R. (ed.) (1983d). "Until the sun breaks down". Review of Hampshire butterflies during the summer of 1983. *British Butterfly Conservation Society (Hampshire Branch) Newsletter* No. 7.

Oates, M.R. (1985). *Garden plants for butterflies*. Brian Masterton Associates, Farnham.

Oates, M.R. (ed.) (1986). *Hampshire butterfly report*. British Butterfly Conservation Society (Hampshire Branch).

Oates, M.R. (ed.) (1987). *Hampshire butterfly report*. British Butterfly Conservation Society (Hampshire Branch).

Oates, M.R. (1996). The demise of butterflies in the New Forest. *British Wildlife* **7** No. 4.

Oates, M.R. (2000). Conserving the intractable – The Duke of Burgundy Fritillary. *British Wildlife*. **11**, No. 4.

Oates, M.R. and Warren, M.S. (1990). *A review of butterfly introductions in Britain and Ireland*. JCCB/WWF.

Pearce, W.T. (1890). Contributions to the entomology of the Portsmouth district. *Entomologist* **23**: 227–231.

Piffard, B. (1902). Lymington and its insects. *Entomologist's Rec. J. Var.* **14**: 287–289.

Pitman, C.M.R. (1960). The march of progress. *Entomologist's Rec. J. Var.* **72**: 49–60.

Pitman, C.M.R. (1963). The New Forest that was. *Entomologist's Rec. J. Var.* **75**: 187–199.

Pollard, E. (1979). Population ecology and change in range of the White Admiral, *Ladoga camilla*, in England. *Ecological Entomology*, **4**: 61–74.

Porter, K. (1983). Multivoltinism in *Apanteles bignellii* and the influence of weather on synchronisation with its host *Eurodryas aurinia*. *Entomologia exp. appl.* **34**: 155–162.

Pratt, C.R. (1983). A modern view of the demise of *Aporia crataegi* L.: the Black-veined White. *Entomologist's Rec. J. Var.* **95**: 45–52, 161–166, 232–237.

Pratt, C.R. (1986). A history and investigation into the fluctuations of *Polygonia c-album* L.: the Comma butterfly. *Entomologist's Rec. J. Var.* **98**: 197–203, 244–250.

Pratt, C.R. (1987). A history and investigation into the fluctuations of *Polygonia c-album* L.: the Comma butterfly. *Entomologist's Rec. J. Var.* **99**: 21–27, 69–80.

Prescott, R. (1983). *Hampshire's countryside heritage: Chalk grasslands*. Hampshire County Council.

Richards, A.W. (1943). Extension of habitat of *Pararge aegeria* in N. Hampshire. *Entomologist* **79**: 224.

Richards, A.W. (1949). Lepidoptera in N. E. Hants, 1949. *Entomologist* **82**: 278.

Richards, A.W. (1957). Lepidoptera of the Aldershot district of north-east Hampshire. *Entomologist's Rec. J. Var.* **69**: 114–117, 140–143, 177–180 and 202–204.

Rivenhall Goffe, E. (1932). The Rev. A. J. Richards' collection of British Lepidoptera. *Journal of the entomological society of the south of England* **1**: 45.

Rivenhall Goffe, E. (1944). Extension of habitat of *P. aegeria* in Hants. *Entomologist* **77**: 60.

Robertson, W.O. (1928). *Argynnis childreni* Gray, in Hampshire. *Trans. Hampshire Ent Soc.*, 1928 (4): 21.

Roig, F.J. (1918). *Papilio bianor*, Cram., in Hampshire. *Entomologist* **51**: 212–213.

Russwurm, A.D.A. (1978). *Aberrations of British butterflies*. E.W. Classey.

Saundby, R. (1948). Collecting in 1947. *Proc. Trans. S. London Ent. Nat. Hist. Soc.* 1948–49: 197.

Saundby, R. (1951). Lepidoptera in Hampshire, 1948. *Pap. Proc. Hamps. Fld Club* **17**: 348

Sheldon, W.G. (1923). The destruction of British butterflies: A suggested remedy. *Entomologist* **58**: 105–112.

Skelton, M. (1999). Successful overwintering by Clouded Yellow *Colais croceus* (Geoff.) in southern England. *Atropos* No. 8: 3–6.

South, R. (1906). *The butterflies of the British Isles*. Frederick Warne & Co. Ltd.

Snell, B.B. (1925). *Agriades corydon* in the New Forest. *Entomologist* **58**: 249.

Sperring, A.H. (1952) *Carterocephalus palaemon* Pall. in Hampshire. *Entomologist's Rec. J. Var.* **64**: 215–216.

Spooner. (1963). On causes of the decline of *Maculinea arion* L. (Lep. Lycaenidae) in Britain. *Entomologist* **96**: 199–210.

Stace, C.A. (1991). *New flora of the British Isles*. Cambridge University Press.

Stokes, J. (1988). Pollination of the wild gladiolus (*Gladiolus illyricus*) in the New Forest, Hampshire by butterflies. *British Butterfly Conservation Society News*. **41**: 38–39.

Stowell, E.A.C. (1924). Entomology in the Alton district. *Trans. Hamps. Ent. Soc.* **1**: 21–28.

Swift, S. and Walker, D. (1998). [Exhibit at BENHS Annual Exhibition, 1997] *Br. J. Ent. Nat Hist.* **11**: 83.

Symes, H. (1961). Impressions of the New Forest in 1961 and before. *Entomologist's Rec. J. Var.* **73**: 182–186.

Tatchell, S. (1916). *Apatura iris* at Bournemouth. *Entomologist* **49**: 214.

Taverner, J.H. (ed.) (1994). *Hampshire and the Isle of Wight butterfly report 1993*. Butterfly Conservation (Hampshire & Isle of Wight Branch).

Taverner, J.H. (ed.) (1995). *Hampshire and the Isle of Wight butterfly and moth report 1994*. Butterfly Conservation (Hampshire & Isle of Wight Branch).

Taverner, J.H. (ed.) (1996). *Hampshire and the Isle of Wight butterfly and moth report 1995*. Butterfly Conservation (Hampshire & Isle of Wight Branch).

Taverner, J.H. (ed.) (1997). *Hampshire and the Isle of Wight butterfly and moth report 1996*. Butterfly Conservation (Hampshire & Isle of Wight Branch).

Taverner, J.H. (ed.) (1998). *Hampshire and the Isle of Wight butterfly and moth report 1997*. Butterfly Conservation (Hampshire & Isle of Wight Branch).

Taverner, J.H. (ed.) (1999). *Hampshire and the Isle of Wight butterfly and moth report 1998.* Butterfly Conservation (Hampshire & Isle of Wight Branch).

Taverner, J.H. (ed.) (2000). *Hampshire and the Isle of Wight butterfly and moth report 1999.* Butterfly Conservation (Hampshire & Isle of Wight Branch).

Taverner, J.H. and Butler, A. (1997). Mass early morning mating of blues. *Butterfly Conservation* News No. 66: 21.

Thomas, J.A. (1974). *Ecological studies of hairstreak butterflies.* PhD thesis, University of Leicester.

Thomas, J.A. (1986). *RSNC guide to the butterflies of the British Isles.* Country Life Books.

Thomas, J.A., Snazell, K.G. and Moy, I.L. (in press). *The conservation of violet-feeding Fritillaries in southern Britain.* English Nature, Peterborough.

Thomas, J.A. and Lewington, R. (1991). *The butterflies of Britain and Ireland.* Dorling Kindersley.

Torlesse, A.D. (1983). *The decline of the New Forest butterflies.* Unpublished report to NCC.

Tubbs, C.R. (1986). *The New Forest.* Collins New Naturalist, London.

Turner, H.J. (1949). The occurrence of *Melitaea cinxia* in Hants and Dorset. *Entomologist's Rec. J. Var.* **61**: 19.

Turner, H.J. (1951). Butterflies in the New Forest. *Entomologist* **84**: 45.

Tutt, J.W. (1905). *British butterflies.* Elliot Stock, London.

Walsh, G.B. (1945). Reappearance of the Wall Brown. *Entomologist's Monthly Magazine.* **81**: 236.

Warren, M.S. (1993a). A review of butterfly conservation in central southern Britain: I. Protection, evaluation and extinction in prime sites. *Biological Conservation* **64**: 25–35.

Warren, M.S. (1993b). A review of butterfly conservation in central southern Britain: II. Sites management and habitat selection by key species. *Biological Conservation* **64**: 37–49.

Warren, M.S. (1994). The UK status and suspected metapopulation structure of a threatened European butterfly, the Marsh Fritillary. *Biological Conservation* **67**: 239–249.

Warren, M.S. (1995). *Managing local micro-climates for the High Brown Fritillary.* in Pullin A. S. (ed.) (1995) *Ecology and conservation of butterflies.* Chapman & Hall.

Warren, M.S. and Oates, M.R. (1995). *The importance of bracken habitats for butterfly populations.* In: Smith, R.T. and Taylor, J.A. (Eds.) *Bracken: An environmental issue.* 178–181. International Bracken Group Special Publication No. 2, Aberystwyth (available from School of Geography, Leeds University).

Warren, M.S. and Thomas, J.A. (2000). *Management options for the Silver-spotted Skipper: a study of the effects of timing of grazing at Old Winchester Hill NNR, Hants.* English Nature Science.

Webb, M.R. and Pullin, A.S. (1996). History of establishment attempts with the Large Copper butterfly *Lycaena dispar* (Haworth) (Lep.: Lycaenidae). *Entomologist's Rec. J. Var.* **108**: 321–327.

Wells, H.O. (1898). New Forest, 1898. *Entomologist* **31**: 198.

Whicher, S. (1918). Larvae of *Papilio bianor* in east Hants. *Entomologist* **51**: 16.

Williams, C.B. (1958). *Insect migration.* Collins, London.

Woodforde, F.C. (1904). Lepidoptera at Market Drayton, in the New Forest and Cornwall. *Entomologist's Rec. J. Var.* **16**: 25–27.

de Worms, C.G.M. (1934). British Lepidoptera collecting, 1933. *Entomologist* **67**: 5–9, 100–103, 131–134.

de Worms, C.G.M. (1950). *Thymelicus lineola* near Salisbury. *Entomologist* **83**: 13.

de Worms, C.G.M. (1973). Memories of collecting in Britain during the past fifty years. *Proc. Trans. Brit. Ent. Nat. Hist. Soc.* **6**: 1–15.

de Worms, C.G.M. (1977). Collecting Lepidoptera in Britain during 1976. *Entomologist's Rec. J. Var.* **89**: 213–220, 232–235.